Beneath the Underdog

BENEATH
THE
UNDER

DOG

MINGUS

Edited by Nel King

WEIDENFELD AND NICOLSON
5 WINSLEY STREET LONDON W1

First published in Great Britain 1971

A portion of the book appeared in Changes, *Vol 1, No. 3.*
"It's Dark Out, Jack" by Kenneth Patchen is from Hurrah
for Anything, *published in 1957 by New Directions.*
Reprinted by permission of the author.

ISBN 0 297 00446 8

Reproduced and Printed in Great Britain by
Redwood Press Limited, Trowbridge & London

I would like to express my deep thanks to Nel King, who worked long and hard editing this book, and who is probably the only white person who could have done it.
And my thanks to Regina Ryan of Knopf—who heard about my book, came looking for me, and was responsible for its publication.

*Some names in this work have been changed
and some of the characters and incidents
are fictitious.*

Beneath the Underdog

"IN OTHER WORDS, I AM THREE. One man stands forever in the middle, unconcerned, unmoved, watching, waiting to be allowed to express what he sees to the other two. The second man is like a frightened animal that attacks for fear of being attacked. Then there's an over-loving gentle person who lets people into the uttermost sacred temple of his being and he'll take insults and be trusting and sign contracts without reading them and get talked down to working cheap or for nothing, and when he realizes what's been done to him he feels like killing and destroying everything around him including himself for being so stupid. But he can't—he goes back inside himself."

"Which one is real?"

"They're *all* real."

"The man who watches and waits, the man who attacks because he's afraid, and the man who wants to trust and love but retreats each time he finds himself betrayed. Mingus One, Two and Three. Which is the image you want the world to see?"

"What do I care what the world sees, I'm only trying to find out how I should feel about myself. I can't change the fact that they're all against me—that they don't want me to be a success."

"Who doesn't?"

"Agents and businessmen with big offices who tell me, a black man, that I'm abnormal for thinking we should have our share of the crop we produce. Musicians are as Jim-Crowed as any black motherfucker on the street and the . . . the . . . well, *they* want to keep it that way."

"Charles, I know who you mean by *they*, and that's ironic. Because don't you remember saying you came to me not only because I'm a psychologist but also because I'm a Jew? And therefore could relate to your problems?"

"Haw haw! You're funny, doctor."

"Ah, you're crying again. Here, dry your eyes, Mingus, and don't bullschitt me."

"Haw! Now I got *you* cursing!"

"You've got no exclusive on cursing. Don't bullschitt me. You're a good man, Charles, but there's a lot of fabrication and fantasy in what you say. For instance, no man could have as much intercourse in one night as you claim to have had."

"The hell he couldn't! Maybe I did exaggerate some things like the weight-lifting and all that 'cause I really don't know how much those bar bells weighed but only two other guys could pick 'em up and their feet sank into the ground!"

"You're changing the subject, my friend. I was asking about the Mexican girls. Why are you obsessed with proving you're a man? Is it because you cry?"

"I am more of a man than any dirty white cocksucker! I *did* fuck twenty-three girls in one night, including the

4

boss's wife! I didn't dig it—I did it because I wanted to die and I hoped it would kill me. But on the way back from Mexico I still felt unsatisfied so I stopped and . . ."

"Go on. . . . Are you ashamed?"

"Yes, because it felt better when I did it to myself than with all those twenty-three dirty-ass whores. They don't love men, they love money."

"How can you know what they love, Charles? Here. Dry your eyes."

"Schitt. Fuck it. Even you just dig money!"

"Then don't pay me."

"Oh, I dig your psychology! You know saying that makes me want to pay you double."

"Nope, I don't want your money. You're a sick man. When the time comes that you feel I've helped you, buy me a tie or something. And I won't call you a prevaricator again. What matters is that you stop lying to yourself. Now, earlier you said you were a procurer. Tell me about it. How did you get into that?"

"Why don't you ever let me lie on the couch, doctor?"

"You always choose the chair."

"I feel you don't want me on the couch 'cause I'm colored and your white patients might be bugged."

"Oh, Charles Mingus! You can lie on it, kick it, jump on it, get on it, get under it, turn it over, break it—and pay for it."

"Man, you're crazy! I'm gonna save you."

"You're not trained to save. I am."

"I *can* save you. Do you believe in God?"

"Yes."

"As a boogie man?"

5

"We'll get around to that later. Back to the subject, your onetime ill-famed profession."

"Well, it's true I tried to be a pimp, doctor, but I wasn't really making it 'cause I didn't enjoy the money the girls got me. I remember the first one I knew—Cindy. She had all this bread under her mattress. Bobo laughed at me 'cause I didn't take it—he said I didn't know how to keep a whore."

"If you didn't want the money, what was it you wanted?"

"Maybe just to see if I could do what the other pimps did."

"Why?"

"That's almost impossible to explain—how you feel when you're a kid and the king pimps come back to the neighborhood. They pose and twirl their watchchains and sport their new Cadillacs and Rollses and expensive tailored clothes. It was like the closest thing to one of our kind becoming president of the U.S.A. When a young up-and-coming man reaches out to prove himself boss pimp, it's making it. That's what it meant where I come from—proving you're a man."

"And when you proved it, what did you want?"

"Just to play music, that's all."

"I've been reading about you in a magazine. You didn't tell me you were such a famous musician."

"That don't mean schitt. That's a system those that own us use. They make us famous and give us names—the King of this, the Count of that, the Duke of *what!* We die broke anyhow—and sometimes I think I dig death more than I dig facing this white world."

"We're making progress, Charles, but perhaps we've done enough for today."

"I wanted to tell you about Fats—I dreamed about him again last night."

"Fine. Keep it on ice till next time. Good-bye, Chazz."

"So long, doctor."

BABY HAD JUST TURNED TWO, on April 22, 1924, out at 1621 East One Hundred and Eighth Street in the city of Watts in Los Angeles County in the State of California.

He was done for—his head split wide open on the corner of a Goodwill-store old-fashioned second-hand-me-down white-folks' bedroom-set dresser. I hadn't realized how important the little fellow was. Everybody got so upset. I found myself outside him for the first time since he was born, standing beside him with Mama and his older sisters, Grace and Vivian. Grace was screaming, "Baby's dead! Baby's dead! Oh, Lord Jesus! My baby brother's gone!"

Here comes Daddy! He's looking down at poor, unconscious Baby. Everything will be all right now. But even Daddy cries out, "Oh my God, he's dying! Mama, get some ice, fold it in a clean cloth, wrap him up good, hold his head up high so he won't bleed no faster, we gotta get him to the hospital! Pray, Vivian! Grace! Mama! All us gotta pray! Oh Lord, save my boy!"

Daddy drove the Chevrolet sedan as fast as he could to the clinic at One Hundred and Third Street in downtown Watts. On the way, they all prayed and cried and pleaded with God to please save Baby. Nurse took one look and rushed him to the operating room. "I'll do my best, Mr. and Mrs. Mingus," the doctor said, "but he's going fast." "God help us! Oh Lord, not now!"

But though they had so much faith in this guy named God, Baby wouldn't respond. I decided to go back inside and take over until he could get himself together. No one seemed to notice as I climbed up on the white table where Baby was laid out and materialized myself into the big hole over his left eye. Just to console everybody, I breathed deep and exhaled and Baby let out his first scream since early that morning when Grace had tickled his stomach till it hurt.

The doctor took the bows and credit. "Don't worry, a week or so and he'll be as good as new. He's lost a lot of blood and we'll need X-rays, of course, there may be a fracture or concussion. Come back in the morning."

I started to leave again when the family did but Baby had hold of me now and was hanging on for dear life, so I stayed with him and I've been with him ever since.

BABY WAS SO LITTLE, but big-jointed, with oversized shoulders and hips. Pigeon-toed and bow-legged, running and playing all day, he was the boy they'd longed for in the family. He'd have his tantrums, falls, thrills—Sunday wading in the tides at Santa Monica, carefully watched, yelled at not to go out too far. The big picnic basket on the grass, the cold chicken a little sandy and tasting so much better than at home. He had a few toys, liked water bugs, and kept ants in bottles. And all—not some but all—of the pretty little girls he saw he loved instantly.

Yet I felt sorry for the little fellow. They all loved him, they said, but they loved him like a puppy. He was becoming a person and no one took notice. They'd poke at him and say, "What cute dimples!" He'd blush browner and feel frustrated that he couldn't ask serious questions because he didn't know how to talk yet. Still, he was so well protected from the world at large that if he were left alone one second outside his big back-yard fence he was completely befuddled.

One day I saw that Baby had a brain. One of the neighbors, a cranky old night-watchman named Mr. Davis, had often complained about Baby's beloved dog Buster sniffing around his terrier bitch. One terrible day Mr. Davis called across the fence to Mama and said, "Your dog just got run over! Better come get him." I was proud of my boy. He had seen Daddy shoot birds out of the sky with his rifle and somehow he knew, he *knew*, that Mr. Davis had shot Buster. He was enraged—he wanted to get Daddy's rifle and kill Mr. Davis's she-dog! But I calmed him and told him to remain silent and that when Daddy came home somehow justice would be done. So Baby waited to see if Daddy would take his rifle and go shoot Mr. Davis. But Daddy didn't even seem to notice the bullet hole in poor Buster's neck. He dug a nice grave in the back yard and Baby put flowers on it and that was the last of his little dirty white male poodle. Baby cried, but Daddy only said, "Son, God will take care of it all."

Hear that name "God" again, Baby? Oh, yes. Baby

silently prayed that God would handle Mr. Davis in some drastic way. But Baby grew bigger and older and nothing happened to Mr. Davis, nothing at all—except he seemed to become aware of the hatred and contempt Baby felt and he began to watch my boy resentfully and never missed a chance to wisecrack about his being so big and clumsy and dumb. My boy said nothing but often while he practiced his music four or five hours a day he thought about Mr. Davis. Much later when he was fourteen and reading a book in the library about a man named Sigmund Freud, he wondered if Freud had known a Mr. Davis in his childhood.

MY BOY WAS FOUR YEARS OLD and he felt pretty strange on his first day of school, clinging to Mama's hand, trotting along on his bow-legs, stumbling over his pigeon-toes, headed for the principal's office. Here went a brown baby with complexes, off to kindergarten to develop more. The kids all laughed as they passed and he didn't know if it was at him or his mother, who had taken off her work clothes and put on her Sunday go-to-meetin's for this occasion. He had over-heard Daddy saying, "Take that damned snuff out of your mouth! And don't dress so damn sloppy. You ain't fit for a pig to come home to!" It had to be true, Daddy was next to God and even sometimes told God what to do: "God *damn* it!" he'd say when he got good and angry.

Weekdays Mama plowed the back yard, planted the corn, tomatoes, string beans and onions, cleaned the chicken pens that held over a hundred hens and roosters, gathered eggs, mended the fence, cut and watered the grass, scrubbed and mopped the house, cooked and washed dishes, patched the children's clothes, made the girls' dresses and covered their ungodly asses with big black bloomers gathered with elastic just above the knee.

Were these strange little people really laughing at his mother? He thought she looked beautiful. He was confused by the yelling and fighting and screaming all around him but he hung on to her and didn't cry.

Mrs. Corick, the big fat white lady principal, was less than five feet tall and wore a short, neat little dress that flowered out to expose her legs, shaped like oversize country-fair blue-ribbon hams. She had bosoms like two strapped-down white winter melons. She looked bigger than a cow! Her face was fat like Santa's, bursting with joy, and she blushed continuously for no apparent reason. My boy wondered if she was rosy all over.

So Charles entered school and his problems with the outside world began. I wanted him to know that he was not alone, that I was with him for a lifetime, so after this day I tried harder to communicate with him. It seemed difficult—maybe I had waited too long and he'd already developed a thinking pattern of his own.

One day he stole. He'd eaten his lunch on the way to school and at recess he went to the cloakroom and I saw him eating a sandwich that wasn't his. At noon another little kid began to cry and I looked closely at Charles's guilty face. I scolded him for that, and he heard. He promised he'd never take anything again as long as he lived.

It was about this time he heard himself called a strange name. Playing in the sandbox he was pouring nice hot

sand down inside his pants because it felt so good. He was
yanked from the box by a teacher. "SEX PERVERT!" she
said. He didn't know what it meant but he soon heard
more on the subject. The little girl was Beulah Clemmons
and Charles hadn't even noticed her that day, let alone
looked up her dress. Besides, at home he'd seen his sisters
in the bathtub and what could Beulah have under her
dress different from Grace and Vivian? He was sitting
on a bench at lunchtime, peeking around a corner of
the schoolhouse, watching the girls and making eyes.
Suddenly Mrs. Pinkham, the spelling teacher, pulled him
to his feet and slapped him and the Truant Officer grabbed
him by the ear and booted him all the way up to the Fat
Principal's office. "Mrs. Corick," he said with satisfaction,
"we caught him looking up Beulah Clemmons' dress!
This boy should be sent to Boyle Heights this time for
sure." Boyle Heights was the school for disturbed and
recalcitrant children.

"Mr. Cuff, be good enough to go down and pick up
Mrs. Mingus," the Fat Principal said. "We're going to stop
this kind of thing once and for all. You nasty thing,
Charles!"

My boy remembered this was his daddy's day off
and began picturing his own funeral. Daddy was quick
with the strap these days and often whipped him for
things he hardly understood, like letting water get into
his boots when he waded home from school in the flowing gutters after a heavy rain—though he was careful
and never knew how it happened. Sometimes there were
two thrashings, one from Mama's switch and the second,
much worse, from Daddy's doubled-up strap.

He thought with terror of the punishment for wetting

his bed. Daddy had warned him one night and the next morning Mama slipped in early and whispered, "Get up, son, go pee—you don't want Daddy to beat you, you know what he said!" But she was too late and Charles began to cry. The bedroom door shot open and Daddy entered like the wrath of God. With his strap and fist he outdid himself while Charles was praying that Mrs. Haynes next door would hear and yell as she always did, "Stop abusing those children or I'll call the police!" But this time she must have been sound asleep.

The beatings at dawn went on for months and it got so sometimes they didn't even wake my boy. Daddy would beat on his body but the child was no longer inside, he was out with me waiting till the agony was over. He tried to find ways to foil these misguided parents, like changing the bottom sheet to the top, hoping it would dry with the heat of his body. Sometimes when Daddy thundered "Did he wet?" Mama, the official pee-feeler, would reach under the blanket and touch the dampness of his long old-fashioned nightgown and, feeling sorry for Charles, she'd give his butt a little slap and say, "I think he's going to be all right, Daddy."

One morning my boy opened his eyes to see his father shaking a bottle under his nose. "Good thing you didn't pee, boy! See this bottle of Lysol? Next time I'm gonna take this stuff and burn it right off!" The words struck icy horror to his heart and echoed through the years as he rose in the early hours and made an extra trip to the bathroom to relieve the damaged kidneys that had gone unattended in his childhood.

It was during this period that Charles asked me to take him away, out of himself, and let him die. When I refused, he no longer believed in me and began to pray to Jesus Christ to wake him up so his father wouldn't burn him or if that was impossible to take him up to heaven with the angels. So I began to watch over him all night and in the early morning I tugged at him and said, "Wake up, Charles!" He jumped up blind with sleep and reached under the bed for the chamber pot. Once in his haste he mistook his shoe for the pot and gratefully made water in it while shouting "Thank you, Jesus!" And so the morning beatings ceased and Charles was convinced Jesus had heard his cry for help. After that he called on Jesus for everything.

He was sending prayers up fearfully now as Mr. Cuff and his parents entered the Fat Principal's office. His father looked straight at him and said, "Now, son, I don't want you to lie to me—if you do I'm through with you forever. This man here tells me you were looking up some girl's dress. I'm not going to whip you if you tell the truth. Where's the girl?"

"Here's Beulah," Mrs. Corick said.

"Did my boy try to look up your dress?"

"Yes. I was swinging on the rings and he was lying on the bench looking up my dress, that's what Mrs. Pinkham said."

"Son, why were you crying when I came in?"

"Mrs. Pinkham was slapping me and—"

"Who the hell is Mrs. Pinkham?"

"The spelling teacher."

"What happened to your lip and your left eye?"

"Mr. Cuff bumped me when he kicked me up the stairs."

"I did no such thing!" said Mr. Cuff.

"Yes, he did, the kids saw him," Beulah said unexpectedly.

Mr. Mingus took everyone outside to the scene of the crime. He had Beulah get up on the rings. Then he had the Truant Officer lie down on the bench, then the Fat Principal, and finally he lay there himself. He was getting madder by the minute and when he rose from the bench he said to Mr. Cuff, "Now, you red-necked son-of-a-bitch, tell me I'm a liar and kick my ass like you done my little boy 'cause you can't even see her from here, let alone see up her dress! You low trash, wasting my time bringing me down here! Lay a hand on my son again and I'll kick your ass all over this county of Watts!" Mama cried, "Now Daddy, you know your temper! You've proven you're right. Let's be respectable and go home."

NOT LONG AFTER THAT INCIDENT, a very spicy little five-year-old Mexican girl named Hoacha showed him how they could prop up their big coloring books on their desks to block the teacher's view, and kiss each other and hold hands. He enjoyed that part but he was puzzled when one day she whispered with flashing eyes that he should get excused and wait for her in the place the *girls* went! When she came she pulled him into a booth, locked the door, stood on the toilet seat, pulled up her dress and slipped down her pants and told him to kiss her. Do you know what my boy did? Climbed up beside her and kissed her cheeks and said warmly "I love you too!" Then he went back to the schoolroom.

One day Hoacha didn't come to school and she never

came back any more. Charles got very worried and ran around the Mexican neighborhood asking "Where's Hoacha? Where's Hoacha?" They said she moved away and he went home that evening with a broken heart. I consoled him and reminded him of all the other girls he liked—Evelyn, Caroline, Juanita, Jacqueline, Lois, Marian. . . . But Charles kept on missing Hoacha till the day he met his next love.

TONIGHT IS THE FINAL REHEARSAL of the Tom Thumb
Wedding. The children are being sorted out and paired
up by anxious, nervous parents. The teachers are all excited—the O'Neills have consented to their son and
daughter joining the procession! The sisters are screaming about Bernard—handsome, so brilliant, just like his
daddy, Officer O'Neill. Charles is left standing alone.
Things are sort of dull for an average seven-year-old
Don Juan. They're all rushing around discussing who
looks good with whom. He hasn't even had a partner at
any of the rehearsals. Who is this kid Bernard, he wonders,
feeling out of things. And then it happens—he sees
Mariana.

Hot dog! Cupid done walked right in the front door
—walks in and unloads bow and arrow, pistol, revolver
and machine gun and blasts away at my boy Charlie's
heart, soul, body and don't miss nary a smidgen or notch
of his entire personage! Grant's Chapel First African
Methodist Episcopal Church on the sixteen hundred block
of One Hundred and Eighth Street is finally blessed with a
miracle, plain as day is from night. Behold, an angel stands

in the doorway!—a spectacle of sacred loveliness, holding the hand of a lady who could be her mother and
standing next to a boy much like Charles. Perhaps a little
taller, that's all, just a little taller.

This girl! This little woman! God, beauty is not the
word for it! Eyes meet and lock. Watch out!—a bossy
deaconess in a black bonnet is trying to link her with another partner! It won't work. Charles and the angel stare
and stare—nothing can stop them from looking at each
other. Mrs. Johnson sees and solves the problem. She puts
them together, both of them blushing, trembling, looking
at the floor, feeling still the other's eyes penetrating to
the soul.

A whistle blows and the procession begins. How and
where will he ever see her again? What's her name?
Where does she live? No matter. Charles knows he'll find
her. This is it! There'll never be another.

Rushing home after rehearsal, getting ready for hours,
washing and washing over and over, practicing walking,
trying to turn his feet out so as not to be pigeon-toed,
trying to get the bow out of his legs. . . . The whole
family is coming tonight and they're betting Charles will
look more splendid than anyone, including Officer
O'Neill's son. He patiently allows them to get the tuxedo
on him and the big bow tie. Dressed and ready, he sneaks
into the toilet, closes the seat, gets down on his knees and
prays like Jesus on the big rock on the Sunday School picture card hanging in a frame over the piano in the living
room. Placing his hands together under his chin, he looks
up at the white bathroom ceiling. "Dear Jesus, make her
love me, please, dear Jesus." Just as he's said amen his

mother calls, her voice starting low and glissandoing up an octave or so. "Char-*rulls!* We're going now!" And Daddy booms, "Come on, boy!"

Grace glows and compliments, "Ooooh, do I have a handsome brother!" Vivian complains, "I don't see what this old Tom Thumb wedding is for. Gosh, do I have to go?" Mama warns, "Now, you all come on 'fore Daddy gets mad."

"I'm already mad now I've spent all that money buying those damn fool rags and still got to buy tickets to get us in! Over a dollar apiece paid admission and my own son in it! I bet the Reverend passes the collection plate to boot."

While the rest of the family get their tickets, Grace takes Charles around to the side entrance. Everybody waits his turn to go with his partner through the swinging doors and down the aisle to the miniature pulpit where the mock ceremony will be performed. Charles has already described the angel to his sister. When she sees the little girl she exclaims, "Oh, yes, you're meant to be together! My little brother Charlie is in love with you, angel honey. What's your name?"

Do you know who she is? The daughter of Officer O'Neill! Entranced, they gaze into each other's eyes.

"All right, parents and children! The procession is about to begin. Everybody out who's not in the wedding! Partners, everyone!"

Grace leaves to go out front but Charles and Mariana stand hypnotized, not even hearing the adult voices. Mrs. Johnson gently pushes them into line. "Partners now!" she calls in her sweet, musical voice. "Charles—

come on, boy, give this pretty little lady your arm so you can march down the aisle together."

As they wait in the dimly lighted lobby, no one sees the little adult hands that moistly intertwine, pulsating and clinging, as they move closer and closer together. Had this moment of pure love lasted forever, I'm sure they could both have survived all life's problems.

The other children are busy preparing for the procession and Mrs. Johnson alone sees this just-born little man and woman now in each other's arms. Her face shapes slowly into a big, moonlight smile. Bending to retouch Mariana's lipstick and wipe my boy's forehead, she gently kisses their cheeks. At that moment the three understand what love is and they are all children together. Charles is thinking churches must be good if this is where you meet people like Mrs. Johnson. He remembers the Easter egg hunt—the eggs were gone, the fastest kids had found them all. Disappointed, he turned to go home. But Mrs. Johnson called out, "Keep looking, boy! Don't ever quit looking." "There ain't no more," Charles said. "Look, Charles, they didn't get them all! Why, here's some right here! Bunny left three in a pile. Old Bunny's left a lotta eggs!" She placed them in his hands. They smiled at each other and he ran after her, shouting back to the others: "Come on, kids! There's a lotta eggs the bunny left!" as time after time she reached in and held her hand under that little old Easter bunny laying colored eggs right in her big apron pocket and he hid them for the littler kids to find. Oh yes, Mrs. Johnson had the Easter bunny in her pocket that day, and tonight she had the secret of life.

The doors swing open. "Don't be afraid, babies. Lock arms. Hold your flowers straight, Mariana. Walk down the aisle. March!"

A hush comes over the audience. These are children physically, but it is as man and woman they are being married to love tonight. Attention shifts from the principals to Charles and his little lady. Laughter rolls over the congregation and ends in a sigh as Mariana follows Charles to the boys' side. The instructors separate them, but Charles runs after her and joins the group of girls. He hears his sister's low voice saying, "It's not Tom Thumb's wedding—my brother's the one really getting married tonight. Go on, brother, marry your Mariana on this fine Christian evening!"

Reverend Jones gives the nod and the mock wedding proceeds with Charles among the bridesmaids, clinging to Mariana. Mrs. Foldy plays the introduction on the old upright piano and Bernard O'Neill—Tom Thumb!— makes his grand entrance,.strutting and striding up the aisle toward the miniature pulpit. Halfway, he stops with a shocked expression, his eyes on my boy in among the girls and hanging on to his sister, but he regains his dignity and overtakes his best man. The little bride, her make-believe father, a tiny tot carrying the end of a super-long veil and a smaller toddler bearing two rings on a pillow are making their way down the aisle. But my boy and his angel are oblivious to them all.

After the ceremony, the Reverend gives a short sermon. Collection plates are hastily passed and after the recession the crowd bursts into cheers and laughter. Parents search out their children. The mock wedding is over. Mrs. O'Neill and her sisters rush toward the only real thing that's happened this evening. Mariana's family are not harsh with her, they're just embarrassed and ashamed and in a hurry to get her into her coat and out of the place. But big, brave almost-white Officer O'Neill can't resist commenting, "I'm wondering if this boy's got all his marbles. What's your name, boy?"

"He's Sergeant Mingus's son," someone says.

"Good evening, *Corporal* O'Neill," says Daddy.

"Why, hello there, Charlie. You still in the Army?"

"No, corporal, I'm not still in the Army. You still think you're white?" Officer O'Neill says nothing and Daddy continues, "Take a good look at my son and your daughter. Ain't neither one going to pass for white like we did. All it got you was corporal's stripes in the Army and flat feet as a traffic director. Wake up, nigger. Times are changing."

"Well, my old friend Mingus," Officer O'Neill laughs, "I see one thing ain't changed is that temper of yours. Let's not worry about our children. They'll forget this little puppy affair."

Mr. Mingus is mollified. "Um. Humm. Let's get out of here and have a smoke, O'Neill. Leave the kids to the women."

And as Mariana with her wrist clasped tightly in her mother's hand walks backwards toward the exit, she and Charles are still busy every second filling their eyes and souls with each other—as if they somehow knew already they'd never be this close together again.

CHARLES WAS EIGHT when his father first asked him what instrument he wanted to play. Trombone, he decided, because that was the only interesting-looking musical instrument he'd seen up to that time—Mr. Young, the choirmaster at church, played one that glittered and glistened while he conducted Watts's largest Afro-American choir. Charles's dream was picked out of the Sears Roebuck catalogue and arrived boxed in wood, wrapped in straw and tissue paper, shining and ready to go. Mr. Young had agreed to teach him but at the first lesson he seemed surprised that my boy didn't even know his lines and spaces. He told him to study the basics with his sister Vivian, who was already appearing in piano recitals. The first thing she taught him was the treble clef and this he learned quickly and he returned to Mr. Young eager to play his beautiful horn, but he was called stupid for not knowing a trombone is played in bass clef and sent home again. My boy was so discouraged that he never went back for lessons but did his best practicing at home alone until Daddy, disgusted, traded the trombone for a cello without even asking him —and this instrument Charles loved right away. Then Mr. Arson came into his life.

In Watts, itinerant teachers—not always skillful or well educated in music themselves—traveled from door to door persuading colored families to buy lessons for their children. Mr. Arson was one of them, out for the few bucks he collected weekly from each of many black families whose money paid his bills in a "white only" section of L.A. He would teach anyone how to play anything even looking like a musical instrument that poor folks might beg or buy second-hand or on the installment plan. Maybe he didn't even admit to himself that he cheated his pupils but the truth was he took no time to give the fundamental principles of a good musical education. His short weekly sessions had to result in satisfying sounds that proved to parents their children were really learning something in a status-building, money-making field. So Mr. Arson by-passed the essentials that even the most talented child must master if he is ever going to learn to read music well, and the parents, as usual, were paying for something their children were not getting.

Mr. Arson saw at once Charles could sing the sounds he saw on paper. Good. Without bothering to name the notes, he showed him where to put his fingers on the cello to make that sound. It was as if a bright child who could easily and rapidly pronounce syllables was never taught how syllables fit into words and words into syntax. I'm sure Mr. Arson hadn't any idea his shortcut method would turn out to be great for jazz improvisation, where the musician listens to the sounds he's producing rather than making an intellectual transference from the score paper to the fingering process. Using simple scales and familiar tunes, Mr. Arson would count as he bowed his muted, sloppy, gypsy-sounding violin with its resin-caked surface and Charles would follow as best he could by ear, knowing only how it sounded and having no conception of the technical processes he should have been learning at that time.

I T WAS ABOUT THAT TIME, I remember, that some of the older boys told him about swimming in the Watts Canal without suits, with little white girls who went in naked too! But there were crawfish in the canal and that scared him more than he was tempted by the other thing. Not to be a sissy, he forced himself to join the fellows anyhow, but no white girls showed up—there wasn't a bare ass of any color without a penis and in addition he almost drowned in the deep and murky canal. I helped him climb out and really felt sorry for him when he discovered someone had stolen his brand-new shoes and pants. Poor Charles had to go home holding eucalyptus branches in front of himself, knowing Daddy would slap him upside the head and send Grace for the strap that hung waiting in the kitchen. When Daddy beat the kids with that doubled-up three-quarter-inch-thick belt, the worse part was not the strap but the blows from the fist that held the strap. I'd say Daddy knew this. I'd say he was a sick man at these times—sick, frustrated at a life spent in the post office when he'd trained to be an architect, and confused in many ways. He taught race prejudice to his children— said they were better than others because they were lighter in color. Grace was hurt when Daddy said this and she cried and complained that by his teaching she was the lowest one in the family because she was the darkest. During these discussions Mama would look in the mirror and say how often she was taken for a Mexican because of her freckles, her thin chiseled nose and tiny feet. She believed she was part Indian. But the kids remembered that Daddy said Mexicans and Indians were dirty greasers with lice in their hair. It was confusing.

That year there was a pretty little Irish girl who sat across from him in the last row in reading class. She didn't refuse his fingers that found their way to the edge of her seat and touched her legs while she buried her head in a book and looked serious. And then his turn would come to pretend deep interest in his lessons while her little hand caressed his thigh.

One afternoon they planned to meet at her house after school—"Mama won't be home till six o'clock," she said. She showed him the big cream-colored house half a mile across a lettuce field near the Hundred and Third Street wildcat oil well, next to the old firehouse and police station.

Charles felt safe trudging across the field carrying his schoolbooks—people would think he was going to the stables like the other kids did to look at the horses her father owned. He crept up to the back door and called her name. Two Mexican boys, not much older than he but far larger, opened the door. "Get out of here NIGGER! Betty's our girl and we don't wany any NIGGERS hanging around!"

My boy was shocked. Daddy'd warned him about playing with "them little black nigger yaps" down the street so how could he be one too? Hadn't those greasers noticed his light color? For the first time it came to him that whatever shade he was, he was going to be nothing but a nigger to some people.

Losing his girl and becoming a nigger all in one day

was too much. Near tears, he ran back across the lettuce field and suddenly three big white men loomed up and roughly collared him by the road. "Here, boy! What you doing over this way?"

"Going home from school. . . ." Charles managed to say.

"Let's kill this little nigger," Red Face said. "Sneaking over here where he don't belong, trying to rape our sister!"

Rape! What are they talking about? Did Betty tell what we do at school? Is that rape?! Charles began to run but in three steps the men had grabbed him and forced him into the back seat of their dirty old car. They held him down on the floor while Red Face drove to the canal and kicked him out and shoved him to the ground. My boy was in terror—were they going to drown him, down in there with the crawfishes? But since they only slapped him a few times I felt they were trying to scare him—his daddy could hit harder than that. I whispered to him to cry and put on, I knew that would please these turkey-necks.

"Let's teach the dirty little yap his place!" said Pig Eyes. "We're gonna watch you the rest of your life, ya yella scrunge!" Dirty Fats said. "Catch you near another white girl and we'll cut your little peter off!"

Charles began to cry and just then two young black boys, the Grissoms, came walking along the canal in the dusk on their way home after crawfishing. The Grissom brothers worked at the market. They were always together and nobody in Watts was stronger and huskier. They took in the scene, and without wasting a moment Booker T. picked up Dirty Fats and slammed him into Red Face while his brother Warthell knocked the other honky down. "This nigger raped our sister!" yelled Pig Eyes. The Grissoms looked at nine-year-old Charles and smiled skeptically. Then Red Face, who had been briefly out cold, rose up and cried, "I'm gonna kill *all* these niggers!" The Grissoms waded in roaring and put the white braves to sleep for the last time. Then they walked Charles home and warned him never to say a word to anyone, for Booker. was afraid he might have killed Red Face by tossing him on those sharp rocks which seemed to have put a lot of holes in his head.

However, all three white brothers survived, so for quite a while the Grissoms met Charles each day outside the Hundred and Third Street School and escorted him home, 'cause they expected trouble. And it came. One day a near race riot developed. Betty's brothers drove up to the school with several other white men and they all got out of their cars. It looked ominous, so Warthell ran to get help from the Tuckers at the market and was back in moments with the Derden brothers (who tossed hundred-pound sacks of potatoes at each other all day) and Tan Blue, about the baddest looking young man you ever saw. Tan was big, ebony black, burly and beautiful, two hundred and seventy pounds of solid muscle shaped like Mandrake the Magician's slave Lothar. He hung out at Steve's Billiard Parlor except during football season, which was the only time he bothered to go to school. He was noted for his exceptional speed—wearing his football suit, he could outrun one of Jordan High's fastest track men, Moulah Johnson.

The odds were about even now, and the Tuckers were

on their way. Tan Blue then spoke to the white men very politely, in his over-cool super-hip style. "I suggest you gentlemen forget whatever you had in mind and go on home. For I must tell you that although the Grissoms and the Derdens and our friends the Tuckers who will shortly be arriving are all sporting gentlemen, I myself don't like fist fighting so I would be obliged to cut you should you get tossed in my direction."

I'm not sure who would have won but Tan Blue's diplomacy saved the day. Soon after, Betty and her family moved up North and Charles always wondered what would have happened at that meeting they never had in the big cream-colored house across the lettuce field.

My boy didn't know how to explain to his family what he had just learned—that this dark and light routine was all the bunk. Because if there's any "Negro" in your ancestry you're a nigger to all greasers, redneck peckerwoods and like-minded folks whether you're coal black or yella like my boy or gray as the palest Caucasian with hazel eyes and sandy hair like Daddy and you better get to know it.

But since Daddy didn't seem to understand this, Charles prayed that they wouldn't come face to face some fine evening when the Grissoms, the Derdens and Tan Blue were walking him home. 'Cause Daddy might blurt out in his ignorance, "Ain't I told you to stay away from them black niggers?" And wrong as Daddy was, my boy preferred not to see his stern parent flying through the air like a bag of potatoes while Tan Blue peeled him with his razor at every pass.

SCARLET FEVER TOOK MY BOY out of rehearsals with the Los Angeles Junior Philharmonic Orchestra. On his first day back nobody told him changes had been made in the orchestrations, so cocksure Cholly Mingus was earnestly bowing away at their simple version of Beethoven's Fifth Symphony and even felt proud as he played on after the others stopped, imagining he was the only one on stage properly following the score.

The stern, angry-looking conductor held up his hand abruptly. "You, there! Who are you? Can't you read?"

"They shouldn't have stopped! They're all wrong—I was right!" Charles cried.

"We're too far along for backward pupils. Get him out."

Charles realized with amazement that the conductor was motioning him off the stage. He made his exit in silence, dragging his cello behind him. Backstage as he put it in its canvas bag he thought bitterly, "They're not doing it right—those white folks can't even play the music they act like they invented!" As he was about to stomp out, Mrs. Churney, his music teacher at school, came back to find him.

"It's all right, I know you can play it, Charles," she said kindly.

"Yes, ma'am, just did! They didn't play *theirs!*"

Mrs. Churney explained that certain bars in the Fifth Symphony were too difficult for young performers of varying skills to play together and had to be eliminated because they didn't sound "clean." "Stay and listen," she said, "and next rehearsal you'll know what to do."

Glad he wasn't being kicked out forever, Charles took a seat in the front row of the auditorium. He listened carefully to the Beethoven and then the Tchaikovsky, never dreaming what the next few minutes would mean in his life. I've always wondered what he would have done if a warning angel had just then pulled aside the curtain hiding the future and showed him all that was to happen to him and Lee-Marie down to the last good-bye, over twenty years away. I guess he wouldn't have understood or believed it, and he would have done the same.

My boy felt nothing at first when a beautiful light-skinned black girl brought her cello downstage and played a Kodály sonata for the teachers with finesse and ease—except maybe a little jealousy when he realized she'd been guiding the cello section and he'd been bowing behind her confident lead. Then, he looked at her more closely and suddenly felt strange. How could a little girl be that good at music and so beautiful too? Her dark eyes sparkled, her black hair was pulled back and tied with a velvet ribbon, and she was dressed so sweetly in blue wool with a white collar and cuffs and white knee socks—nothing at all like the sweaty little girls that played basketball during recess at school. She was like a princess—a movie star!

His excitement grew stronger every day as he went downtown to rehearsals on the big red street cars with a boy named Malcolm Walker who played trombone in the orchestra. Charles practiced harder at home now, and what show-offy scales he ran in the tune-ups and in the breaks and what flashy solos he dashed off before and after rehearsals! When the others applauded, she never clapped her hands but sat with her ankles neatly crossed, turning her Madonna face toward him with a tiny smile. He sat so near her in the cello section that he could even smell the delicious soap she used. Everything about her was bewitching.

After rehearsals her skinny, stuck-up-looking mother was waiting to take her back to Southgate—more than ten miles from Watts. Sometimes her father came instead —a huge man with a face like an Indian, wearing a gray bank guard's uniform and a big revolver, and it seemed to Charles he glared at him with cold suspicion if Lee-Marie so much as waved good-bye.

But my boy could feel in his insides they were going to be together somehow. He knew she wanted to—her eyes always followed him down the long aisle of Philharmonic Hall. He decided to ask for her music teacher's phone number, pretending he wanted to study with him— though he was sure it wouldn't be possible, since Mr. Warner taught in Southgate and probably charged too much anyhow. Lo and behold she gave him her own phone number and he pocketed it with a thrill—it meant she wanted him to call her and she might even invite him to her house! After that hardly an evening passed that he didn't find himself at the phone in the hall by his bedroom with his heart beating fast as he asked the operator for the

Southgate number, praying that Lee-Marie herself would answer. Getting her mother on the phone was bad—she'd usually say Lee-Marie was busy with homework—but getting her father was worse. When that stern voice answered, it always informed him, "My daughter is not at home," and he wasn't even asked to leave his name.

At last comes the night of the annual Junior Philharmonic concert. It ends in wild cheers and applause and the parents swarm up onto the stage. Charles drops his bow accidentally on purpose and leaning to pick it up whispers in Lee-Marie's little tan ear, "I love you!" She turns to look into his eyes and he hears her father's voice —"Well, girl, we did just fine, didn't we?" Mrs. Spendell kisses her daughter and smooths her already perfect hair, but Mr. Spendell's stony eyes are now fixed on my boy. "Who's your friend here?" "Charles Mingus Junior, papa," murmurs Lee-Marie. "Oh, is that so," says Mr. Spendell. "This the boy who's got such a bad memory he has to call up every day to get your teacher's number? What was that name, Charles *what?*"

"Charles Mingus Junior . . . sir."

"Well, I'm the young lady's father and she's too young to have boys on her mind. So no more of that—no more calls, you understand?"

Charles understands. He closes his eyes in despair and sits quietly as Lee-Marie is hauled away. Once again love is being taken from him and there's nothing he can do about it. What was wrong with parents, anyway?

SINGLE HOPE REMAINED. Come each summer in July, the First African Methodist Episcopal Church amalgamated with other colored churches in the area for one grand union picnic, and my boy began to live for that day. For weeks beforehand the parish ladies consulted with each other preparing batches of food in their home kitchens to add to the group-cooking projects at the picnic site. This year Mamie Mingus made gallons of potato salad as the family's part of the Grant's Chapel contribution. When the great day came, children, food and all were packed into Daddy's Chevy sedan and they headed for Lake Elsinore. The lakeshore was crowded with what looked to Charles like a million milling people and he knew somewhere among them was Lee-Marie Spendell. Excitedly he ran along the sand in the brilliant sunshine among the shouting, ball-tossing, muscle-flexing throng of bathers. A space cleared before him like magic and there she was, all alone, wading in the warm shallow water, wearing a little orange-colored swimsuit and with her shiny black hair hanging down nearly to her waist. They were drawn together without a word and gazed at each other smiling, the whole world closed out. Moving in and out of the currents that mysteriously changed in temperature from warm to hot and suddenly to cold, they splashed water on each other with their feet and stepped around each other slowly in a sort of natural mating dance, like birds—deaf to the shouts from their families on the shore: "Lee-Marie, don't you go wandering out too far!" "Charles! Can't you hear, boy? Get back here and help unpack the baskets!" But Charles and Lee-Marie kept staring at each other in a silent oneness that seemed endless—an eternity went by, till the voices became so angry and insistent they couldn't be ignored any longer. Then each one went reluctantly back to his parents, who were so busy passing plates of food around that they knew nothing of the miracle going on before their very eyes and kept jabbering on about pickles and stuffed eggs and barbecued ribs and how much punch should be drunk if you're going back in the lake again. None of it was really heard or understood by two children sitting silent and separate waiting for the moment when they would come together again and resume their secret shy communication of love.

On the way home Charles is very quiet. (*What's the matter with you, boy, you sick? . . . He didn't eat a thing, daddy! . . . Oh, he ate all right, I saw that pile of chicken bones—don't you worry 'bout Charles eating!*) But his heart is singing. Saturday! She's coming to Watts Saturday with her brother and sister to see the towers Mr. Rodia is building! Next Saturday afternoon! He thrills when the tallest spire comes into view, and then they're back at a Hundred and Eighth Street and home and he goes straight to his room (*Mamie, I told you something's wrong with that boy! . . . Oh, let him alone, daddy, he's just worn out with all the doings and goings on. . . .*) to live the afternoon over again and wonder how he can keep his mind on anything else till next weekend.

T THAT TIME IN WATTS there was an Italian man, named Simon Rodia—though some people said his name was Sabatino Rodella, and his neighbors called him Sam. He had a regular job as a tile setter, but on weekends and at nighttime, under lights he strung up, he was building something strange and mysterious and he'd been working on it since before my boy was born. Nobody knew what it was or what it was for. Around his small frame house he had made a low wall shaped like a ship and inside it he was constructing what looked like three masts, all different heights, shaped like upside-down ice cream cones. First he would set up skeletons of metal and chicken wire, and plaster them over with concrete, then he'd cover that with fancy designs made of pieces of seashells and mirrors and things. He was always changing his ideas while he worked and tearing down what he wasn't satisfied with and starting over again, so pinnacles tall as a two-story building would rise up and disappear and rise again. What was there yesterday mightn't be there next time you looked, but then another lacy-looking tower would spring up in its place.

Tig Johnson and Cecil J. McNeeley used to gather sacks full of pretty rocks and broken bottles to take to Mr. Rodia, and my boy hung around with them watching him work while he waited for Gloria Scopes, one of his classmates who happened to live just across the street. Some people called her Charles's "girl," but he didn't feel that way about her—he was only stringing her along for something to do.

Mr. Rodia was usually cheerful and friendly while he worked, and sometimes, drinking that good red wine from a bottle, he rattled off about Amerigo Vespucci, Julius Caesar, Buffalo Bill and all kinds of things he read about in the old encyclopedia he had in his house, but most of the time it sounded to Charles like he was speaking a foreign language. My boy marveled at what he was doing and felt sorry for him when the local rowdies came around and taunted him and threw rocks and called him crazy, though Mr. Rodia didn't seem to pay them much mind. Years later when Charles was grown and went back to Watts he saw three fantastic spires standing there—the tallest was over a hundred feet high. By then Rodia had finally finished his work and given it all to a neighbor as a present and gone away, no one knew where.

LEE-MARIE HAD PROMISED to come around three o'clock, but Charles began meeting the streetcars in front of Steve's Billiard Parlor at two to be sure he didn't miss her. In between he'd run back to the towers, in case her plans had changed and she came from another direction. No one was around today—Mr. Rodia must have gone away on one of his trips to collect shells and pebbles and pieces of glass down on the beaches. Gloria Scopes was popping in and out of her house across the street, though, and Charles could tell she knew something was going on.

He arrived for the fourth time at the car stop just as the three-fifteen local pulled in and Lee-Marie got off with her little sister and brother. But then a very large woman stepped down and took the hands of the two younger children. Charles stopped dead—oh crap, she wasn't alone! Well, at least it wasn't her mother and this lady had a friendly look. He ran up to them. Lee-Marie's face flushed when she saw him but she kept her cool dignity. "Hello, Charles. My Aunt Ridey came with us. This is Charles, Auntie."

The big Creole-looking lady smiled and nodded at him and the flowers on her hat bobbed. "You going to show us the way, Charles?"

"Yes, ma'am!" And Charles eagerly led them down San Pedro Boulevard next to the tracks and turned left on One Hundred and Seventh Street to the Santa Ana dead end. For the next two hours he was in heaven as he and Lee-Marie whispered together, always under Aunt Ridey's eye but often out of her hearing. The smaller children clambered around, climbing up as far as they dared in the towers. Charles pointed out Mr. Rodia's little fountains and stone flowers and other wonders as if he had made them all himself. Aunt Ridey served ginger snaps and lemonade from a thermos bottle she had brought along in her string shopping bag, and while they had their refreshments Gloria Scopes sat on her porch staring across at them resentfully, though my boy was hardly aware of her presence.

It was too perfect to last. Two white teen-age boys Charles had never seen before were coming down the middle of the street toward the towers, kicking rocks in front of them, sparring and throwing punches at each other. Their raucous voices rang out: "Come on, you mother!—got you that time!" "Try that again, schitt-face, I'll out your ass!" They bounded over the wooden bannister onto Gloria's porch. "Hey, Gloria, what's doin'?"—

and quieted down as Gloria began whispering to them. Charles noticed them all glancing at him sideways and he began to worry. Sure enough, soon the two boys, hands in pockets, swaggered across the street toward him and he knew he could expect the worst. He'd seen those narrowed eyes and sly smiles before—they had meanness on their minds, they were going to say something in front of Lee-Marie and he'd have to fight and he'd get trompled into the dust!

Aunt Ridey rose up, calm and smiling, brushing crumbs from her vast bosom, gathering up the lemonade cups and tidying the children. "Time to go!" she said. "I promised your mama I'd get you home early for supper." She moved away like a big ship, shooing the children before her. The two boys stopped and stood waiting. Charles's heart was pounding—he knew he was still in for it, but it wouldn't be so bad if nobody was watching. He'd stand his ground as long as Lee-Marie was in sight, then if he had to he'd hit back and run like hell.

Suddenly Aunt Ridey turned and called in her deep bass voice: "Charles! Ain't you coming now to take us back to the car line?" It was the voice of command, the order of a general who must be obeyed—even the Mexican boys saw that and they made no move as Charles ran to join Lee-Marie and her family and escort them to safety.

Aunt Ridey knew what had happened—he saw it in her kind old eyes when she patted his head as she climbed on the streetcar after the children. My boy waved goodbye and wished with all his heart he was big and strong enough to be the protector Lee-Marie thought he was and Aunt Ridey had made him seem to be.

THE GREAT LONG BEACH EARTHQUAKE of 1933 reached all the way to Watts and cracked the walls of the One Hundred and Third Street School and the building was condemned. Now every day Charles walked with his cello down the winding San Pedro railroad tracks on his way to the One Hundred and Eleventh Street School, wobbling and balancing his pigeon-toes on the rails. Sometimes his home-room teacher strode briskly past on the weedy dirt path paralleling the tracks and gave him a warm smile. Charles glowed and thought Miss Tuckfield must be the nicest person he knew—except Mrs. Johnson, his Sunday school teacher who knew the Easter bunny.

Thinking about Mrs. Johnson, he remembers the frightening evening—was it only a year ago?—when for the first time in his life he witnessed sudden death.

It's Sunday night, services are just out, and the congregation is crowding the lawn and steps outside Grant's Chapel First A.M.E. Church on the corner of One Hundred and Eighth and Compton Avenue. My boy sneaks around back, opens the fuse box and flips the switch the way Foster Driver taught him to do when he was only five. Instant darkness descends on the church grounds.

Ooooooooh! goes up from the multitude. Charles is tickled —he's giving them a thrill, the feeling of a real miracle! But nosy old Mrs. Vaughan who thinks she runs the town is already racing back to grab him, shrieking and shaking her finger in his face—"Turn those lights back on, you mean ugly nasty boy!" Fuck her with King Kong, Charles says to himself. "Next time you touch that switch," she shrills, "I'm going to pray that GOD WILL STRIKE YOU DEAD!"

At these awful words my boy turns cold—now some dire thing *must* come to pass! Everything freezes—it's like the hush between lightning flash and thunderclap. And in the next second the Devil rushes up from hell, unleashed by Mrs. Vaughan's blasphemy. Mr. Johnson is walking across the street from his gas station to meet his wife coming out of prayer meeting, smiling, holding his day's receipts in his hands. A car shoots toward him like a rocket. A sudden scream—the grinding of brakes—the squeal of rubber—and a terrible thud as a tired old body is flung high in the air and smashes to the ground! Coins fly up and shower all around, tinkling, jingling, chiming, spinning on the pavement. The congregation stands in deep, shocked silence. Greenbacks flutter like broken-winged birds and drift slowly down. A dime rolls into the gutter with a final clink.

The crowd understands and groans its knowledge: he can't live. This is their decision—crowds know. He's gone —Mr. Johnson, who worked his whole life through for the daily handful of paper and copper and silver that has now fallen on his grave.

Cora Johnson's loving, moonlike face is hovering over her husband. Is he still breathing?—their friends press close around them, sniffling and moaning. "Oh, my Lord, he's dying! They've killed him! Oh Jesus, who's next?"

Mrs. Johnson speaks. She's wise, very wise. "Quiet now, don't frighten my husband. He's all right, I say. One of you call Dr. Bledsoe, quick. How's my darling, beautiful husband? You'll be fine, I know you will."

The Reverend Jones is coming. "Pardon me, folks, let me through. Some of you brothers stand down the road apiece and wave those cars down so we don't have no more accidents."

"Reverend Jones, this ain't no accident," Mr. Foldy says. "It's murder! If this was a white neighborhood there'd be a stoplight here where one belongs—we asked for it enough times!"

"Yes, brother, we asked for it!"

"Now, now, Mr. Foldy, we can't know the Lord's way."

"*This* ain't the Lord's way, Reverend. This place took too many lives! Johnson saw it himself—he stood over there in his station and saw lives lost and now he's taken too. If they can't give us everything that goes with free-dom they shouldn't of given us nothing—it's better to be slaves. At least as slaves we got a chance to die standing up fighting 'stead of getting knocked down and run over like fools!"

"Now, Brother Jackson, we can't get everything we want so fast. Look around you, there's children here—Mr. Mingus's son Cholly and little Laura Comfort and her brother Joe. These little kiddies don't even know what the word slavery means."

"They *should* know!"

"Brother Jackson, you want to discourage them chillun and make them think their forefathers weren't nothing but ignorant slaves? If you ain't got the whole answer it's best not to say nothing to confuse them. We got this man hurt here—now's the time to be praying, not talking politics."

"We *know* the answer, Reverend! We ain't ignorant— we just cowards!"

"Oh . . . my back . . ."

"My darling husband! Oh, Lord—please, please everybody be quiet. Reverend, ask them to be quiet!"

"Everybody listen to me now. When I pray you listen with all your might, you hear? Oh, Lord! Hear me, Jesus! One of our brothers has been struck down by that devil's machine over yonder, and oh Lord, hear us this evening! Everybody say Amen, Lord, out here on this street!"

"AMEN, LORD!"

"Brother Johnson's one of your best servants, Lord. When he paid, Lord, he paid. His sins was forgiven every collection plate. Yes, Lord, to my recollection Brother Johnson is neeeeded! Ah! Oh, Lord, don't let him die! We need, need! We need Brother Johnson! We need his spirit, Lord! His gas! Yes, Lord, heal our brother! Anoint his head with *oil!* All your forgiveness if he done something we don't know about! Lord, heal him! Everybody say after me, heal Brother Johnson! Heal Brother Johnson!"

"HEAL BROTHER JOHNSON! HE-AL BRO-THER JOHN-SON!! AMEN!!!"

"Wa ta sa ga bo toe gomba, a ta la so bo goum! Hallelulah! Ma so buta blombo! Reta goosa la-po co-ro da-le!"

"Talk in tongues, brother! Get that devil Death out of here!"

"All right, all right, all you sisters and brothers, move aside. Pardon me, Reverend Jones."

"Thank God you here, Doctor!"

"Did any one of you black Christians call an ambulance?"

"I did, Doctor!"

"That's fine. You can't pray no ambulance here—that's why God let Mister Alexander Graham Bell discover the telephone. Spread back, everybody, little air there! No fans necessary, sisters, just spread back—the air's for me. Some of you sisters been shouting and jumping a little joyously here. A little fresh air, please, so I can breathe something besides your overworking perfumes. They say they was sending the ambulance right away?"

"No, sir, Doctor, they said was he colored and I said yes and they said well, it would be here in a while."

"Somebody step there! Hurry and get Officer Slaughter to call them white sons of—pardon me, folks. Tell him to say an important *white* gentleman been run down by a car. Then they'll get some them ambulances down here!"

"Oh Lord, get that ambulance on the way! Our brother needs Your Healing Hand! Amen!"

But at some moment while the fervent prayers and pleadings were rising into the dark Watts skies, Mr. Johnson had quietly died.

After all this time, tears of sorrow for poor, beautiful Mrs. Johnson came to my boy's eyes as he walked on down the railroad tracks toward school.

T HE NEW SCHOOL was all black except for a few Mexicans and Noba Oke, a Japanese boy whose family owned the most pleasant and fairly priced grocery store in the district. Noba's brother Mosa was a straight-A student at Jordan High. His young sister Miko had been crippled by polio. They were a nice family and tolerated the adolescent Negro drop-outs—called "delinquents" in those days—who hung out in front of their store smoking and shooting craps all afternoon and in the evening went over to Steve's Billiard Parlor on Watts's main street to shoot pool. These tough kids wore jackets and windbreakers painted with skulls and dragons and the names of their clubs—Panthers, Blue Devils, Crusaders. One of the leaders was so thin, cold and hard-looking he was called Boneyard. Then there was Teddy Poole, with the loudest mouth. Most of his family, brothers and all, worked in the post office or carried mail. Teddy had all a boy needed at home so it was hard to understand why he was such a bully. Feisty Page was already in high school but he hung out with the grammar school toughs because his age and size gave him an advantage. He wore expensive black leather basketball shoes, and walked with a cocky bounce, heel to toe, up and down, and he knew ten times as many dirty words as any of the others.

Though he tried to avoid them, the gang sometimes cornered my boy when he got out late from orchestra rehearsals nearby. He was twelve now and not small but still timid, and they loved to crowd around and torment him, kicking at his cello, feigning punches, calling him sissy, Mama's boy and schitt-colored nigger till they finally made him cry. Noba often came out to rescue him. He'd shoulder in, smiling and friendly, saying "Want to wrestle with *me*, Teddy? Come on, let's wrestle, Boneyard! Feisty?" Nobody accepted Noba's playful-sounding challenges and for very good reason.

This time, after fending off the gang, Noba said, "Come on, Charlie." Inside the store while Charles dried his eyes, he said, "Don't worry, those guys can't fight, they just talk. Come back and meet my mother."

My boy followed, realizing this was an honor. No one he knew had ever been invited into the living quarters at the back of the store. Noba pointed to a corner. "See Papa sitting there? Nobody can see him from the front but he can see the whole store reflected in that mirror. He sees when the kids take things. Sometimes we even let adults get away with stealing."

"Why do you do that, Noba?"

"Well . . . you know, they must need what they take, right? We *have* all we need. . . . Charles Mingus, this is my mother, Sumi Oke."

She was a short, strong, beautiful woman and she greeted Charles warmly. "Ah! You good boy. Mama-Oke know good boy. Noba good boy too. Boys out front bad, end bad in jail. Noba show you how to help self, so if they bother, you knock them all together. No more bother. Come, we show you."

She led the way back to a large storage room made into a gymnasium with straw mats covering the floor and swords, screened helmets, stitched bamboo sticks and padded garments hung along the walls. "All right, Charlie, lay your cello aside now and watch me," Noba said. He took a formal stance and held it for an instant—hands extended before him, one leg lifted to the side. He was strong and graceful, like a dancer. Swiftly he sat down, rose easily, sat and rose and sat again. He rolled back over his head and onto his feet all in one movement.

Charles watched fascinated. He didn't know then that his friend had a Fifth Dan Black Belt in judo.

Mosa came and stood in the doorway, relaxed, bracing himself with both hands against the door frame, swaying back and forth. "I have a better solution," he said in his cool, sly way. "How long's that sharp metal peg in your cello, Charlie?" My boy told him twenty inches. "A good weapon," said Mosa. "File down the point and give those guys a few jabs. Or maybe you'd like to borrow my samurai sword. I once chased them all the way down to a Hundred and Third with it."

"Come on, Mosa, let's show Charlie some judo," Noba said.

Mosa removed his glasses and slowly walked to the mat. The brothers stood face-to-face and bowed. Then Mingus saw a lightning-quick succession of throws, rolls, flips, flops and falls that he thought for sure would kill any of the bullies out front—except possibly Feisty.

After that they showed my boy how to bend his knees naturally and fall or sit fast so that if he got thrown—even on pavement—he'd be cushioned against the shock by his buttocks. Then they demonstrated how an attacker could be repulsed to a degree equal to the strength of the assault, and Noba said, "Train your eyes and reflexes to respond to the law that governs your opponent's mind and body. Forget yourself. Your life depends on what your enemy is doing. That's why, Charlie, if I fought any of those punks outside I'd have to hold back. Because those poor guys, their lives are so hard they're on the edge of insanity and whether they know it or not they want to kill, so I could just accidentally kill *them*, you understand?

Feisty used to test me by throwing boxer punches. I'd let
him hit me, ride with the punch, grab an arm and lift him
right off his feet. If I'd followed through on the roll he
would've flipped over and cracked his skull or broken his
back on the sidewalk. If you know judo, there isn't any
need to hurt anybody. . . . Now I'll show you how to
follow through if you ever need to. When I swing at you,
tune yourself to the law that governs my motion and grab
onto my sleeve, about here. Sit, roll back and kick up in a
pushing motion and let go of me just after you kick."

Noba swung in slow motion. My boy did what he'd
been told and Noba flipped over in a six-foot arc and
bounced up smiling. "Good," he said. "Now I'll show you
why a little knowledge isn't enough when two people have
studied the same subject." Again he swung and Charles
responded as before. Noba's feet flew up but this time he
held on to my boy's sleeve, spun in mid-air and grabbed
his leg and Charles somersaulted into a belly-flop, lungs
emptied of air, and found his left arm in a backlock vise.
Noba released him. "If you had known the third step, my
own force would have landed me on my back. But you
quit, Charlie. You stopped my motion and started your
own, which is an attack. In judo the man who attacks is
at a disadvantage. If you had followed me through instead of trying to save yourself from the fall, you would
have landed on your feet in a crouching position, understand? . . . Okay, that's all today. Don't forget, this is
just one lesson. You come here after school, and at lunchtime we can practice in the sawdust bin. When those
guys see you wrestling me they won't bother you any
more."

Mosa smiled. "That's right, Charlie. Forget your cello. Be a fighter."

"No, no!" Mama-Oke interrupted. "Noba speaks to his friend wisely. Good boy, Charlie, good boy. Noba and Mosa, take Charlie to Japanese school Saturdays. Teach him to be proud man. Then he play cello *better*. Charlie, call your mama, tell her you eat with us. Papa! Miko! Come! Dinner now."

T THE DINNER TABLE Mingus struggles with chopsticks in embarrassed silence until Mosa, amused, brings Western silverware. "You've practiced enough Oriental arts today. Eat your sukiyaki the easy way."

Charles is quietly thinking about what he has learned, and the Oke family, laughing and chattering musically in Japanese, leave him to his thoughts. For the first time in his life my boy has been taught something about self-defense. He wonders if he's a coward because he doesn't like to fight. But then he's never known how. Once he had asked his father to teach him and Charles Senior butted him with his head clear across the room and said, "That's your first lesson, son."

He thinks back to an embarrassing episode with Chester Lightfoot last year. One word led to another and Charles had doubled up his fists. Chester Lightfoot did the same and Charles noticed quite a difference as he looked at his own hands compared to Chester's big fists with the fingers curled tightly into the palms and thumbs locking over to form neat, compact sledgehammers—such deadly weapons that Charles cringed and turned and ran into his appropriately yellow-painted house, straight through and out into the safe, fenced-in back yard. His dog, Buster the Second, came over to comfort him.

Chester Lightfoot wasn't a bad guy though. He understood why Charles had picked a fight and he forgave him. But neighbors had seen and word got around and the gang teased and bullied more than ever, filching money from his pockets, threatening his cello and doing so many little meannesses that almost every day he was provoked to a wild, crying, helpless, fist-flailing rage.

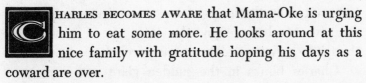 HARLES BECOMES AWARE that Mama-Oke is urging him to eat some more. He looks around at this nice family with gratitude hoping his days as a coward are over.

After supper he asks if he can leave his cello in the store overnight. He knows his father will be home by now and Mr. Mingus doesn't like the sound of children scratching on those damn instruments. Also he feels he should have both hands free in case he encounters Feisty and the gang.

The Oke family all stand smiling and bowing as he leaves. Mosa winks. "Charlie, don't you need your cello peg?" In answer, Charles drops to the floor, rolls back, kicks up with both feet and springs into the classic defensive stance and departs with their applause in his ears.

Y BOY USUALLY takes the long way home at night, the well-lighted main thoroughfare, Compton Avenue. But now he feels he can handle any situation and he heads down the dark San Pedro railroad tracks even though it does cross his mind that a neighbor, Johnny Mendosa's brother Manuel, had been stabbed to death here one evening as he walked home from band practice.

After One Hundred and Eleventh Street the tracks curve to the east. All's going well. Only a few blocks more. At One Hundred and Ninth he can see the Sander family playing on a homemade swing suspended from one of the few tall oak trees left in Watts. Mr. Sander has big bright lights strung over his yard to discourage thieves who might be tempted by the heaps of junk he collects, Lord knows what for. Maybe he enjoys the status title of "junkman"— though he survives mainly on county relief.

Charles blinks in the sudden glare and remembers how he used to wake before dawn in his soaking bed with the overhead bulb shining down in his eyes and Daddy standing over him with the strap. He's convincing himself he can hold his pee till he makes it home when a voice bellows out of the darkness and shocks him back to the present: *"Hey, you fat-ass half-yella schitt-colored nigger! I'll beat your ugly ass off! I'll knock your eyes out, mother-fucker!"*

Oh Lord, he thinks, it's the voice of Teddy Poole, the nastiest guy in the gang! A barrage of stones falls around him. Panicky, my boy scrabbles on the railway embankment for rocks and hurls them into the shadows toward the hoots and laughter. They crash into metal and Mr. Sander's great piles of old fenders topple with a terrible din. The ruckus brings people running from all directions—the Sanders, the Smiths, Moses, Harold, Minnie, C. I. Pauling, Walter Johnson, Mary Price, even Anthony Duane.

Duane wasn't a bully. His pastime was teaching younger boys to masturbate. If he was successful at that, he tried to persuade them to give him oral satisfaction, which he was glad to demonstrate to show there was no harm or evil in it. I'd say this young man observed carefully the Golden Rule, which urges us to do unto others as we would have them do unto us. There was a story that Thomas Bradley had succumbed to Anthony Duane's offer to teach him how such things were done and Thomas had literally flooded him, mouth, eyes, all over the face, with the substance of his response. Bradley held the Watts record for ejaculating—he could fill a pint milk bottle a little over three-quarters full. No one was ever able to match that, even with the stimulation of the underground French-style comic books full of amazingly humorous positions—Barney Google, Toots and Casper, Popeye and Olive Oyl and best of all, Snuffy and Betsy Smith. I do believe that Thomas Bradley's record is unbroken even in this atomic age of today.

So tonight in the eerie glare of Junkman Sander's lights Anthony Duane assumes his usual role of instructor, drawing a big ring and announcing, "I'll referee." Teddy dances about shadow-boxing. "I'll kill the little yella coward! Come on, schitt-face Charlie! Come on, bow-legs!" Charles is hoping he'll remember Noba's instructions as he tries to kick the broken glass and sharp rocks out of the arena. Impatiently Teddy runs forward and hits him in the jaw.

Wow! Does my boy react! He screams with rage! "Scum! Sissy! Coward bluff! Punk! Punk! Punk!"

Teddy is taken aback. His prey has turned on him, the target's exploding in his face! Charles is still scared but he prays to Jesus and his language improves. "Come on, do that again, you sonofabitch! Swing, dog! Motherfucker!" Teddy recovers and throws a tremendous roundhouse right. Charles steps in close, takes the punch, grabs Teddy's arm and rolls back on his haunches, jackknifes and pushes up hard and Teddy lands several feet away on a heap of broken glass and old bottles with my boy on his feet, crouched, waiting for the next assault.

Mrs. Sander runs out yelling. "Police! I'm calling the police! I'll tell your mother, Charles Mingus!"

Teddy just lies there like he's dead. Really frightened, my boy runs over to him. "Teddy, Teddy, I'm sorry! Come on, get up! You can beat me easy—I don't know how to fight!"

Slowly Teddy gets to his feet. "I'm not through with you yet, Mingus," he says dizzily and though Charles backs away there's something in his face that warns, "Don't push too far, man—'cause I know now you ain't schitt." Their eyes meet in understanding and Teddy says in a lower tone, "I'll let you go this time but next time you get whupped all over the streets! Come on, gang, he won't mess with me no more!"

Charles turns toward home with deep relief. But Teddy's closing statement echoes in his mind. Was he crazy, or them? Then as he walks down the weedy railroad tracks in the dark a big smile comes over his face and seems to warm his whole body. I am a little bit mystified with

my boy at this point. Here he's learned to fight, so why
didn't he finish Teddy off instead of giving him that "I'm
sorry" business? Oh, what's the use, there he goes again:
"Thank you, Jesus! Dear Jesus, thank you!" Charles, boy!
If Noba Oke hadn't taught you—oh-oh, now he's on
another tack: he's blaming himself for not stomping and
kicking Teddy when he was down, in the face, balls, anywhere, like he saw some men do outside the Compton Bar
on a Hundred and Twelfth Street. He's debating with
himself. One minute he believes his actions were soul-
saving and he's glad he didn't whip Teddy, for that would
humiliate and destroy him since that's all Teddy had. The
next minute he wishes he'd beaten the life out of the punk.
Then he decides he could never do that under *any* circumstances and hates himself for having destructive thoughts
about any human being. He figures he must be somewhere
in between Jesus and the Devil—closer to the Devil but
unable to perform a perfectly evil act. Finally he's grateful
that at least now he doesn't have to dread being out with
Lee-Marie some day and getting beat up right in front of
her eyes. That fear is almost gone. Of course, there's still
Feisty. But she'd understand if he hesitated to fight a boy
already in senior high—wouldn't she? But if Feisty went
too far, he'd certainly have a perfect right to split his head
or break his back with judo on the pavement, railroad
tracks or even off the Empire State Building!

And he reaches home thinking sadly of Lee-Marie.
He hasn't seen her since the day at the towers, but nothing
will ever change. He had phoned her the very next day
and she cried and said she could never see him again.
Aunt Ridey had told he was with them—she didn't know it

would do any harm—and her father beat her and locked her in her room. "Please, darling Charles, don't ever try to call me any more," she said, sobbing, and hung up.

"Fuck Mr. Spendell," Charles says to himself. "I'll call her tomorrow!"

AT THIRTEEN, my boy Charles arrived at the conclusion that there was more to life than people have time for. Important things came in such rapid succession that he'd hardly begun to solve a problem before another arose and each day burning questions were crowded out by new ones and disappeared into the past unanswered.

He began to realize he had some sort of mystic powers. He felt he was able to touch people, to contact certain souls in the next room or miles away or even those who had died. In later years he had this special kind of empathy with Farwell Taylor, an artist friend of his in Mill Valley, and they often experienced a mysterious awareness of each other while in different parts of the world.

Ever since Elsinore and the afternoon at Mr. Rodia's Charles had felt a telepathic communication with Lee-Marie. He was sure they were having the same dreams and thoughts and feelings at the same moments in time. So he wasn't at all surprised when he boldly asked for her number and she answered herself and said immediately, "Oh, Charles, I knew it was you!"

As if it were the most natural thing in the world and

they saw each other all the time, he invited her to go to the show at the Largo in Watts on Saturday afternoon. He knew she'd say yes and she did. The rest of my boy's week was full of anxious calculations. He'd already spent a nickel of his twenty-five-cent weekly allowance and he knew better than to ask for an advance. Admission price, a dime apiece. Ice cream sodas, fifteen each. He rummaged in Daddy's vest pocket, stuffed with Chinese lottery tickets and poker chips, found an extra quarter and copped it without a qualm. Total, forty-five cents. Five cents short can be as big a problem as five hundred dollars short, depending on circumstances. He knew he had to cut-rate his way in somehow. The kids told him Stewart Harrington, the Largo Theatre doorman and ticket-taker, was beyond bribery, but you could get an usher to sneak you in the back door for a nickel. Then you'd go out front, ask for a return pass, meet your girl at the candy store, pay for the sodas, take her back to the theater and buy her a real ticket and you're both safe inside. Total, forty-five cents.

All goes well. In the dark theater they sit side by side, full of the love they've saved so long, dying to kiss and touch and hold each other but scared of being noticed by Lee-Marie's sister Patricia sitting close by with their little brother. They think she must be aware of their wandering hands and uncontrollable deep breathing and fraudulent concentration on the movie screen they're staring at but neither of them really sees. Charles' hand, loving carefully, perfectly, slips into her sleeve to touch her naked little breast. Timid fingers feel around her nipple's areola as it swells, hardens and throbs. His hand slides down and tugs and finally her blouse is pulled free of her skirt. She covers

58

her lap and naked stomach with her coat as her slip is pulled away. His fingers crawl down the edge of her elastic panty band and press pleadingly. Her skin tightens to his touch, she bites her lips together with her teeth. Her stockinged foot caresses his leg. She spreads her thighs. Pains of delight crawl and squirm. Beads of warm perspiration seep into his palm as his fingers smooth the soft, fine little fuzz that grows from her navel down to her damp, hot pubis where a few scattered long hairs roll and twist around his fingers. This child, this woman, this wife! He holds her wrist as it slides inside his unbuttoned fly and his jacket covers her innocent, kneading hand. At last in a single thought together with little or no movement both reach a climax and turn to look into each other's eyes, slowly nodding their heads as the gradual letdown comes. Their moist fingers untangle. They rise. Lee-Marie leans toward her sister and whispers, "Stay here. I'll be back." Together they go out to the unromantic theater parking lot. Without a word they open their mouths to each other, drink each other's love taste, swallow, and in their magic oneness say at the same time: "I was you!"

"Is that what love is—being *one*, Charles?"

"I don't know. But I felt your thoughts. I read your mind."

"I did too!"

"We've always been like this, Lee-Marie." Charles takes her little hands. "But we can't do this again until we're grown and old enough to be married. We're going to wait." And she cries, "But I love you, I love you! I'm yours and you're mine now, tomorrow, forever!"

He buttons her blouse beneath the coat draped over

her shoulders and they look deep into each other's eyes, living for a brief moment on an isle of thought that exists until this very day.

FUNNY THING ABOUT LOVE. My boy was thirteen years old and he understood that in the eyes of the world they were only two small children and their passion was against every rule of God and man. "Man" was the powerful and dangerous adults surrounding them.

He stayed away from her for five long years after this happened. Sometimes he'd ring her on the phone, listen to her voice and hang up quickly, or go all the way to Southgate to walk past her house hoping to see her moving about inside the imprisoning walls. Sometimes she waved from a window and he could see her smile and he wondered if there were tears in her eyes, for there sometimes were in his. But he felt she knew his love and it was only a question of time before her family would consent to their courting.

ON MY BOY'S FIRST DAY at Jordan High, he arrived to find the older students conducting the traditional rite called "pantsing." As Charles entered the schoolyard six pairs of pants already flapped high on the flagpole before all the thrilled little girl onlookers. He was quickly spotted by Feisty. "Get that motherfucker with the cello!" he hollered at Peter Thompson and Snooky and the gang.

A mob is like a large cowardly animal with several heads and each head has a large, loud mouth backed by strong lungs and a frightened, overworking heart. Whether taking off pants or lynching a man, it has no ears and can't be reasoned with. Charles knew this and he had made plans. Running into the boys' lavatory, he tore off his shorts and flushed them down the toilet. Then he dressed and ran to the principal's office. "Mr. Doherty, they're pantsing fellows outside! I'm leaving my cello here."

Mr. Doherty, who weighed a solid three hundred pounds, stared at him coldly. "My father's a policeman," Charles lied. "You better protect this property—there's a mob out there!" He left his cello and went back to face the music.

"I oughtta hit you in the goddam mouth, nigger!" Feisty screamed. "You squealed to Doherty!"

Doherty appeared on the porch and graced the building with his picturesque broadside and bald-spot head. For a second Charles thought he was saved. The crowd quieted down as the principal addressed them: "I'm not going to say what you're doing is wrong as long as nobody's hurt and it's just good clean fun," and added, with a benevolent smile, "but don't be late for classes."

My boy jumped up the staircase above the principal's head, unbuckling his belt and swinging it around and shouting to the advancing students, "I don't have drawers on! I flushed my shorts down the toilet! If Fatso Doherty lets you strip me naked, what's the girls' parents gonna say?!" The girls murmured excited Ooohs! and Oh, mys! "Yeah, come look down my pants, you dumb thrill-seeking brawds! And when you do I'm gonna pull off every girl's pants in this crowd!"

The gang hesitated, struck by this great idea. Growling like a dog Charles jumped down and lunged among the girls, grabbing skirts and urging the boys on. "Go for the *chicks,* you dumb bastards!"

The girls began to scatter, running and screaming. "None of that now!" Doherty shouted. "Stop that, all you fellas!" But the boys were in full cry and one by one they caught the shrieking girls and then stood stupidly looking at my boy, waiting for his order to take their underpants! Charles suddenly realized his power and opened his mouth to say "Now!" He would have made history if all the neighbors hanging out of windows overlooking the school-yard hadn't started yelling: "Cops is coming!" A squad car rolled up and Doherty strode out to meet it with Charles at his heels. "No trouble at all, officers, just a little initiation fun with the boys! It happens every year." My boy capered around. "Yeah, good clean fun! Look, officer, I don't have no pants on!"

"ALL RIGHT BREAK IT UP YOU LITTLE NIG-GERS!"

The schoolyard cleared rapidly and Charles saw that Feisty and his gang had just faded away. He went back to get his cello thinking with astonishment that these were the very boys who had made his life a nightmare in grammar school and that with a little guts and know-how it wouldn't be hard to be a better leader than Feisty or any of the rest of those schitts.

ORDAN HIGH SCHOOL Symphony Orchestra, lacking a cello, had been waiting for my boy Charles, the child prodigy from One Hundred and Eleventh Street Grade School who had been so long with the Los Angeles Junior Philharmonic. But at fifteen he still wasn't prepared for difficult sight reading and worked mainly by solfeggio. With proper training his natural talent could have developed into superior reading ability if he hadn't been advanced to the Senior Orchestra under the direction of Mr. Lippi. On his first day such complicated pieces of music were set before him on his stand that he couldn't keep up and Mr. Lippi said so loudly, in front of everyone, adding in a patronizing tone, "However, I've noticed that most Negroes can't read."

Il Signore had a Florentine bias against any possible

63

descendants of the great Hannibal of Carthage who crossed the Alps in the Third Century B.C. stomping asses all over Italy with his less than forty elephants and over one hundred thousand big, black-jointed soldiers. When the conquerors, now reduced to thirty thousand, cooled into the cities it is historical fact that the young white ladies and women looted and raped the black soldiers for their *hardwares*, which may account for certain very dark Italian offspring down to this very day. And it is known that those few of the so-called aristocracy that are entirely blond and unmistakably blue-eyed look a little shady in the arm and leg pits.

Poor Charles kept watching his sister and wondering how she could sit there with all those other violins and play to Mr. Lippi's satisfaction when she couldn't read as well as he could at home and Mr. Arson had been her teacher too. Then he realized that Grace was following the other violins. But there was no other cello and he couldn't make it alone so he got up and went home and put his cello in the closet and lay down and said he wanted to die. Okay, I said, and started to cut out on him. You should have seen him jump out of that bed and start figuring out how to make it somehow.

He did go back to school but he was forced to stay in the band and orchestra classes, so he began playing around with the bass horn or any instrument that didn't need to show up for parades, football games or assemblies because inwardly he had quit. He felt he wasn't good enough to play again in public. Of course that feeling didn't last forever. A boy named William Marcell Collette who played clarinet in Mr. Lippi's Senior Orchestra had seen my boy's humiliation. He was an exceptionally good musician, already classically trained, and he just laughed at Charles's despair and commented, "You're a funny kid." That was Buddy, who later got him onto bass and helped brighten up his musical talent and finally his soul.

WELL, PREJUDICE from Signor Lippi was to be expected. After all, he thought of himself as white. But Watts had its own pecking order like any average American community of working Negroes still too busy slaving as free men to evaluate themselves and their true position in society. Some of the fellows, three, four, five years older, selected Charles as the underdog because, well, he was kind of a mongrel, lighter than some but not light enough to belong to the almost-white elite and not dark enough to belong with the beautiful elegant blacks, the kind that make a man like Bud Powell say to Miles Davis, "I wish I was blacker than you." There really was no skin color exactly like his. So he changed from burning his hair with his mother's hot-comb hair straightener to wetting it to make it kink up for the real beautiful natural dignified wiry and woolly look. Nobody accepted him, kinks or no. The black hate in the air for Whitey was turned on him, a schitt-colored halfass yella phony. Others could hiply call each other *black son of a bitch* or *nappy-headed nigger* but they took no "brother" schitt from him as he found out the hard-knuckle way at a party when he walked in and greeted Snookum Young with "Hello, Blackie!" and somehow found a knife swishing at his person. It could have been the day of his death. He was so careful after that he called the blackboard a chalkboard.

Whenever he looked in the mirror and asked "What am I?" he thought he could see a number of strains—Indian, African, Mexican, Asian and a certain amount of white from a source his father had boasted of. He wanted to be one or the other but he was a little of everything, wholly nothing, of no race, country, flag or friend.

So finally Charles gassed his hair straight and ran around with the other mongrels, the few Japanese, Mexicans, Jews and Greeks at Jordan High. The light Mexicans called themselves Spanish, the light Chinese said they were white. But even with them there were difficulties for they all spoke other languages and could shut him out when they chose. All he wanted was to be accepted somewhere and he still wasn't, so fuck it!

He became something else. He fell in love with himself. "Fuck all you pathetic prejudiced cocksuckers," he thought. "I dig minds, inside and out. No race, no color, no sex. Don't show me no kind of skin 'cause I can see right through to the hate in your little undeveloped souls."

I understood what he was trying to do. I've met a few other people who live on that colorless island.

DURING HIS SEVENTEENTH SUMMER he shined shoes and walked at least fifteen to twenty miles a day with his shine box, weaving up one block and down the next all the way uptown to Compton City's main street boulevard or five miles to downtown Los Angeles and on some weekends fifty miles out to Santa Monica and back traveling on his Union roller skates. He disappeared from his usual hang-outs and his friends didn't see much of him anymore.

He had a funny makeshift shine box that he'd found in the garage one day and he got some rags and brushes out of the house, fastened his belt to it for a shoulder strap, bought some shoe polish at the dime store and went walking out into the streets looking for business.

He was busy reading everything he could find in the library that went beyond his Christian Sunday School training—karma yoga, theosophy, reincarnation, Vedanta— and sitting on park benches he often became so engrossed in finding God that he forgot about shining shoes.

Sometimes down by the Million Dollar Theatre he'd see Eden Abez, a poet-mystic who wore long white robes and later wrote a song called "Nature Boy." They'd look at each other and speak with their minds in silent thought about the God of love and nod their heads and walk their separate ways.

This day as he leaned against a lamppost at the corner of One Hundred and Third Street and San Pedro reading a book and waiting for customers, a tall handsome young black man walked up to him and said, "Are you the kid that plays cello? Remember me? I'm Buddy Collette." He introduced the boys with him—Major Harrison, Charles Martin, Crosby Lewis and Ralph Bledsoe, who were all laughing and grinning though Charles failed to see anything funny.

"How'd you like to make bread and wear the sharpest clothes in the latest styles?" Buddy asked. "Look at yourself. You dress like a hobo."

"I don't dig clothes any more."

"How'd you like to have the finest chicks in town?" Charles said he wouldn't mind that at all.

"All right, join the Union," Buddy said. My boy knew he didn't mean Local 47 of the A.F.M. The Union was a private Watts club that had started out collecting dues from shoeblacks, newsboys and soda jerks in return for providing "protection" against bullies and rowdies like Feisty and his crew. All the victim had to say was "I paid my Union dues" and he was safe. Lately the Union's interests had shifted to music and their private parties and social gatherings were causing plenty of gossip and speculation all over Watts.

"Go get yourself a bass and we'll put you in our Union swing band," Buddy told my boy. "We can use you."

"Get a *bass*?"

"That's right. You're black. You'll never make it in classical music no matter how good you are. You want to play, you gotta play a *Negro* instrument. You can't slap a cello, so you gotta learn to *slap that bass*, Charlie!"

Charles liked the way Buddy talked and admired his proud carriage and adult manner and extreme good looks so he went home and discussed it with his father, explaining he had a chance to make a lot of money if he traded his cello for a bass. His parents, as usual not really knowing but hoping for the best, agreed to help. Next day he and Daddy Mingus went down to Schirmer's on Broadway in midtown Los Angeles and turned in the cello for a brand-new German-made double bass and Daddy forked over one hundred and thirty dollars in addition.

E WAS IN A HURRY to begin dating the finest chicks in town so my boy called Britt Woodman and asked for Joe Comfort's number. Joe was the bass player with the Woodman Brothers, the best young jazz band in Watts.

"How can I learn to play bass, Joe?"

"Got one?"

"Yeah."

"Turn on the radio and start right in playing with it. That's how I started."

Not even knowing the names of the strings or how to tune his instrument, Charles began practicing hour after hour standing by the RCA Victor console radio in the living room and after a few weeks he began to get the feel of it. He could follow what he heard, using cello fingering.

He called Joe Comfort again and said, "I think I can play it now. How do I tune it?"

"How you been tuning it?"

"I just left it like it came from Schirmer's. Top to bottom it goes zom zom zom zom." Charles hummed E A D G.

"Man, that's backwards! That's violin tuning. You gotta start all over again. Tune it G D A E."

"How does that go?"

Joe Comfort hummed the notes. "Tune it up right like that and keep practicing with the radio and get some records too. When I meet you on the street I'll give you a lesson."

"Take the cover off my bass on the street?" Charles asked, astonished.

"No, man, play it with the cover on. You learn it better that way. When you take it out there's nothing to it."

Later Charles discovered that Joe could play any instrument by ear. This was his thing. He never even tried to read. He'd hear the parts and go on to the right notes. Britt said Joe could hear a note before it started to vibrate. "But anybody who isn't as fast as Joe," Britt said, "better learn to read a little. Anyway don't worry, Charlie, because mainly all bass players do is keep time."

10

WHEN CHARLES WAS LITTLE I used to see him run to meet his father shrieking with joy "Daddy! Daddy! Guess what happened to me today!" and I sometimes wondered if his father heard him at all. "Um," was all he'd say or "How're ya, boy," and pass on by. I watched my boy's attitude toward this unresponsive "Daddy" person change through the years till he was greeting him with a disinterested "Hello" and finally when he became a little-too-hip young musician with simply a cool "Hey."

Though he wasn't conscious of his longing for a father anymore, it was still there. So when he met Buddy's father at the Collette house after a rehearsal he was emotionally stirred and deeply envious. There was such an air of friendship and ease between this father and son and Charles admired it so, he thought if he wanted to know anything about life he'd ask Pop Collette, not Daddy Mingus.

One day Pop Collette said to him, "Charles, you're a handsome young man. Got any money?"

"Not yet," said Charles, embarrassed. "Nothing's happening."

"Why, a handsome boy like you should be able to get money from all those pretty little girls you know at school. They all got a dollar or two for books or a few cents for candy. Their papas and mamas, they all got some money. You should talk them out of it. You got to start thinking about that."

Charles had never heard this kind of talk before or any kind of talk at all from a grown man, though he was now sixteen years old. His father never told him anything and it was flattering to have Buddy's father treating him just like another fella. Charles began to frequent the Collette house and the youthful-seeming father now and then gave little lectures to the boys on the art of making love.

He told them sex was important and not meant to be dirty. "Don't waste your youth," he said. "Don't masturbate. Learn to control yourself. Find out about girls. It's a lifetime tease if you let them go on fooling you. Listen to me and you'll see they want you more than you want them. This is the whole art of sex between a man and a woman. They'll pay for this understanding kind of a man because most men think a woman don't like sweets the way he do, that she thinks it's nasty what he wants to do to her. So when she accept it in the end, he treat her like she's a receptacle, a come machine. He don't even pat her on the head when he's finished. There was a wise old man told me a story once. He said, 'If you try what I'm going to tell you, every woman you touch will come back for more of your sweets and she'll tell you these same words: she'll tell you she ain't never had nothing like that done to her in her life before.' That's what the old man said, and I should charge you boys for this advice. Someday you gonna walk right in and hand me some money and say, 'You sure was right, Collette.'

"What this old man told me was, for those who don't have the natural talent, here's some good rules for fucking. Kiss her. Play with her awhile. Then insert your peppermint stick, just the knob, the head of it. Rub it all up her split for a long time over the clitoris, in just a little bit and out, from bottom to top and around until she's warming up to you. You gonna make love like this for hours, kissing, playing, sucking her breasts and fingering that good pussy till she's begging for you. Then you don't just ram it in. You put the head in sorta gentle and easy."

All this was shocking coming from an adult. Charles was blushing but Buddy was smiling, he'd heard it all before. He and Charles discuss those lectures sometimes now in their manhood.

Pop went on, "After it's good and moist, seeping all through the sheets, you don't give her all that white-folk freaky stuff. Just plain old good fucking. The best position that old man found was on one side with her on her back, 'cause he was a big man. She's about dying from waiting now, but you're just teasing, gradually giving it to her. Stay in for just a little while to let her know what kind of sweets you got but pull back if she reaches up for it, all the way out and around the edges of the lips. Then all of a sudden you hit it hard and deep as you can and hold it there firm and tight and rock from side to side. Then draw back, almost out. Tease. Move every which way but so easy she can barely feel it move. Tighten and loosen its muscles. That gives her a throbbing sensation. She'll start reaching for it again. Pull away. Just when she gives up and settles on her ass hit it in hard and deep as you can, draw it out fast and hit it quick again. Don't move for an instant after it's all the way in. Hold it tight and rock, then draw it out again easy. This time let her soft flesh cling to you—she'll try to follow and keep it up inside her. Now she starts to beg you and everything to hit it for her like you just did. Don't do it. Just play and tease some more. If she ain't never done anything like this, she'll start getting frantic, crying and begging. Then—*when you make up your mind to*—let her have it again hard, fast and deep. Hit it and hold it in there and rock from side to side, kiss her and hold her in your steady rock. Then ease it back and pretend you're gonna quit. Take it out. And if she don't grab you and plead and beg you to please fuck her *your* way then you can have one of them Cadillacs sitting out there! . . . Now, Charles, you try that on the next little girl you get. Watch the difference to her response. See if she don't tell you these very words: 'Charles, I never had it done to me like that in my life!' And see if you don't want to pay me fifty to one hundred dollars for the results you get."

11

WHEN MY BOY CHARLES WAS SEVENTEEN and a Junior in high school his pal Britt Woodman rushed up to him one day. "Man, I had a rehearsal for a record with the greatest bass player possible! He sounded like a horn. His name is Red Callender, did you ever hear of him?" "No, but I'd sure like to." "I'll ask Les Hite if I can bring you to rehearsal tomorrow."

GEORGE CALLENDER was a tall redhead with light brown skin and a freckled face and the physique and build of an athlete. He was super-cool, his movements were slow, and in everything he did he seemed at ease. He was only two years older than Charles although the books said different because California state law required that a person working on the premises of a joint selling liquor had to be at least twenty-one years of age.

Charles went to the record date and the minute he heard Red play he wanted him to be his teacher. He told Britt, "Man, in the break he was sitting alone playing

75

'Body and Soul.' I was so surprised to hear anybody
doing that with a bass—using the bow like in the things
Menuhin and Heifetz play—up high in the harmonic positions, like, you know, Bartok's violin concerto—de ya do,
do e de la—Britt, when I start really learning to play
people will see me big, with a big bass, but when I want
it they'll hear a viola, my magic viola that plays high as a
violin and low as a bass and gets rid of all the muddling
undertones and produces a pizzicato sound with the
clarity of Segovia! Callender was doing something like
that—I've got to study with him."

Red was married to a girl named Irma who had two
children by a previous marriage and they shacked at
Irma's parents' house. My boy went there once a week and
Red taught him bowing and Franz Simandl's funda-
mentals of bass playing. He charged Charles two dollars every time and then spent it taking him to the local
movie houses after their work was over. A brotherly
friendship and lifetime relationship grew out of these
lessons.

Now Charles was becoming so involved in composing
that Buddy thought he should go to Lloyd Reese to study
piano too. Reese and his wife, a classical pianist, had a
conservatory on McKinley Avenue in Los Angeles. He was
considered the greatest all-around teacher and a fine
instrumentalist himself. He was said to be able to hang
a trumpet on a string from the ceiling and play a high G
by use of the buzz system—blowing into the mouthpiece
without touching the horn with his hands. Many of the
boys who later became famous studied with him and
played with his big student rehearsal band on Sunday

afternoons. Eric Dolphy worked his way through Reese's school by cutting the grass and hedges. He used to sit on the steps watching the band rehearsals. He was younger than the others and my boy didn't know him then but years later in the East he became a mainstay in Mingus groups.

So Charles was having a very full musical life, what with the school orchestra, studying with Callender and Reese, playing what gigs they could get with Collette and the Union swing band and using any leftover hours to practice and compose at home.

About this time a beautiful Mexican girl named Manuela came into his life. His sister Grace's high school girls' club gave a dinner party called "A Trip Around the World" and each dollar ticket buyer could visit a whole series of homes to sample their native cooking—Spanish, Chinese, East Indian, Greek, Jewish, Italian, American Indian, Japanese, Mexican—Watts had them all. The evening would end at midnight when the whole crowd gathered for a soul food feast with the entire repertoire of slave dishes right down to rattlesnakes.

But when Charles arrived at the third family on his list, the Rodriguezes, he took one look at their daughter Manuela and decided to stay put. Suddenly he became an aficionado of their south-of-the-border food and stayed on asking for seconds and thirds till the family were so flattered they opened a big jug of wine. And sitting there eating and drinking and laughing with these friendly Mexicans he felt so at home he found himself telling them about his longtime love for Lee-Marie.

Some weeks before, he had heard she was going to be

in a fashion show in Watts. He hadn't seen her in so long he couldn't stay away so he walked downtown toward San Pedro Boulevard and who should pull alongside and offer a lift but Mr. Spendell himself! Charles was overjoyed at this sign of friendship but Spendell wasted no time making it plain that kindness was not his motive. It turned out he knew all about the Saturday afternoon at the Largo Theatre four years before and of Charles's recent efforts to see his daughter again. Charles tried to explain how they'd stayed apart of their own free will all these years, but now that they were getting older . . . Mr. Spendell looked at him as if he were insane. "Maybe you didn't hear me," he said. "I'm ordering you to stay away from Lee-Marie *forever*. Or else we'll have to do something about it like finding you an alley to sleep in." The threat didn't frighten Charles though Spendell was in his bank-guard uniform and wearing a gun, but he was deeply hurt and sad as hell, for hard as it was, hadn't he and Lee-Marie made their own decision to stay apart because they thought it was right? And they'd waited so long. . . . Looking at Mr. Spendell's hard face, he felt like weeping.

At the fashion show Lee-Marie saw him standing far in the background. Their eyes held as if the last day for love were now. He went home without speaking to her and composed at the piano long into the night, feeling her there with him, sad as he had seen her, swaying, bowing, as the breeze blew the pretty gowns she wore in the outdoor fashion show of Watts's Elite Department Store.

He told Manuela's family this story and they sympathized because Manuela too had been hurt by a lover. "You and Manuela are both lonely," her brother Juan said. "You can be friends." And at midnight Juan and Manuela and Mingus took off for the wind-up of the evening, the Harlem-style party—whew! That fried chicken! Those steaming chitlins, all those sweating jitterbugs! Too much, too much! Mingus was almost happy that night.

E AND MANUELA went swimming together and he took her to dances and movies. His respect for her and for her family and the fact that he constantly heard his parents reminding his sisters that all men wanted was to get into their bloomers (a ridiculous thing—those big, black, blousy homemade drawers!) kept him from pressing her to go further than a little light petting.

It was Manuela who became impatient and it turned out she had advanced ideas. The flat-topped garage in her backyard had what they called a "roof garden," with a hammock and shrubbery and overhanging trees. One evening when he brought her home she took him up there and after they had kissed a while she pulled up her dress —"I no wear pants, see, Charles?" She begged him to feel the long hair over her "pinchy"—how black yet soft like cornsilk it was! "Feel it, Charles. It's for you, because of your kisses. Look when I open my sweater. See my *chichis?* I never wear nothing on them. See how they don't fall down? We don't use brassieres in my country. We are real women. We're not ashamed to show we have bosoms that are hot and that we love to get them sucked.

We can tell when a man is ready and hot and good to fuck. We love to fuck with him too. Fuck me now, Charlie. Oh! I knew your *macoula* was hard and hot for my ace! Oh! Oh, I love it! Push it up hard. Fucky, fucky, fucky. I fuck you, you fuck me everywhere! No one can see us under the trees. Now fuck between my *chi-chis*. See, I kneel. Ai chi wow wow! I like your taste. Here now, we lay in the hammock some too. *Madre mia,* how you stretch me when your fucks start! Like this, like that . . . *Chingala, chingala tu madre!* Oh, I'm coming, Mingus! Come in it, juice my split, fuck, Mingus!"

"You chile cunt bitch! You got me now! Come on, baby! Sloppy pop your cunt!"

"Oh, I love it, I love it!"

IT WAS A WAY-OUT EXPERIENCE for a few months and then my boy began to get nervous. All Manuela wanted to do every night was go up on the garage roof and take out her big titties and press them in his face and mouth and finally make love in every possible way for hours. He felt her parents knew what was happening but they didn't seem to care and she was so wild she didn't want him to even use the rubbers he bought at Raleigh's drugstore. He was afraid he'd give her a baby and then what would happen?

He began to see more of other girls, especially Rita Reed, a smooth-complexioned black girl so beautiful that he and Buddy called her "the race horse."

But the day he dreaded arrived. For some reason—maybe she thought she was losing him—Manuela discussed their relationship with her parents. He was so shamed by their civilized reaction that on impulse and maybe trying to justify his behavior he heard himself proposing to Manuela in front of her entire family and he was accepted on the spot. Fortunately he was underage by California laws and had to get his own parents' permission to marry. Daddy came through as Charles had hoped with a violent refusal and added that insanity ran in the Mingus family and that Charles was just lucky so far to be more or less in his right mind. He accused Manuela of being immoral and unfit to be a wife anyhow. Charles indignantly defended his girl but he knew and he realized his father knew he knew that they were playing out a scene and there was a secret smile between them of which poor Manuela was unaware. This private understanding brought back hopes for a new closeness and love between him and his father but it was years more before it came about.

THOUGH IT WAS CLEAR no marriage was possible at present Manuela was eager as ever for the roof-garden scenes and even more demanding. At last he hatched a wild scheme to break away and one evening at the playground in front of her brother Juan and his Mexican friends he announced he was going to kill himself because his father refused to let him marry Manuela. He had been drinking wine and he poured a whole bottle of iodine in it and gulped it down dramatically. The police ambulance came—he'd counted on that—and he was rushed to the Watts clinic, the very same place

Baby Charles had been taken with a hole in his head. They pumped out his stomach and put him to bed.

Soon Manuela arrived with her brother and mother, in tears. They said they understood and would wait. "As long as Manuela's happy, that's all that matters. You can even live with us, if your father will let you," said Mrs. Rodriguez tenderly. Juan said, "My brother, don't do things like hurting yourself. You're our friend. Our people are not funnies like gringos—my house is yours and my sister too. But not my wife or my father's wife, you understand. You get some rest and then come home with Manuela."

Manuela stayed after her mother and brother left. "Mingus, we can love each other as much as you please. You no heard Juan? Don't worry, I will not have baby. I'm a woman, not a stupid child. Ai, we fuck because we love it. You never said you love me. I don't care. We fuck better than anybody. So I tell Papa and Mama we marry some day. But don't worry, we don't have to marry to fuck."

My boy Charles closed his eyes hopelessly, thinking he was not sure he ever wanted to fuck again.

12

CHARLES HAD BEEN STUDYING with Red Callender for about a year when one Saturday afternoon he was in his room at home working out an arrangement of "I'll Never Smile Again" for the Union band and the phone rang in the key of F flat. "Hello? Hey, Lee Young, how you, man? . . . Art Tatum? Sure I know Art Tatum—'least I've *spoken* to him at sessions. What? You kidding? Wow, I'm honored! My ego's gone up one million points! Sure I can make it—when? What's the address? Got you, Lee. Thanks. Listen, say hello to your brother Lester and the other guys in the combo—Bumps and Red Mack and Red Callender—you know he's my teacher? O.K., Lee, I'll sure be there and thanks again." . . . Wow! Did my boy know Art Tatum! Everybody knew about this wonderful blind pianist out of Toledo, Ohio, who had caused great excitement among musicians when he turned up at the Onyx Club on Fifty-second Street in New York and at the Three Deuces in Chicago and was now a legend at the age of thirty-one.

"Dad, how about a ride uptown? Lee Young just called and said Art Tatum wants to see me! I've gotta be at his house at four p.m. to rehearse for a duo! I'm gonna work with a genius, Pops!"

"All right, son, I'll run you up to Tatum's place. Mamie, fix this boy something to eat and we'll be getting out of here. . . ."

"There's the house on the north side of the street, Pops—thirty-eight twenty-six and a half. That's it, right there!"

"All right, all right, I see it. Can you get home on the streetcar with that bass?"

"Sure, I'll just take the V car line back to Watts. Thanks, Pops, 'bye. . . . Hello! I'm Charles Mingus. Mr. Tatum sent for me!"

"Come in, Charles. Remember me? I'm Carol. Your sister and I were best pals at Jordan High."

"Why, hi, Carol! I remember you before that. I used to go to your father's grocery store sometimes when I'd visit Britt, remember?"

"That's a long time back. You were just a little boy then."

"Well, I'm in my last year at Jordan High now. Where shall I put my bass cover? Is he here?"

"Yes, I'm here, boy. Hello there, Mingus. Callender's been telling me you're coming along just fine with your fiddle. Well, we'll see in a minute. You just stand here by the piano and I'm going to work with you and show you what I'm doing. Later, if we get something going, I'll tell my agent and we'll try it out on the people."

"Okay by me, Mr. Tatum!"

"All right, here's how I do 'All the Things You Are.' One, two, three, four . . . . Now let's take it again.

84

Look, I'll show it to you slow. You still taking piano and composition over at Lloyd Reese's? Good. Now digest this on the piano first, so you can get the voicings and the nuances. . . ."

The rehearsals continued for several hours a day for many weeks. Sometimes they went on playing together all afternoon, whatever came into their heads.

"Come on, son. Least we can play for some kicks, I don't believe Whitey can stop us from that. Got the change I showed you in D natural on 'Night and Day'?"

"Yeah, Art, I got them on piano, dig? Go on."

"Hey, watch out there, boy—you stealing my stuff!"

"Aw, Art. You're—what can I say? There's Jesus, Buddha, Moses, Duke, Bird and Art."

"Wait a minute, son. You added an E flat in that A flat chord that descends chromatically. Now Buddha wouldn't done that. Just A flat and G flat in the left hand. See? B natural, D natural, F sharp on top. It's pure, son, pure beauty. That E flat don't go in there, that goes in another kind of composition."

And afterwards Mingus would go home on the streetcar, lugging his bass, exhausted, happy, and knocked out with musical ideas.

But though my boy could hardly wait, no bookings ever came up for the duo and finally Art Tatum went on the road as a single again and it was a long time before they played together professionally.

BUDDY COLLETTE had this little 1935 hunter-green Auburn sports touring car and ran around with the downtown chicks—Indian, Mexican, colored, white brawds—any kind that liked to be worked on Union style.

This particular Sunday night they'd planned a Union bash and Charles was going to get his chance to check out Pop Collette's theories of conquest. Buddy and the guys had picked up some new downtown girls at a party the night before and Charles had a date with Rita the Race Horse—tall, ebony black, a beautiful, graceful girl, about the most beautiful woman he'd met so far in his life, with soft, fuzzy, woolly hair cut neatly to fit her elegant bone structure. She was a wild and sexy-looking brawd and her arrogance showed she knew it.

Buddy called a meeting. Major Harrison, Charlie Martin, Crosby Lewis and Ralph Bledsoe were there. "No gas money tonight," he said. "We're gonna have to hit the can, I guess. It's your turn, Chazz."

My boy didn't know what that meant so Buddy explained the method. "After dark, we take this can here and cruise around looking for a healthy tank. It takes twenty-seven minutes to fill a five-gallon can with this douche-bag hose we use and if someone comes out and sees us we gotta run and it means get the can, man! The car don't slow down so you gotta be fast. Mingus puts the can out and Crosby's the retriever. Mingus, you know how to siphon?"

Charles said he'd learned how when he worked at Mr. Woods's garage.

As it grew dark they drove around looking for a gas-tank prospect. Buddy said he could usually tell from the appearance of a car whether or not the owner had enough money to fill his tank every payday.

There's one now! Right in front of the old Baptist Church in Central Gardens. Everything's quiet, services are going on inside and the neighborhood people are having supper. Mingus drops off the running-board with the can and Crosby's right behind him as the lookout. Buddy cruises on at normal speed. Nobody's around. The parked car is under a tree, shaded from the overhanging street light. It's good and dark. Wow! A healthy tank! Charles puts the can under the bumper. It doesn't even show. He adds a rubber band to each end of the hose to make it stick tight. He sucks a mouthful of gas and spits it out. He thumps the hose to make sure the gas is flowing.

He and Crosby catch Buddy on the run at the corner of Grape Street, two blocks away. They drive around awhile waiting out the time. Crosby comments approvingly on the rubber bands. "This time it's okay, Mingus," Buddy says, "but from now on don't improve on Union methods without consulting the prez."

After twenty-five minutes church begins to let out. Mingus, wanting to prove himself, begs Buddy, "Let me retrieve. I'll hit it on the run." "Nope, too risky now," Buddy answers. The next time around the block the owner is leaning against his car and the preacher stands by his big beige Cadillac with the sisters crowding all around him giggling and vying for his attention and telling him what a wonderful sermon it was. As they drive slowly by they see the can has overflowed and the gasoline is running in the gutter. "Damn!" Major says, "I *thought* that hose looked wider than the one we used to use."

"That sure is a healthy tank, though!"

"Buddy, go by one more time. I'm gonna get it."

"Don't be stupid, Mingus. You want to get busted?"

"Well, now," says Buddy, "we can't chicken out when a new member comes on strong and sincere like this."

"Thanks, Buddy, I won't let you down. I can run the hundred-yard dash in ten and nine-tenths flat wearing a football suit."

"Yeah? Then you better break your record tonight 'cause we come in at fifteen miles an hour and don't slow down. You drop off and get the can. If you don't catch up, too bad. Meet us home if you don't get caught. If you do, no squealing. Remember the Union!"

Again they circle the block. Major leans out and covers the license plate with a handkerchief as they start their fifteen-mile-per-hour steady run. A quarter of a block from the car Charles jumps out and sprints past the Auburn. Elder Washa Moola stands at the curb puffing a big cigar and twirling a gold watchchain, the big cat-eye size diamond ring on his little finger glittering like a tiny sunbeam. He's wearing an English bowler hat, gambler striped pants, black sports coat, white tattersall-checked vest and patent leather shoes. He casually flicks sparkling red ashes into the gutter and remarks, "Sisters, we certainly stirred the spirit here tonight. All them sinners gonna burn in fiery hell!"

A puff of smoke and blue-red flames shoot up above his head! Black smoke billows toward the sky! My boy grabs the can and runs for the far side of the Auburn. Women are screaming—"Oh, my Lord, save us! He done created a miracle! Amenhotep! The world done come to its sinful end! Praise his gracious name!"

"Oh, my Lord! Them boys done stole my gas! Catch that yella one running there!"

Old preach runs out, swishing at my boy's ass with his straight-edge razor. Charles sidesteps. The reverend's knee buckles, his other leg shoots up in a jitterbug kick and throws him into a spin that lands him on what Jesus Christ sometimes rode into the city to speak to the people. "Lawd, my britches busted open!" he yells. "Holy Moses, look at my Cadillac, all smoked up from them flames! Wipe off the Lord's chariot! Call the police!"

"There they go!" people are shouting. "Catch 'em! Get their plate number! Lord save our place of worship from fiery ruin!" Horns are honking, cars are starting all over the place. But Charles has made it back to the car and Buddy says coolly, "Keep the rag over the plate, Major. Here we go. Hang on, fellas."

He guns to fifty, sixty, swerves onto the straightaway and surges to seventy, eighty, ninety and flying, we take off at one-hundred-and-twenty miles per ´hour up San Pedro Highway. Mingus is scared. He's never traveled that fast except on the roller-coaster. But suddenly everybody is patting him on the back and laughing as Buddy slows down to the speed limit and turns off toward downtown. Charles feels good, born again. He's finally in with the fellas, accepted. "Wow, Mingus, we gonna tell Rita what a bad cat you are! We gonna have a ball, man! Like kings with harems and all that schitt tonight!"

They fall by Rita's to pick up the chicks. Then they get

mustard, marshmallows, bread buns, beer, wine and pot for a Union-style wienie roast and head out for the beach.

Mmmmmm! Long wienies roasted black till they're almost bursting and dripping with juice, splashing in those red-hot charcoals. Mmmmm! Hot juicy buns split open and French-style mustard daubed all inside them. Toasted coconut marshmallows held over beautiful white-ashed black and red glowing coals, their white syrupy insides foaming out, dripping down, sizzling and spitting as they're scorched to ashes, their sweet aroma seeping through the fresh salt air. Flaming red-hot fireballs popping and crackling in the hole dug deep in damp sand. The still sound of silence behind the sea breeze. Down below, the waves splashing and the white tide washing against the cruel granite rocks near the underwater cave that those who knew called the Cove of Love.

CHARLES IMPROVISED a poem of pure seduction to Rita's eloquent ebony silhouette as the moonlight haloed her bosom and hips and classic statuesque form. He was enchanted, exalted to heights of sensual ecstasy he'd never felt before. Lee-Marie had been the pure object of his soul's love, Manuela the over-willing and over-submissive passionate aggressor. But tonight he intended to conquer a goddess. He was going to get that fine ass.

Everyone was noisy now, getting high on beer and wine, smoking pot—except for Buddy who calmly drank soda pop, examined and compared bosoms and legs like a judge at a beauty contest and played his clarinet and

Major's drums—sock cymbal, snare and brushes. The girls were dancing and running around pulling off their clothes, bucking the salt air, seductively slipping a brassiere off a shoulder, doing the breakback and slyly pulling their panties aside at the groin.

Rita fondled Charles's ears, bit gently into the back of his neck. Marian stripped completely and danced to the drums, shaking up close to Major's face. He took the warm wienie from his bun, sucked and licked off the mustard and suddenly grabbed her as if he had just become aware of her nudity, threw her back, sucked and kissed her breasts. Then all down, and he left the wienie where he'd put it and began kissing all over her, breathing deep and fast, sucking the air in between his teeth with a Whew! "Marian, cock your jelly roll buns up here higher to me." He moved the wienie in and out and at first we thought he was eating it, but he was eating high above it with long sucking breaths, popping his tongue inside his mouth, *tut tut*. And finally he ate the wienie.

Rita called out "Mingus!" and ran easily toward the surf, undressing. Charles followed, tearing off his clothes and shouting, "I'm swimming nude with Cleopatra tonight!"

"Cleopatra hell! I'm a purer, prettier black than that black bitch!" Rolling over and over in the churning, splashing, raging sea, the white, angry foam seeming to float between the dark water and the dark sky, Rita was swallowed by the ocean. It covered her heavenly curves except for the shining buttocks and as she turned and floated on her back, her swelling bosom. The sparkling waters swished and foamed between her thighs. Mingus stood startled and erect till she tumbled in with the waves and they were kneeling on the wet sand, seaweed twisting and entangling their ankles, salt water tightening his smooth hard neck and wrinkled foreskin, tiny wet grains of sand biting teasingly into his swollen, throbbing heart-shaped head. Rita stared at this primitive, savage beauty, stiff out, harder than it ever was at the peak of self-gratification. She reached her hand out and pointed him higher toward the sky. Her smooth hands caressed gently over and around the neck and tight drawn-up sac protecting two tremendous black pearl pendants and handled them with studied care. She bent her head to them and said "You're colored, like me. Big, beautiful, hard, with these Taurus sacs—black as I am, Mingus!"

For the first time Charles felt completely accepted by a black Negro. He swayed, trembling. Caressing and stroking Rita's soft, fuzzy hair was a new and electric experience. It tickled his palms and fingertips. He thought with distaste of the girls with processed hair. She pulled him down to the sand and moved over on top, straddling him, her breasts dangling over his face, then leaned back and spread her knees wide, reaching under her legs and caressing him into her loin. Warm ocean waves splashed over their bodies and ran out smoothly and splashed in again. A shadow loomed behind them.

"Buddy! You big lanky black bastard! You been spying! Go on back, you got your two but not this one."

"Naw, you got me wrong, Mingus—Major and the girls swam out to the cave, I'm taking some food and stuff in this oilskin, see? We're gonna build a fire. Want to join us?"

They could see Major and the two girls bobbing beyond the big rocks. The entrance to the secret cavern was a hole a yard below the water line. Surfacing, you came up into a space the size of a living room with dry, sandy ledges.

"Later, man," Mingus said, and Buddy waded in and struck out for the rocks with his bundle on his shoulder. My boy drew Rita back into the warm waves and held her close. Slowly, slowly and deliberately, he began to move and make her move with him until she yielded to his rhythms. Then he held back and she began to beg. "Don't tease me, baby, fuck me! You go so easy, baby. A little while ago I couldn't take it in me. Now I want it and you just give me the head! Fuck me, man! Give it to me, daddy! Now, right now, please! Oh! Yeah! Um! You bastard! Bring it back, daddy. *Please*. Keep it in there. Rock it in there deep! I'll hold it with my muscles. . . . I'll make you stay!"

"You're kind of strange, Rita baby. . . It feels like you got a crazy mouth inside chewing and biting me."

"That's my muscles, daddy. I gotta put my dogs on you! I used to hear my Daddy say to Mama, 'Lord, baby, get them dogs off me, I'm helpless!' Oh, Mingus, come back, you dirty motherfucker, damn you, come back in —what are you doing to me?"

"Practicing."

"What?"

"How to make a bitch ask for more. Come on, let's swim out to the cove."

"I ought to kill you, Mingus, for leaving me wanting it like this!"

"Who's leaving you, you fine-cunted whore? There's

more coming and the way to get it is do what I say. Come on."

Charles swam toward the rocks and Rita submissively followed. My boy laughed out loud with his new feeling of power and thanked his stars for Pop Collette.

13

CHARLES FELT EMBARRASSED because the girls from the sixth period gym class in their white blouses and black shorts were hanging on the fence and watching the football players and giggling, though by now he should have been used to having them make fun of his bow-legs and pigeon-toes. And he was conscious every second of the presence of Lee-Marie, standing alone and apart and not seeming to know he was there. He went close to the fence and whispered to Rachel and Kate, "How come you didn't laugh over at Buddy's pad last Friday, girls? You saw more of my bow-legs than I'm showing now. Up to *here*, dig, baby?" He walked away thinking to himself I don't dig no bitches that can be talked into making love to two cats at a time anyway—made me sick watching 'em.

He trotted out on the gridiron, aware of Lee-Marie, who never was looking at him when he glanced her way. But somehow over and under the laughter and cheers and boos from the fellows and girls clinging to the fence he knew she was speaking to him though her lips didn't move. The call became so strong that at the end of the quarter he had to go directly to her, not knowing whether

95

she wanted it or not, but when they looked at each other through the steel-link barrier it felt as though she were inside him—like they were one again.

"What were you saying to me, Lee-Marie?"

"That I love you, and that you need me now. Have you forgotten me?"

Charles held onto the fence, looking down at his pigeon-toes, shaking his head. "I don't understand."

"Then listen. I'm a woman now and I've waited over five years since that day at the Largo. You haven't tried to come to me. Oh, sometimes at night in bed I'd hear you calling my name outside when you'd been drinking wine and I heard the pain in your voice, and I knew it was you throwing things against the side of our house in the middle of the night. But Charles, my little Mingus! Why haven't you ever come in the daytime, openly, why, why?"

"Baby . . . Your father . . ."

"What could my father do? My father's carried a gun for thirty years and never shot anyone."

"When he spoke to me he was serious, Lee-Marie. And he had a right to be at our age."

"At our age? Do you know how *long* ago that was? How long must we wait? I know about Buddy's pad and all the chicks. You think girls don't talk? They say you and Buddy are tramps, male whores, easy to get. Charles, I'm not proud of being a virgin. That's your fault. But needing you is natural to me. I can't change what we taught each other—maybe too early in our lives—but it was a sacred thing to me and it would be sacrilegious with any other man. And now I have to hear the girls saying that you and Buddy are the best lovers of all. . . ."

"Baby, hear me, you hear me. You hear me, Lee-Marie? I have goofed, not slightly. I have balled chicks and really made the whole scene. But even while they're doing what I teach them, I know that using sex this way is mocking love."

"Oh, darling, I'm not jealous but I'm selfish, I want the other half of me. I'm burning for you, here, now. We're not children any more—we don't belong in school. *These* are children all around us, playing and waiting to grow up and love or marry or go to bed with someone, and I'm afraid this society is beginning to make *you* a child again. When you were only ten you were more of a man than you are today. You said nothing could separate us, but today you dream of me as your sacred bride and take tramps to bed. I know you hear me, Charles, I know you still understand—even the silence between us tells me that. Oh, hell, I love you! Say you love me! Isn't it true?"

"Hey, Mingus!" Peter Thompson shouted. "Come on!"

Lee-Marie held my boy's eyes pleadingly but he couldn't speak a word.

"Mingus, get your ass on out here and play!"

Charles looked toward the field and, sobbing, Lee-Marie turned and walked away. He followed along the fence until she disappeared into the back door of the rehearsal hall and the doors closed behind her.

N THE LOCKER ROOM after the game Charles is slowly dressing. Britt Woodman strolls in and sits down on a bench.

"Hey, Britt—what you doing here?"

"Hey, Chazz. I came to see Mildred Ray. She acts bashful since I graduated, every time I come around she runs home. Hey, I saw you talking to Lee-Marie."

"Yeah."

"Well, I don't mean to be butting into your business but it seems you got a good chick there who loves you. You're kind of lucky—look how confused Mildred keeps me."

"Britt, lay off, would you mind? Oh, schitt, I don't know what to do."

"Well, if it's like that, ball spot, I'll help you, I'll center the ball for you. See, Charles, like you and Lee-Marie are a sign for all of us that everything in life can be all right. Mingus, she's—I don't know how to say. Like once William Luke hit on her."

"Oh, yeah?"

"Now wait, Mingus, just a minute. You know Luke's polite, pretty style—what are you getting steamed up about?"

"I'm sure she took care of him."

"Look, ball spot, you hardly ever speak to her, let alone go around with her."

"I'm waiting."

"On what?"

"Till we're of age."

"Lemme see, Lee-Marie must be near eighteen. You oughta be through waiting, as of today. Charlie, love don't come in ages but she ain't a girl no more, she's a woman, you can't miss it. Like when Luke started jiving her, she took him through technocracy, autocracy, philology, economics, ethnology, anthropology, the whole scene. Luke was glad to get away. But now take Nathaniel Raven."

"Who?"

"Rags Raven—you know, his father peddles fruit from that old wagon. What do you think of him just offhand?"

"Well, sort of like his name implies. Trampy. Don't care about his person. A hog. Slouchy. Like me, except he's dirty at times. Still, he's a kinda nice, quiet cat."

"Charlie, about a year ago Lee-Marie's parents let her go to a party and Rags was standing out front; he told me. She came running over—she thought he was you at first. She invited him in and danced with him all evening, talking 'bout you. He said he fell in love with her that night and still is, but your name is ringing in his ears all the time. And don't forget there's lots more guys around out there that's got eyes."

"Britt, she's not like that. She'll wait."

"Maybe so. *May-be* so. But you know, a need is part of you, no doubt about it. You can die from a need of heart. . . . Well, let's go."

"Yeah. I'll lock up."

"Charlie, I'm just your old buddy wishing you luck in whatever you do but I'm sure hoping you two get straight together at last."

EE-MARIE? . . . Can I take you home?"

"Charles Mingus Junior darling! Are you following me? I'm sorry I walked away today."

"Come on get in."

"A Lincoln! Isn't this a bit fancy for a schoolboy?"

"I borrowed it. It's mine for the week. Do you mind?"

"Oh, Charles, don't answer my silly questions. I apologize for prying into your private life. Darling Charles, how are you?"

"I love you, that's how I am."

"Are you happy, my darling? I mean really Happy-Pappy style, like Red Callender's tune."

"I guess I don't know what being happy really means."

"Do you sleep with me in your mind's eye, do you cry out to me in the darkness? I do, Charles, I do. That's my happiness, it's all I have."

"Lee-Marie . . ."

"Of course, Mr. Mingus, you fully understand that now that I'm with you I'm not going home. You are personally taking me to that famous pad of yours."

"It's not my pad. I live at home. It's just a place Buddy and I use sometimes for rehearsals."

"Then take me there."

"I don't want to take you there. It's not the kind of place for you."

"Then will you promise never to return to that house of ill-repute again? Except on business."

"Business? What kind of business?"

"My father told us some of the boys are procurers."

"They're what?"

"Panderers, pimps. Are you and Buddy in that business too?"

"Oh, Lee-Marie, no—of course not."

"Then take me to your rehearsal place. So we can be alone just a little while. Please, Charles."

My boy drives more and more slowly as they approach the white frame house on the east side of town that he and Buddy rent for thirty dollars a month from Tan Blue's brother Amos. He feels it's wrong somehow to take Lee-

Marie into this place, the scene of so many parties and conquests. But she jumps out of the car without hesitation and runs to the porch and he follows and silently unlocks the door and pushes it open. She walks in and stands still, looking around curiously. What did she expect to find? It's just a plain little house, plainly furnished. She goes quickly all through the four rooms and comes back and stands close to him, looking into his eyes. Almost with a sob, he puts his arms around her.

"Oh, Charles, Charles, to be in your arms again! Hold me tight! . . . No, let me go, let me do whatever I like— oh, I don't want to be a lady any more! There—catch! Wheee! Catch! My shoes! My dress! Everything! Oh, I'm with you, we're alone, alone, alone! And I'm going to seduce you, can you tell? Stand still, you're fighting— don't fight me, darling. Look at me, look! You've never seen me naked before! Are you shocked, darling? Give me your tie—there, I have it loose—and your shirt—"

"What are you *doing*, Lee-Marie!"

"Oh, I know what I'm doing! Give me these . . . lift this foot . . . now the other . . . what big-kneed pants, such tiny cuffs! You're certainly not a conservative-dresser, my darling. Oh, look, your cute bow-legs—and I love your knees!"

"Oh, baby, you've gone crazy!"

"Put me down—you mustn't stop me! I want to tell them *I* seduced *you!*—no one can hurt you then. I'm forcing you—I'm forcing you!"

"Baby—not here where all those bitches—"

"Shut up! Come close, don't pull away! You started this a lifetime ago."

"Lee-Marie—if it's going to be tonight it's not going

to be here or any place like this. You're just too much, baby, you're too much beauty for this outhouse. Not here. I want to see you in some lovely, crazy place—"

"Oh, Charles, you're right, this isn't good, because when I don't come home they'll know I'm with you and they'll come looking for us here."

"If your father touches you—"

"He won't, he won't, because I'm kidnapping *you*— and I'm taking you to—I have it all planned—Elsinore!"

"Oh, baby, that's beautiful—but it's a long way, must be a hundred miles."

"I don't care, do you?"

"You're not afraid? Because if we go I'm not bringing you home tonight. You wouldn't be sorry?"

"Not any more. I don't care if we never come back."

"Here, baby, put your things on!"

"No, I don't want my shoes, I'm walking bare tonight. I won't wear *anything*—just my coat—and put all my things in your raincoat pockets—see?"

So not knowing whether it was right or wrong, feeling happy and reckless and so much in love, my boy committed himself. "We have a right," he thought, over and over. "We've waited half our lives."

I, CHARLIE, FILLERUP?"

"Yeah, Bubba. How far is it to Lake Elsinore?"

"Come on in, I'll show you on the map. . . . Say, boy, ain't that Spendell's daughter with you?"

"Bubba, please don't say nothing to nobody no matter *what*."

"Oh, boy! I ain't saying nothing but you really asking for it, Charlie. Where'd you get that car? Don't it belong to that actress, what's her name, Lupe? Whew, boy! Shot guns, both barrels! Cars and under-age chicks! You crazy, boy, you can't fight Sidney Hall! But don't worry, I ain't saying nothing."

ET ME LIE with my head in your lap, darling Charles. Ummmm! You feel so good."

"That won't be necessary all the way, baby. I'm only human."

"Could you ever get tired of me?"

"I don't see how."

"Then I'll lie here all the way and do anything I feel like doing."

"Don't let things get out of hand, baby, I might lose control."

"Love like this is getting out of hand? You're funny, darling."

"I mean control over this steering wheel. I'll tell you something, Lee-Marie, if I didn't know you so well, if you were some other chick, with that poetic bag you're working out of you'd sound like the greatest con artist on earth."

"Con?"

"Line. Jive."

"Maybe lovers have to be con artists on this poor earth, to convince each other that such a wonderful thing can exist. . . . Yes, darling, move closer, Charles, love inside me, in my mouth. I want to taste you there."

ABY, see up there around the lake, that ridge and the mouth of the canyon and the higher mountains beyond? That's where we're going to live. We can have a cabin or tent or sleeping bags, whatever you want."

"A little house to live in? And do as we please? Oh, I want that, Charles. When?"

"We have enough money to see us through for a week or two. Are you afraid?"

"You're the frightened one."

"Come on, let's go in the lake. Leave our clothes here. There isn't a soul in miles."

"Look at the moon! Look at all the planets, Charles!"

"Yeah. . . . You know, baby, the next summer after the church picnic I came back here with my family, and stood right *here* where we stood that time, and missed you so much I cried. And my Dad yelled, 'Come on, wake up, have some fun—we'll be going home soon!' They were always yelling at us, weren't they?"

"You really *love* me, Charles!"

"You know I do."

"Then catch me! Stalk me, ancient man who loves his mate! I'm the *tiger* woman who loves her man and will have no other! Screaha! I'm yours but you must tame me, I'm wild! Screaha!!"

"You're crazy, baby—you scratched me. Come here, you wild—"

"Say it, say it! Wild *bitch!* No other bitches can keep you from me any more—I'm your clawing, scratching, loving *only* bitch! Catch me, Mingus, catch me! You can't, you fumbler, you'd rather catch a football or hold a cello or play with a piano!"

"Come here, woman! I'll catch you by your heaven-sent ass! You're in my hypnotic power!"

"Minggggussssss!"

"The water won't help, baby, you can't get away. You called it anyway, so how does this feel, bitch? No no no, you're no bitch, you're an angel who's never been fucked or had her ass kissed or slapped! Hold still, you slippery witch! You almost made me hurt you, I've got you, damn you! If you can't swim you better learn now, mama, from here on out it gets deeper and I sure can outfloat you."

"I love you, Charles. I'm tired. I can't fight anymore."

"Feel how hot it is where I'm standing."

"This lake is strange, just over there the water was cool. Look, it's getting shallower, the water just covers my shoulders. Now it's down to my chest and it keeps getting hotter. Now, it's—Charles!"

"Yes, baby, that's me."

"You're drowning me!"

"Bitches don't drown, they just float a while till the water gets shallower, shallower, until there's just damp, hot, soft, fine sand."

"Oh, like a warm, soft feather blanket beneath us. Let my legs, oooh, slide downnn easssy. Oh, Charles, hold me to you."

"I won't hurt you, darling."

"Hurt me."

"Don't have to, baby, there's time, lots of time. Go on, put your teeth in my shoulder, bite, if there's any pain for you I want to know it too."

"Oooooooh . . . darling. . . ."

RE YOU RESTED NOW, baby?"

"Charles, it was like being willing to *die* for you! . . . What have you done to me—I'm a baby crying like this—what have we done? Oh, Charles, I'm frightened. I fainted, I went blank—"

"Oh, baby, I told you we should wait."

"I can't ever go home."

"Don't worry, baby, everything's fine, you'll be all right. Come on, hold on to my shoulder, it's deep here."

"It looks so far back. I'm frightened."

"Just hold on to me. Easy sweets, don't break nothin'. We can almost walk out now."

"Do you think I'm bad for loving you like that?"

"Oh, Lee-Marie."

"Then, after you kissed me everywhere else, why did you stop before you kissed me down there?"

"It's just that—oh, hell!"

"Go on, Charles."

"Whatever you heard those slut tramp cunt bitches say is so much a lie that I—oh, damn it, I haven't really *made love* to nobody except you—and I wanted to kiss you all over you, inside and out, everything and anywhere, but that's sacred to me so I just hesitated when I found myself there wanting to love all the ways in the world that people make sound so perverted and dirty because they don't dig what love is. I wanted to get down with it and love every, any and all ways possible but I just wish they didn't make it sound like the most popular style worn this year, invented by some French freak."

"Is it dirty, Charles?"

"Not with you, Lee-Marie. But if people knew we made it like that they'd call us freaks, teen-age perverts. Suppose we were caught here like that, we'd be arrested and they'd call you a whore, do you know that? By the time we were released you'd be raped or forced into some act with any white cop that felt he wanted a colored girl and if I couldn't get you out they'd send you to a woman's jail where some Amazon homosexual matron would get at you and threaten to kill you if you said anything!"

"Mingus, don't upset yourself trying to think it all out now."

"I don't ever want to stop thinking, it's the only way I can go forward."

"No, darling, please. Let's go see about our cabin where I can cook and take care of you like a sweet little wife and love you where no one can find us or see us. . . . But who is Lupe Madrid?"

"What?"

"Not what. Who."

"Why do you ask that?"

"I tried not to. I didn't want to pry into your life again. But in the glove compartment there's a little handbag with room keys from the Dunbar Hotel and pictures of you and Buddy and two girls and that name is written on the back. Is this her car?"

"Yes, it is."

"Who is she?"

"Just a girl. A showgirl at the Million Dollar Theatre."

"And the girl with Buddy, who's she?"

"Her name's Pat. She's a Sioux Indian. She's like us,

she doesn't feel she's treated as an American. I saw her grandfather's picture in the Los Angeles museum—he was a chief. Me and Buddy met these chicks when we were all working as extras in 'The Road to Zanzibar.' Haw haw! Big deal. They cut my scene with Bing and Bob—I was standing behind them holding a spear saying 'Yes, Bwana.'"

"I don't think I like Lupe Madrid furnishing our honeymoon transportation. From now on we're taking the bus."

"Talk like that is getting you someplace in my mind you could never imagine. Do you know how far Tijuana is from here?"

"No, why?"

"That's where we're going. We're on our honeymoon now, Mrs. Mingus. Ahead of time. We're celebrating our marriage which takes place not more than five days from now."

"Charles—"

"Lee-Marie, Lee-Marie, your mouth is so nice. Come, baby, it's still a long ways up to the top of the canyon. . . ."

TWO DAYS LATER my boy took Lee-Marie to Mexico in Lupe Madrid's car and they were married. Neither one of them had even finished high school and the world didn't look kindly on what they'd done and God did not bless their union.

14

A YEAR HAD PASSED since Elsinore and my boy had graduated from high school and gone up north away from places and people that reminded him of Lee-Marie and the incredible things that had been done to them both. He played a few gigs in San Francisco, made some records with a big band for Harold Fenton, delivered mail, worked at odd jobs, anything to get by. Art Tatum was in town and Charles's one great pleasure was sitting in with him most nights at an after-hours place called Jimbo's. It was a hard, sad time for my boy. He'd been told Lee-Marie's father had sent her out of the country—he didn't know where and if he had he couldn't have done anything about it and he was sure he would never see her again.

During high school he had played sometimes with Herman Grimes's group and when he got a wire to rejoin them he came home to Watts. Herman was a versatile black-key piano player and a wizard with spoons, forks, knives and bones so it was appropriate that their dates were mostly in hotel dining rooms. He looked at the job as a lesson in uncommon keys, for Herman never played in the naturals but mainly in F sharp, or D, A and E—which were not often used in ordinary jazz.

His old school friends and Union brothers were going their separate ways on the road, into the Army or east to the Apple. When his own draft notice came he was not very enthusiastic about it so he put powdered sugar under his fingernails and peed his way from 1-A to 4-F. But in a way the joke was on my boy because when he changed his mind and tried to enlist in the Navy he was rejected anyway.

He and his old buddies, those who were still around, got together now and then at the municipal playground and lifted weights. One afternoon Brother Woodman called up. "Hey, ball spot! Hear about Britt? He's leaving with Les Hite's band."

"Wow! Guess that leaves me pretty much alone. Buddy doesn't care too much for outdoor sports."

"Britt wants us to meet him at the playground right away, okay? We'll see if I can still beat you pickin' up the load."

"I'm pretty good now, Brother—'way over two hundred press and two-fifty jerk."

"You get 'em up, ball, and I'll double whatever you do. Fifty dollar bet?"

"Check and race you to the playground, Brother Rabbit. On your mark, get set, go!"

EY, MOM, make me a bean and onion sandwich?"

"You sit down there and eat those nice pigtails and rice I fixed for you."

"All I want's a sandwich. I'm going to the playground."

"Might as well sit down and eat your food. You can't be running like the rest, you're an old man's son."

"No schitt, Mom!"

"What'd you say?"

"I said what's in the *skillet*, Mom?"

"Some greens to go with your tails and rice. That's healthy."

"What do greasy pigtails do for nutrition?"

"You just eat your food and get strong. Remember he was past fifty before you was born."

"Who? Your President Roosevelt?"

"Son, you don't even listen to me. Old men's sons aren't strong like the rest. You'll kill yourself trying to keep up with normal folks."

"What facts are you basing that theory on?"

"The Holy Scriptures. It's in there someplace. I seen it."

"Did Jesus ever pee, Mama? Do the Scriptures say anything about that? And when he did Number Two did he use toilet paper? Or was it a corncob or his robe or maybe just a leaf? . . . Mama, that's the last time in your life you're gonna hit me! You got it, all by yourself! I'm too old for that. You're not my real mother anyway and you handed out so much hate you lost my father and you been taking it out on me ever since!"

"You devil you! Let go my hands and I'll beat you within an inch of your life!"

"You won't do schitt but sneak and eat snuff and sneak off to Mr. Marvin and sneak into his bedroom. Be still!— can't you see I'm not fighting you? Let's get this thing settled. No wonder the Spendells thought their daughter was too good for our family—I got a sneak Mama who eats snuff and dresses like a witch! Go tell your old gossip cronies what *you* do, tell 'em about Mr. Marvin and Duane too!"

"*Who?*"

"You know who—Tony Duane's father! . . . You should see that look you just gave, like the old Mexican lady in our alley you used to call a witch. Aw, wake up, Mama! You fooled the neighbors and church and Daddy's friends but not me. You used to judge Daddy for just dropping some lady off at her house and you made us take your side till he felt so bad he finally left us all forever. You know why he left? When we went to visit him in the hospital he had some ice cream Mrs. Garrett brought him and to you that was an act of fornication! You couldn't even let a member of your church give Daddy a pint of ice cream without you accusing him of adultery when he was close to death in a hospital. That's when Daddy put you down finally for keeps in his mind. He shook his head and his eyes watered and not a word came out, he just shook his head like no, no, not this, Lord, this woman really hates me! You made our family *extinct!* You killed the spirit in all of us. Mama, you're a witch who heals old women with your hands and destroys your husband and children with your hate!"

"Son . . . son . . . you don't know all I've been through with your father."

"What, Mama, tell me what?"

"You saw him throw a book and almost knock my eye out."

"After years of nagging! And what else?"

"You saw him beat and knock me down."

"How many times, Mama? I remember *one*. He rose out of his chair and shouted God give me a moment's rest around this house!—and grabbed your hair and threw you against the wall."

"Lord, he almost killed me! Son, you remember that?"

"Yeah, Mama, I got a very good memory, I'm an old man's son. I remember getting beat for wetting the bed and getting whipped when it rained and my feet got soaked. You didn't care. You say Daddy's cruel? You're the cruelest person I've ever met because your heart is full of hate!"

"Oh Lord, everyone's against me!"

"Yeah, cry! Drown out the truth. When my father came back from the hospital with his leg amputated he was seventy-two years old and he had to go and take a room with Mrs. Garrett to save his sanity! You have a mean, evil, filthy mind, Mama, and what's more you haven't taken a *bath* as far back as I can remember! . . . Yeah, go ahead, cut me with your butcher knife, beautiful Jesus Christ-loving mother! And tell me again to honor thy mother and I'll go to hell as a gold star sinner 'cause I won't honor an evil old bitch! . . . For God's sake put that knife down and shut up and listen while I remind you what you did to your own blood mother—my little Grandma Newton. You were too busy doing nothing and too selfish to look after her so you said she was crazy and sent her to the crazy house! She came to my room the night before she ran away, you didn't know that, did you? I loved her. I still do. She was the only thing I knew about love at that time. She was eighty-seven years old and she

113

asked *me* to help her escape! We packed her things and I took her over to the Drews and just by the gate I begged her Grandma, Grandma, let's run away together! She told me no, son, you got to get back home and learn them white man books so you can get out of this mess of poverty that keeps black folks in ignorance. She told me all kinds of things that night and talked to me like I was as capable of understanding them as she was. She told me she was born a slave and remembered when the white men snatched her from her mother's arms and raised her separately—she only saw her mother now and then in the cotton fields. She told me things she knew, like when the white man came to Africa he acted friendly at first and tried to show the tribes his superiority in magic—but our people's medicine was as advanced as his and *more* so when it came to tropical fevers and diseases. The white man had one magic we didn't have—he could write, he could write down ideas and this amazed our people. But the white man couldn't transmit thoughts from one mind to another like the Africans, he had to talk. Yet a thousand of his words could be said in the African sign languages just by the raising of a black brow, the trembling of lips, shaking a head from side to side, squinching the eyes, moving the fingers, grunting—oh, Grandma Newton knew a lot. She could have taught us all a power greater than the white man's magic. And when she had to run away you still wouldn't let her be—you told the Drews you'd have them arrested for kidnapping! So she came back all by herself with her belongings tied up in a little bundle. Another part of me died that day. How could you and Daddy pass judgment on a beautiful old woman like that? Was it her

money you wanted? Then you lied and made her believe
Norwalk was only the old folks' home and even took me
along to make her feel secure. When she realized she was
in the asylum she screamed and screamed—Tell them,
boy! You know your old Granny ain't crazy! I was crying
and wanted so much to help. They grabbed her like she
was a mad dog and I heard her yelling at you—I'll die
here, I'll die in a few days and it will all be on your hands!
But you and my father walked out and on the way home
you talked about how you did the right thing! Why
couldn't you let her stay with us and have a ball the last
year of her life? You killed your own blood mother, you
over-holy Bible-quoting witch! Now I'm going over to the
playground and think of you and beat every motherfucker
on earth!"

Jogging toward the playground my boy felt sick at
heart. Why had he said those cruel things to Mama even
though they were true? Some of it had been buried so
deep he hadn't known it was there till it came out. The
pain of the confrontation was too much. He tried not to
think about what he'd done.

The guys were clustered in a corner of the playground
—Brother and Britt, Brady Whitehouse, Bubba Lee,
Booker T., Warthell and Travis Grissom, Vechi Lopez—
"Hey, Mingus! Ball spot! Ball spot rabbit pig, you slow!
Hey, Fat Face! . . . Mingus, look at this—they got our
weights chained!"

"The new playground director says we gotta sign them
out and put a deposit on them before we can use them.
Got any money, Charlie?"

Rage flooded through him. Without a word, he took

the dumbbells one by one and turned them end over end, twisting and tightening the chains until the rusty iron links broke. "There's your weights," he said, rolling them out free on the playground. "And here's their deposit!" He flung the broken chains over the fence.

He heard a soft voice in his ear—"You young men will have to take up a collection to pay for these chains you've broken"—and turned to see a strange and attractive young woman at his side.

"Who's this bitch?" Charles says furiously. "These are our weights, we made them ourselves from train wheels and crow bars! What's your name, girl? If you want respect, introduce yourself. What're you doing here anyway?"

"My father's the new playground director and I'm helping out temporarily. He chained the weights because they're the property of the playground."

The guys are whistling and swooning. Brady Whitehouse snickers, "Hey, little fine ass missy, come here and set on these bells and let me pick you up on them so I can get a close look at your pretty ass!"

My boy turns. "Brady, I been looking all over for you! If you don't bring my tool kit back I'm going to break your back, you hear me?"

"You saying I stole your tool kit?"

"Yeah, I am. Go get it."

"Aw, you're crazy. Go hide behind your cello like you used to, you motherfucking coward."

SPLATT! WHAM! BONK! STOMP! KICK!

"Mingus, stop, he's out, you'll kill him if you ain't already!"

"I'm sure trying to—hah!"

"Oh Lord, you kicked his nose and teeth all in!"

"Let go of me, Brother! Brady started it—he picked on me for thirteen years! I *want* to kill him!"

"Booker T.! Britt! Somebody help me—he's crying mad and he's got the strength of a devil!"

"Charles!"

"Let him die, if that's the Lord's will! Die, mother-fucker! Stop breathing!"

"Charles!"

"Go away, Lee-Marie!"

"I'm not Lee-Marie. My name is Barbara."

My boy stops dead and turns to look at the girl.

"Don't hit that boy any more, Charles." She picks up his coat and brushes it off and hands it to him. She takes a little handkerchief from her pocket. "Here, let me wipe your face." My boy submits. "Now will you boys please sign for the weights before you use them and leave a deposit?"

"Bubba Lee, help me get Brady to my car," Brother says.

Charles takes the registry book from the girl and scribbles his name. "Okay, I signed. Where's my wallet? Oh. Here, is this enough for a deposit?"

"That will be fine. Thank you." She turns and walks away and my boy watches her and then follows.

"Whee whee!" says Booker T. "First Charlie goes crazy and now he's tryin' to make out with the fine new playground director! Come on, Travis, let's see what you can lift."

"I hope you don't think I'm crazy like they said, Barbara. That guy did steal my tool kit."

"No, but I think Brady Whitehouse is crazy. I saw him taking money from a six-year-old, and he was locked in the girls' room with the little Barton girl—she can't be past twelve. But you should learn to control your violent instincts."

"I been controlling my instincts with Brady since I was seven years old. I'm glad I did it. It felt good. All the Thompsons and Feistys and Johnny McDowells, all of them who ever picked on me died just then. 'Cause I know I've had enough. No one will ever pick on me again. . . . Barbara, you know, I don't mean to sound corny but I felt like I wanted to protect you. I feel strange when fellas who don't know any better whistle or make smart remarks at a woman like you. Can't they see you're a lady? Aren't they glad there's still some around?"

"Oh, I'm used to it. They don't mean any harm."

"That's what the playground director before you said, but she made passes at some of the guys, even me. Pie Bailey couldn't keep his hands off her. She didn't mind, but some of the local mothers saw it and she lost her job."

"Well, I'm not that way, Charles."

"I can see that. You make me think of someone I used to know who was nice like you. You sounded like her for a moment. Like in a dream."

"I think you mean Lee-Marie."

"How did you know that?"

"I heard about you two, she goes to school where I do —Compton College."

"You mean she's here in California? Her father said he sent her out of the country!"

"She was away for a long time, but now she's home."

118

They walk into the playground office and my boy sits down, feeling confused, half-dazed. To know she was so near again!

"I'm sorry to remind you of all that, Charles."

"It's just that—I thought she was still away. I didn't know where."

"Let me look at your hands. See, they're all cut! Suppose you had broken your hands—a musician can't afford that."

"Well, I hope that was my last fight. Unless someone attacks me. I hope so anyway."

CHARLES AND BARBARA sat in the little office through the afternoon and he told her about Lee-Marie and how it had all ended and even showed her the bullet scar in his shoulder. She didn't say much but looked at him gently and sadly.

"Barbara, do you believe some men can die when they want to, when they feel they have worked out their karma?"

"Karma?"

"Their personal understanding of themselves in relation to creation."

"I wouldn't know, Charles."

"Barbara, you'll think I'm really crazy but anyway I'll tell you. I've already achieved the point of remembering birth and I'm sorry I have. And last year in San Francisco I was supposed to die."

"I don't understand. Do you mean kill yourself?"

"No. I learned how to meditate into a trance and leave

my body and it became more and more difficult to return. So I left San Francisco and came back to Watts to my father's house to leave earth, to die of divine self-will. I didn't want my family to have the expense of bringing my body home for burial, I thought it was better to die at home. I achieved a level of meditation where my heartbeat slowed and stopped. Thank God and my lucky planets I found out in time I had not properly packed my suitcases for death. Like Red Callender said, I was a lucky coward."

"Was your death wish because of Lee-Marie?"

"I don't think so. It was the whole American scene, it seemed like hell. I thought yoga had a new instruction but it almost took me before my time. Laugh at this if you want to—I feel I must tell someone, you dig, Barbara?"

"Of course."

"I wonder if one of my problems is I've never been the greatest at anything. For instance, I can chin four times with my right and once with my left, I had to learn that much, but Britt Woodman is the best in chinning I've ever heard of in America, maybe in the world. He can cut everybody to death—nine with his left and fifteen with his right. Oh, Britt was Olympic Games material for sure. It seems no one notices high school colored talent. We covered all the playgrounds some time ago just for the hell of it because we felt the white boys didn't like us or want us showing off around their girls. Mostly we didn't even know the girls were around, 'cause what the Man says is, don't see my women. I still don't. Anyway we'd go to these playgrounds and act dumb about the equipment and the chicks would gather around and the white fellows who were good would come around to cut us. At first we'd do just what they did and no more. We had a little con going. Britt would say 'You do it this time, Mingus, this fella ain't up to my form yet,' if it was something I was good at, and if it was something I couldn't do as well as Britt I'd say 'You got this one, Britt, I don't even feel like wasting my time.' So the two of us looked like we did everything better than the white gentlemen performing, and their girls would turn red and get goosepimply and come up close to us and talk about our muscles. Sometimes we'd give them a little sample of hand-boxing—Britt trained at Robert Hannibal's gym and he's the most beautiful boxer. Hannibal's father taught him—he used to be Dynamite Jackson's trainer. Britt had an extreme faith in himself—he felt he was a Sampson—Sampson in Britt like God was in Jesus. Am I boring you, Barbara?"

"Of course not. You're a good story-teller."

"But anyway, I did try to die of my own free will through yoga. I had a stepbrother, Odell Carson Mingus was his name. At that time I thought he was square. He believed in Jesus Christ and God and all. After his wife left him, he preached shyly in church, read, meditated, spoke very seldom and lived a secluded life. I felt hipper even though he was older than me. But when he got sick it came to me he had a death wish in his mind, he was planning and premeditating his own death. When I saw him in the hospital the death mask was on my brother. But at the last minute he changed his mind, he wasn't so sure he wanted to go. He cried out, 'Help me, Charles, I don't want to die!' because he knew where I thought I was—my pride in having the great answer to life's secrets.

I didn't even go to church like my family and here—look, all you Christians!—my brother was saying 'Help me, Charles!'—to no one but me! I said, 'Odell, it's up to you. You can change it if you want to.' But after that I didn't see him. They'd only let my mother in though I knew he was frightened and wanted me with him. All his church friends came to the hospital and sang and prayed. I remember a black nurse came out and saw them and she was ashamed—ashamed of her colored people's faith. I think I could have saved him if I'd been there at the end. . . . But later when I mistakenly thought it was *my* time to leave, I heard my dead brother's voice. A bird came to my window sill and sat. I knew his sound. This same bird had followed me around for quite a while. My body didn't move but I went closer to the window in my spirit form to listen to this bird calling. I heard my brother's voice! 'Better get back there to your body before something else does! Return to your bed and return in your time—' And so it was finally my brother who saved *me*. Anyway, it's better I didn't die before my time, even though the white man makes dying seem preferable to what he metes out to us. But I still have to get myself ready. And I thought someone—I don't know who she'll be now—could help me figure it out before it's too late."

It was getting dusk and they sat silent for a while. Then my boy asked, "Can we talk together sometime again? Do you want to come and watch the strongest men on earth lift weights tonight? Come on, Barbara, I like you 'cause you listened to my funny talk. Who knows, maybe I'll break my own record with you standing looking at me with those big pretty eyes. Do you work here every day?

"Just after school."

"You're going to be my new girl."

"What makes you think I'm available?"

"I just feel it like I know. You know it too, Barbara, don't you?"

15

"HEY, DAD! How ya doing? I thought I'd come and talk to you about a few things."

"Why, hello, son, I was hoping you'd be over to see me one of these days. Come in, sit down, make yourself at home. I been hoping to see you ever since the day you handed me my gun."

"Oh, Daddy, I didn't know what I was doing. I was so hurt you were leaving me—why doesn't he kill me, I thought. Then I saw the look in your eyes when I gave you the gun."

"I'd of killed *myself*, son, if I'd thought it would help change things. That woman kept me so mixed up! But you're my flesh and blood and I love you. Oh, Pearl! Would you close the door? My son has come to visit me."

"Hello there, little Charlie."

"Hello, Mrs. Garrett."

"Now Ming, you leave those sweets alone, you know what the doctor said. Don't let him eat them, Charlie."

"Oh, bosh! I'll live to be ninety. Doctors! They discover a mole and they cut off my leg! The Lord had a remedy called penicillin there waiting for me but they couldn't find it in time. Bosh!"

"All right, Ming, all right, I'll leave you two men alone."

"Okay, shoot away, son."

"I always wanted to ask about—you and her, Daddy. Do you? I mean, can you still get a hard?"

" 'Course! Or I'd be done left this earth long ago. That stays good. Oh, it might drop now and then if the fire ain't right, but I warm her up and everything comes out fine like it always did. Now your stepmaw, she thought that was dirty. And she wouldn't use all the modern equipment, she didn't believe in it. Lord, she's got pretty silk underthings I bought her fifteen, twenty years ago, still in their boxes. Instead, she'd cut the legs off my old winter long-drawers and pin 'em 'round her waist. When I'd go to kiss her I'd get a sniff of snuff and sneeze my lungs out. Oh, there's definitely something wrong with the old girl. She don't seem human like a woman, she was even jealous of me putting flowers on your mother's grave. But I didn't enjoy that anyhow. Silly custom. To hell with tombstones, graves, the whole mess! It's only making up for what should have been done for the deceased while they lived. Yeah, son, that's a lot of wasted good soil. When I go, don't make no mess over my remains."

"Dad, you remember the time I came home and heard your car motor running in the garage? I almost fainted from the carbon monoxide when I opened the door. I saw that red tube in your hand that you snatched from the exhaust when you stumbled out of the car. You said 'Go on in the house, the door's open. I'll be in in a minute, son.' I was afraid to tell you I knew what you were doing but I know God sent me to tell you to wait your turn."

"That was a bad day, son, but I'm glad now you showed up."

"I'm sorry I misjudged you so often, Dad. I could have learned so much from you. Like when I joined the Masons I found out that you're one of the few Thirty-third Degree members in this world! And after you left us I found books of yours in the house—remember the one by Herbert G. Wells?—with notes all through—really intelligent analysis. Yet you never talked to me."

"I tried, son. Maybe you don't remember."

"Even you leaving Mama—people say you left on account of Mrs. Garrett. Well, it would be different if you left for a younger woman, that would be a sign of weakness. But you're a man of seventy-six and you went with a woman suitable to your own age. And she's a person with pride in herself which means that the mind has a great deal to do with your relationship and that's normal and mature. So now I'm going to ask for your advice about my own life."

"Son, you're crazier than a loon in lots of ways but you did turn out pretty good and your old man is proud of you. That's enough for me—you didn't try to be no president. Like who's really got time to father the world with all those nuts out there? How's your job coming? What do you call your group?"

"Pick, Plank and Plunk. We're getting work. Buddy and Britt want to form a co-op band, we can start anytime at Bobo's on Central Avenue. Only thing is, the money'll be less than half of what I'm making right now and I'd like to get married."

"Married, is that so! What's her name?"

"Barbara Jane Parks. Her father's John Parks, that big,

proud, black, Tarzan-looking cat, you know, the Twenty-second Street playground director."

"Oh, yes, Parks. How long you known this girl?"

"Nearly a year. We want to get married right away."

"Why right away?"

" 'Cause for some reason I feel guilty sexually about her like we shouldn't have sex until we're married. We went boat-riding the other day and it brought about another petting situation and that's got to end one way or another. I don't want to think of her as just a girl I want to bed. I feel I've done too much of this. I lose respect for myself and I'm confused as to what else a woman is for sometimes."

"I saw you walking her a few times, son. She carries herself real careful, like she's saving it for a special occasion. Well, that's all right but you don't go into nothing like a marriage just for no sample or any other reason 'cept love. Look how long I took that woman's abuse to keep you children together—it might have been better to put you in a home. Yet I doubt it. It's hard to find a good woman to come and take another woman's children and love them like her own. When you look at it that way it almost makes me want to go back and hug old Mamie. But she's so ornery she can't forgive me for what she thinks I did. Anyway, she's all the mother you know and you be as kind to her as you can."

"Last year Mama and I had a talk and I told her the truth, Daddy, I told her off. We got along ever since, we're even polite now. You remember she used to think you were fooling with every woman on the block? What would you have done if it was the other way around?"

"If I caught it in my own house? Remember how I

used to shoot sparrows out of the sky—shoot 'em flying, right in the eye? Remember how I shot Buzza Perkins and Turk Hawkins right in the asses when they was stealing our chicken feed? If that's what I done to Turk and Buzza about my chickens, what do you suppose I'd do about my woman?"

"Remember when I was a kid and you were shooting your rifle off one day and you told me the story of your birth? Was that a true story?"

"As true as I'm sitting here now. You children are blood heirs to the same family as Abraham Lincoln's family."

"Daddy, I don't want to be related to no white folks."

"Well, dammit, you are! You can't change it. That story ain't no lie, it's the God-blessed truth, I wish it wasn't. I don't tell it to boost you. Don't you realize I wouldn't lie about you being from the same family as Abraham Lincoln? My daddy, your grandfather, was a slave on the plantation of Lincoln's first cousin, she lived there with her husband and sister and brother-in-law. My father was in love with Abe's cousin and she with him. No one knew about this and they were never caught. Finally Mingus—that's one of the few real African names—run off, escaped. She helped him to, so she could join him one day. I was only fourteen the time my mother got so mad with her husband she came out and told him she was in love with Mingus and that Charles—me that he thought was his son—was part colored. Her husband and his brothers come after me shooting to kill. 'You dirty son of a bitch!' they were yelling, 'your father was a filthy nigger like *you!*' I ran to the barn for my rifle. They were hiding, ducking, running, but

they didn't dare come near once I got my hands on a gun.
I was such a marksman I could shoot their eyes out. I shot
buttons off their jackets, the heels off their shoes, guns out
of their hands—I didn't want to hurt *them!* I was crying
hurt 'cause I still loved them! I felt like throwing myself
out in front of their guns—I always thought they were my
own people. Toward evening I got out of there and into the
fields and didn't stop running till I was a long way off.
They didn't come after me so I guess they thought I was
still in there. That night I saw a red glow on the horizon
and I always wondered if they burnt that barn. I just
kept going till I got two states north and I joined the regular Army. This was about, oh, 1880. Later I tried to get
word home to my mother through a neighbor friend I
wrote to, and they wrote back and told me my mother left
not long after me and they heard she went to Massachusetts. But I never did know where she went to for sure.
And here I was in the Tenth Negro Cavalry feeling just
like a Southern white man, the way I was raised! From
then on through my life, from time to time, I passed for
white whenever it seemed like a good idea. So, son, you can
take it either way you want—say you got the blood of
Abraham Lincoln running in your veins or just say I was
raised on a plantation as a white boy till I was fourteen
'cause one of the black boys got some woman's nooky, it
don't make no difference to me any more. It took all these
seventy-six years to find out it's all so much hogwash. Isn't
that the way I told it to you, son, when you was little?
'Cause that's the truth."

"Yeah, Daddy, but I ain't thrilled. I say fuck Lincoln.
He ain't freed the slaves, he just helped hide us."

"Well, son, this is your century. In mine, people did a lot of talking about freedom. But I see now it's a waste of time 'cause even a slave could have inner freedom if he wanted it."

"That's brainwashing by the white man."

"Careful, boy—*you* ain't totally black. And don't you be cussin' your kinfolk the way you did back there. Now what's this about you marrying John Parks's daughter? Did you ask for her yet?"

"They didn't give me a chance to ask. I was over there visiting Barbara one evening—they have a *big* house, too big for three people. Everything inside looks unused, brand new. Someone else cooks and serves the meals and they even have a driver for her mother's car that wears a uniform. After dinner Mrs. Parks said she was going to Watts and she'd be glad to drop me off, so I had to go with her. In the car she started asking all kinds of questions into my life, like who are the Minguses, what have they done. I guess I got a little salty, then she said we're mongrels and have no culture or racial pride and she didn't want a half-breed coming around her daughter. She called our house a shanty and said they had lots of those they rent out to their workers in Pasadena. She said John Senior worked as a playground director because it was socially valuable work. I don't understand this black man's class system she tried to drop on me—schitt, their family's from a long line of hamhocks and beans!"

"That's a card they pull on you, son, this pure-dee black class stuff. So tell them your grandfather was an African chieftain named Mingus and keep the Abe Lincoln business to yourself."

"Daddy, don't you remember how you used to be telling me I was better than other people 'cause I was a little lighter colored? I never believed that either, none of that crap reaches me. Telling the Parkses your father was an African chieftain has the same sound to me as the white man telling me I'm a nigger. Somebody—the God of love or someone—seems to believe the world can make it with all these races here or things wouldn't have gone this far. Anything on this earth is bound to have some evil mixed into it. The white man isn't really together with his own people—to think so is overestimating his power. People who want freedom should consider the white man's weaknesses too—his greed and wastefulness, his suicidal tendencies. He's insane! He rapes and kills his own, robs his own banks, cheats his own system, ignores his sick and helpless and old. They throw each other into ovens and make lamp shades and upholstery from their own hides. Then they lie about these things to each other in their newspapers. They're sick and maybe it's our duty to care for them, to be their doctors and nurses and heal them—or else we might catch the same disease and infect our future and wreck our hopes of ever living in a truly free world—and that would be more dreadful than the atomic bomb! No, Daddy, Barbara's mother can belittle me, my body, my family, my house, but I don't dig badges, skin colors, blood lines. I'm not using any of the rules. If you hadn't grown up—in your seventies—I doubt if I'd be talking to you now. What has the fact that you went to bed with my mother got to do with anything? The only father I have is God. Your only duty was to see me to an age to think for myself. You owe me nothing but the truth of your journey. Some day I may choose another father to teach me and you may choose another son to teach. If I sound loveless and it hurts you, I'm sorry, because then I'm not making myself clear. I'm here because I love you—it's not your power over me as the author of my being that drew me to you at this age. The man you *were* once drove me away. What brought me back was your true self, the man I'm talking to today."

"I do understand you, son. You think and speak just like your mother Harriet. You make me think somehow she never left you, though she died when you were a little baby. Lord, it kind of frightens me to think of it—that you're her in spirit. . . . Well, let's get back to your problems today. If you're getting married, I figure you'll be taking a day job."

"I've tried that before. Last time, the big white man's sign at the factory said LABORERS APPLY IN ROOM 1, SKILLED WORKERS IN ROOM 2. So I went to Room 2. The man said, 'What can you do?' I told him I studied drafting for four years. He laughed, like I was a joke. White makes me bite into iron. Sometimes I think if all black people were like me there wouldn't have been any slaves, they'd of had to kill us all! Anyway, I didn't belong working in no place like that. No human being does, actually. Naw, I don't like it here, Daddy. You can have this bullschitt freedom."

"Son, you asked for my advice and here it is. Don't get married to anyone. Go to Europe or some place where you can get a chance to express yourself."

"Maybe someday I'll do that for keeps. But tomorrow I'm getting married."

"Tomorrow, is it? And where you gonna live?"

"There's a vacancy coming up on Vermont Street next

door to Jake and Bess Baines. In the meantime we'll stay at Vivian's. And I just picked up the blood test reports from Dr. Bledsoe. We're both cool."

"Well, son, I wish you all the luck in the world. But don't push that luck too far after you're married."

"Not me—I'll be True Blue Charlie, I won't even look at another woman, I've had that. No more. And I'm going into Bobo's with Buddy and Britt for less bread than I'm making—*some* of us have got to like to play for more than money. And Red Callender is setting me up for some record dates, and he wants me to leave him now and go to a classical teacher—Herman Rheinschagen, his name is. He was the principal bassist with the New York Philharmonic. I'll stay him out, then I'll do what Casals and Segovia did—work out my own fingering system. So those are my plans, Daddy."

"Well, son—all the luck in the world."

OCTOBER

"CHARLES, SING OUR SONG to me again, the one you wrote."

"Baby, you know I can't sing."

"*Say* the lyrics then. Please?"

"All right, baby, for you on our last night together as boy and girl. Come sit beside me and I'll play it for you. . . . 'Boy meets girl on a cloudy afternoon, woman needs man so they say. Love at first sight—oh what a day that was—picnics—boat-rides—strolling through the park—watching fireflies light up the dark—' "

"Go on, Charles, the part you wrote when Mother tried to send you away."

"Maybe it's bad luck, Barbara."

"It's just a song. I love it. Please!"

" 'Came the rains, washing away all our dreams. No one's exactly to blame, we failed at the game of love and understanding. Each one is trying to learn that life is just a lesson. If you give and take in turn, love is what you earn. Now you've heard my story, now you know why I'm blue, I lost my Barbara Jane and I don't know what to do—until my baby's back guess I'll just have to die or sing the blues. . . .' "

"Darling, don't look so sad. Those last words will never come true."

MAY

"WE SHOULD STAY HERE, we're doing all right. We shouldn't move to your mother's. At least we have our privacy."

"Charles, when you're working nights if something goes wrong—you know, like the baby, mother will be there to look after me."

"Barbara, I don't dig it, we're better alone. She accused you of everything but being a whore before our marriage. Now she wants me to call her 'Mother.' She still doesn't believe we didn't ball before and *have* to get married."

"When the baby arrives in September then she'll know."

"Who gives a schitt? It's nobody's business when my son was conceived."

"Oh, listen at you! Suppose it's a girl?"

"It's written I'll have a son. I'll have all sons till I want daughters."

"*I'm* thinking girl."

"Don't confuse my son. He hears you talking. Hey, you, boy, man in there! Charles the Third, you hear me? See? He poked me right in the jaw!"

JULY

"CHARLES, HURRY! Dad'll be here in a minute to pick up our light things."

"Okay, you finally got it your way. We're moving in with her and I'll even call her 'Mammy.'"

"How dare you! My mother is no bandana!"

"Don't get salty. I bet your grandma wore one."

"Here's Father now."

"Well, well, is the little mother ready to go? Hello, son."

"Hi."

"Now I want to tell you, Charles, I have nothing to do with the decisions the girls make. You and I are going to become buddies. All right? Shake on that?"

"Ouch! Wow! Dammit, you trying to disable your grandson's father?"

"Why, that's just a little old friendly handshake."

"Squeeze back, Charles. Daddy thinks he's stronger than anybody. Show him you can make him holler."

"Squeeze, son, try your luck. . . . Hey! Oooheee! Let go! You're pretty good yourself there."

"Okay, we're even."

"Fine. Now both of you men use those great muscles and get these things in the car. Away we go."

SEPTEMBER

"NURSE? I'M MINGUS. Is my wife all right?"

"Oh, yes, it's a nine-pound healthy baby boy."

"Wow! That's cool. But how about my wife, is she all right?"

"It was a very long, hard labor but Barbara's fine now. You may go in."

. . . "Oh, Charles! He's so beautiful—an angel! Have you seen him?"

"Not yet. Are you all right?"

"Of course. Oh, Charles, wait till you see him!"

"They all look horrible at first."

"Not him. He's looking around at life like he's already grown! Nurse, my husband hasn't seen our son."

"Any time, Mr. Mingus. Last door on the left. They'll give you a mask."

"Charles . . . thank you."

"For what?"

"For Charles the Third."

ORRY, SIR, we only show the babies once a day."

"Now listen, I'm not waiting till tomorrow to see my son!"

"Oh, you're the father. Sorry. There was a tall man here before. . . ."

"That's his grandfather Parks. I was late getting here. You see, I brought my wife in yesterday . . . or was it the day before? I don't know. I waited here till 9 p.m., then I had to go to work. This is Sunday, isn't it?"

"No, it's Monday."

"Wow! When was my son born?"

"Three o'clock this morning."

"How about that! Right on the nose, nine months to the second! I usually get home from work around two-forty-five."

". . . This is your son."

"Hey, boy! Hey, my man! Hey, Charles the Third! Wake up! Open your eyes! . . . Well, you better take him back for now. He's out cold."

"The other nurses were saying you're Charlie Mingus, the musician."

"Not Charlie, please. I'm definitely not a Charlie. Not that Charles is much better. I don't particularly care for any name in this society. Well, we'll all be numbers soon anyway."

"Do you play any other instruments besides bass?"

"I'd say I play piano. And I've fooled with trumpet and trombone. Most instruments, I guess."

"Where are you playing now?"

"The Lounge in Santa Monica."

"I may be out to see you one night. Would you like that?"

"Sure. Be my guest."

"I play saxophone a little myself. I have one. I guess it's a funny instrument for a girl."

"Alto or tenor?"

"Oh, I don't know what it is. I just love to have it around. I may take lessons some day. You know a good teacher?"

"Look up Lloyd Reese, he's in the phone book."

"I was hoping *you'd* give me some kind of lessons. Just one lesson would be more than I'd ever be able to pay you for, I'm sure, but maybe the great Charles Mingus would be nice to a poor underpaid nurse and wouldn't even charge her at all? Do you think that's possible?"

"Anything is possible, baby."

ELLO, DARLING, you've been gone so long. Did you see him?"

"Yeah. He was asleep, but he's great. Listen, Barbara . . . I'm sorry."

"Sorry for what, darling?"

"Oh . . . I dunno. Because I'm stupid. Forgive me."

"I don't know what you're talking about, Charles. Come hug me."

"Barbara . . . why do women think in a special way about musicians?"

"I think in a special way about you, but not because you're a musician."

"Don't you remember how your mother used to warn you musicians had a girl on every corner?"

"Oh, she was being silly. All parents hate the man they think is going to take their daughter away. But in a way— I mean I guess I couldn't blame you if you did have girls."

"What do you mean?"

"I've been so worried about us . . . the way I can't let you come inside me."

"Baby, did you tell the doctor?"

"I told him how much it hurt. He said there's nothing wrong."

"I'm beginning to think it's in your mind."

"It's not my mind that hurts! *You* hurt me—you're too big. I don't think I'll ever be able to stand it."

"I'm not as big as my son that just came out of there."

"That's different. They used ether."

"Maybe we should get some ether."

"That's cruel, Charles."

"I'm sorry."

"But we're happy today, Charles, aren't we?"

"Very happy, Barbara, very happy."

17

IT'S AROUND TWELVE MIDNIGHT at Bobo's on Central Avenue. They're playing Collette's "Bedspread" in the next to the last set and Timothy Mark is soloing. My boy has been feeling very low, driven half crazy with guilt feelings for balling another chick and on top of that losing his wife by confessing. Barbara's back home again with Mama Parks, who is happy to remind everyone that she always knew the marriage wouldn't work. The lights and smoke burn his eyes, he can barely see the faces in the crowd that fills the room, and he's playing in another world.

Damn! I'm getting confused, hung up. I can't switch the blame to my father and excuse myself forever. I think I'm becoming a reflection of him. His dormant impression on my unconscious is not easily erased. The very act of recalling those early images makes me dwell on getting revenge—but why do I take it out on the people I work with? Oscar and John and Buddy and Givons here—they're not to blame for my spare-not-the-rod parent who gave me a friendless, fatherless childhood. Of course there's love as an antidote and I've tried to stay open to it. But there's no way of coming through on that wave length when the

listener—me—has turned off his receiving set and is sending a many-directed program of his own. I guess I'm as
bad as other people—I only call on God in an emergency
or to solve some selfish material problem, just like my
parents did. I seldom even say "Thank you, Jesus" any
more. Maybe I've begun to think He's me or I'm Him. One
night I tried to walk on water to show that Jesus had
nothing on me. That worries me. If that was my true Soul
thinking such thoughts it would send me to sure ruin. I am
the sheep that senses it is Death's feeding time and leaps
and bounds over all the others to his slaughter. . . .

My man Mingus stumbled off the bandstand and just
as the mythical axe descended toward his head a hand
reached out and touched his arm and someone said,
"Where are you going, you beautiful, independent motherfucker?"

He looked down into the face of the girl who had
telephoned several times to no avail and finally sent a
mash note saying she'd be in one night to see him. On the
bandstand Timothy Mark had just announced a twenty-
minute intermission and began to whistle "Mingus Fingers"
into the microphone. He winked at my boy and segued to
"Pennies from Heaven."

Mingus sat down at the table. So this is Cindy. She
looks as good as any Hollywood bitch. Let me get real cool
and quiet with this broad, like Buddy. Crossing my legs is
a real drag, I'm getting too fat to cross them comfortable.
Damn if I know why my father's flashing through my mind
again. You know why, Charles. Your father used his hands
to help him cross his legs in front of his bitch on Forty-
eighth Street. You hate yourself for being fat and using

your hands to cross your legs, like him—it makes you remember his philandering—and your own. You're fat and greedy. That was your father's escape too—food helped him forget for a while the misery he was creating. He suggested a pattern for you to live by. . . .

"Hey, wake up! I'd give a million dollars to know what's going on inside your head," the girl said.

"A million for that, Cindy?"

"That and a few other things."

"I didn't think you drove all the way down to Spooksville to pay for nobody's thoughts. Every colored musician in town knows you bought Tim Mark a Cadillac."

"He's not the only one."

"Yeah, those are well publicized articles. The next man should get a Rolls."

"Wow, you're a crazy little motherfucker. It so happens a girl can buy only so many of those things before her allowance runs out. It'll be a year till I have that kind of money again."

"So come back next year."

"Why, you conceited ass! What makes you think you'd even be worth a Ford?"

"I've already got a Ford. Am I wasting your time?"

"Of course not."

"Well, you're wasting mine. You could start me off with a bank account at least. Give me some money now so I can get us some smokes."

"Here, you chilly bastard. You got a pocket-sized air conditioner stuck up your butt. Take it, it's money."

"This hundred don't impress me none too much. They print fives and thousands too. . . . That's better, bitch. Ha! I'll be back."

"You'd be back if I didn't have a dime. Wouldn't you?"

"That's right, baby. Because you're wonderful. A beautiful, lady-style woman."

EY, TIMOTHY, did you say this bitch was rich?"

"She is, man, but she's tired of having cats take her bread and cut out."

"She gave me a hundred when I sounded about smokes. Then she flashed this five-C note when I told her I wasn't impressed."

"Let me see it, Ming. . . . Yeah, it's good. Keep it. Keep it all, and think about bigger ones to come. Don't look around, she just held up a fistful and gave me the wink. I'll tell her you're waiting outside in her car. But we gotta get back on the stand in about ten minutes, c.p. time. Love her up a little. Take her purse and take every penny for flashin' like that."

"Take *everything*? What if she needs gas or something?"

"Man, don't go for that schitt. You can bet she's got a few bills in her stocking or up her ass. Take it all. You can strip a woman buck naked, take her belongings and lock her in the room, and when you come back she'll be wrapped in ermine and the walls all lined with gold."

"Okay, send her on out, Timothy. But what I got here is enough. I feel self-conscious. I ain't got that cold act down yet."

"You will. Don't forget the stocking top."

"Later, Timmy."

THIS BITCH talking about she ain't got no money? Big white convertible, white top, white sidewall tires—damn!—white leather upholstery! White sable coat, white satin shoes, that platinum hair—a pure-dee white woman—except for those blue veins and green eyes. I definitely got me a white woman. Schitt! Where is that bitch?

"Timmy said you wanted me."

"That's right, baby. Get in. Crazy car."

"Uh huh, and you can't have it."

"I wouldn't want it. Too light for a heavyweight like Mingus. Next I'm going Lincoln Continental. On my own."

"Are you really, you big, sweet bastard!"

"You crazy white bitch! Yeah! Love me!"

"Oh! Oh! Umm. I can't get close enough in here, baby. Hey, my purse! What are you doing with it?"

"Just some insurance."

"That's all I have—I gave you the rest!"

"Come here, bitch. I ought to take this from you too, for lying to me."

"All right, take it, motherfucker! You bastards are all alike. Take it! And here's some you missed!"

"Baby, baby, you'll tear your pretty blouse. Here, I'll unbutton it for you. That's not a nice place to keep dirty old money."

"Oh, you . . . ! My! You fine motherfuuu . . . ! Kiss me again like that!"

"Baby, get yourself together and come back inside. I'm due on the stand for the last set. Later, sug."

Got to rush back inside before Bobo sees I'm late. That wasn't too hard to act out, just like Timmy said. It seems so easy for him, sort of natural, but I'm amazed at myself. I thought it would be hard to take money from a chick. I wonder if the truth is anything like the Bible says, about hell and all that for sinners. . . .

ORRY, FELLAS," my boy says, stepping onto the bandstand. Timmy smiles. "So you did like I said. I can tell."

"Hey, Mingus!" yells Oscar. "Now you got rich, old Oscar could sure use a new set of tubs."

"Yeah, ball, hear you scored. Turn us on?"

"He scored with a crazy chick, not some crazy schitt."

"Oh oh, gone! Loan me ten, then? Pay you next Saturday pay night."

"Let's go," Buddy says. "One, two, three, four. Ba coo pah che pee doup la ca singala coupa la caah!"

"Hey, Mingus, Mary the waitress said while you was out you got a phone call from your mother-in-*law*. She says you don't have to come visit tomorrow or never—just leave Barbara alone."

"Again?" says Oscar. "What a drag. What makes the old folks keep fooling with your marriage?"

"You cats talking on my solo is what's a drag," Givons says.

"Barbara's parents want me to quit music. I'm not gonna quit music, I'm gonna quit *them*—except for my kid, I'd die for him."

"Stop talking 'bout dying and look out there at that beautiful bitch, Ming. That chick can save you."

"Her money can," says Tim.

"Old commercial Timmy! Haw haw!"

"So I'm commercial, but I'm the only cat here with a classy short—it ain't no raggedy Ford, it's a Cadillac. Nice clothes, a diamond ring, and a nice wife too."

Oscar whispers to Mingus. "Wow! Nice! His nice old lady is got the craziest head which is distributed all over town."

"Oh yeah? Is it like that?" Chazz says, looking away.

"I'm tellin' you, that bitch make you holler, man, she won't let go. Wow whee! Talkin' about good knockin' on wood till I get that hood. Sure hope she ain't misunderstood when I'm aboot to could. She eat my pudding cream while I dream and shake that thing!"

"Damn, Oscar! How can you smile in the cat's face and tell me you balling his old lady?"

"Balling! She calling my ding her dolling while she give up her noggin I'll be taboggin and soggin while she hoggin and toggin, tuggin while I'm pluggin and huggin her muggin buggin fuggin!"

"Cool it, Oscar," Britt says. "Tim can hear you."

"Yeah, man, I hear and I been hearing. Next time Oscar sees her he's gonna pay."

Oscar looks at him, shocked. "What, man, what?! What you talking about?"

"Man, I been knowing about you and June. When I said pay I meant pay money and I still do. No man can make a woman do what she don't want to. So should I be mad at you for doing what any man would do? Blow on, Givons."

"All men won't fool with another man's wife," Britt says quietly to my boy.

"You're right, Britt. But should a guy tell his friend if his friend's old lady has eyes for him? I sure would want to know."

"So you could turn her out like Tim?" John asks.

"No, man, if I was true to her I'd have to get some kind of satisfaction that hasn't been invented yet."

"Like murder the bitch," Givons says angrily, "and all the sons of bitches who talk over other people's solos."

Timmy laughs. "Each his own. Some cats shoot themselves, some shoot the chick and the other cat, some just let it go. Me, I send the bitch to Tijuana or someplace where she can get it out of her system and get paid besides. When she comes back, she'll be glad to meet some of the gentlemen I know."

"How can you be sure she'll come back?" Charles asks.

"When you got her son and reason to kill the whore besides, she'll come back."

"What about love, Tim?" says Britt.

"Love I can do without. But money and I are inseparable."

"Naw, Timmy, that's not the way I'd feel. I'd be hurt," my boy says.

"Why you cats all putting me down? You'd feel hurt because you're jealous. Take this Cindy out there—she's balled two guys at least, maybe a thousand. I don't care and you don't care, but after tonight she's *your* old lady, I ball her and you care. You only care about who comes after, see what I mean?"

"Something's wrong with that philosophy," my boy says and Tim laughs.

"What you gonna do? Shoot yourself? Get a new wife every time one does what she wants to? Watch her all the time and worry? Or wake up, let her have hers and you have yours and admit you're both adult enough to get paid for your weaknesses."

"But it's more to life than just fun and money!" Britt says.

"That's what they told my paw and grandpaw, haw haw, but they never found it."

"Hey, it's two a.m.," Britt puts in. "Take it out. Theme. One, two, three, four . . . See you cats."

"Later, Britt."

"Later."

"Night all."

INDY? COME ON, baby, we're on our way. Where do you live?"

"Up in Laurel Canyon. Want to drive?"

"I'm not your chauffeur, bitch, especially on Central Avenue in front of all the cats."

"Man, that's sure corny."

And Charles thought, "Yeah, she's right, I came on square race-wise. I got to act older and hipper with this chick." When they got in the car he took the wheel.

S THEY PULLED IN the driveway of her house high up in the Hollywood hills, Cindy said, "Zip up and come on in. Oh, I see Sally and Nancy are still working upstairs." It crossed my boy's mind that this

148

was a kind of funny remark for a fancy white so-called playgirl-heiress to make.

As soon as they were comfortable in the living room, she asked the Filipino houseboy for "the usual" and he brought a tiny pipe with tamped tinfoil spread over the bowl, filled with little chopped green leaves mashed into a gummy-looking substance like catnip in tar. Givons had once rolled something like this and called it *moto*. "First class pot mixed with hash," he said. "Two pokes of this will ice you out."

He hoped Cindy didn't know it but this was his first time to get really frozen high. Gradually she began to look like a Greek goddess-virgin freak and as my boy floated around the room, so slow and natural, he was convinced he was the greatest lover—fuck Casanova!—that ever was and his joint was the longest and biggest on earth. It had a mind of its own, the head was equipped with a mouth and tongue and oh how square all the whole world is! When the goddess's eyes, that seemed to change size, met his, the two of them were at opposite ends of a powerful magnetic beam that centered in the base of the brain and went down their spines out her ass and electrified his dick and balls. When one turned his head, left, right, up, down, the other would feel the motion vibrating in the beam and would have to do likewise. "I'm high!" Mingus said. "Yeeeaaah—Charles baby—let's keep on fucking and sucking like this in our heads till we can't stand it— so cool this way, lots of time to cool."

Yeah!—this was the way he'd *always* felt but never got deep enough into himself to find. He was a thousand times soberer than anyone in the world, more so than people who never got high, really himself, and he knew all Cindy's thoughts and she knew his. Wow, this crazy tall bitch!— we should make it wildlike all over this joint! After what seemed like years Cindy smiled at Mingus and said, "Pepe, that'll be all. Blow, and don't come back till I call you. . . . Charles . . . why don't you start doing some of those things you're thinking?" He knew what he wanted all right but he could hear Pop Collette telling him, "Always let 'em cool awhile till they get to wanting you more than you want them." So he just lay back and said, "Make me feel at home, baby, do some of the things *you're* thinking," and in a second she was all over my boy. He let himself go limp and extra relaxed as if it were barely interesting but things started getting a little less cool and less and less cool till they both turned into their animal selves, wild, uncivilized, and clawing.

INGUS IS AWAKENED by laughter. The girl called Sally stands over them throwing a purple satin spread across the couch—"At least you two could cover yourselves!" He wonders fuzzily "How'd I get in *here?*" and reaches down to let the other half fall on Cindy, crouched asleep near his feet. "So you finally got the great Mingus!" Sally cackles. "Now we won't have to be listening every day, thank God, to how much he knocks you out!"

Cindy wakes up, stretching and yawning. "Don't boost his ego, honey, he's already more expensive than anything else we have around here."

A blooming-bosomed young woman with black hair

slung over her shoulder down to her navel walks into the room stark naked and yells out, "If you bitches are going to have your nigger pimps running you all over the place let me know first! I almost lost a regular hundred-dollar trick this morning. When I take my john to the door there's that black ass laying on the sofa and Cindy all over him stoned out of this world! My trick says 'Isn't he colored?' So I tell him 'Sure and so's she—that's our maid and chauffeur.' I hope he believed me!"

She turns a protruding ass, poses with legs spread apart and hands on waist for a moment and then goes off toward the stairway. Cindy casually rises, in the nude as she has been for the past eleven hours, and sneers: "Whore!" Nancy whirls. "Whore yourself—Madam *Lanky!*" She runs full-breast against Cindy's front, hooking her leg around Cindy's, trying to topple her over. Cindy bashes Nancy's jaw.

Screams and yells, tongue and teeth, fists and nails and fingers full of platinum and black hair from all parts of the anatomy! Mingus tries to jump into his shorts and somebody's foot catches him behind. Cindy attempts a hammerlock but Nancy manages to throw them both off balance and they fall to the floor headlocked in each other's legs, rolling over and over as Sally rushes in with a bottle of seltzer water and sprays their faces and asses. "A minute ago they were battling—now they're in each other's arms!"

Cindy frees her head from between Nancy's legs, and breathes deeply. "Nancy, you're a bitch! I kicked your ass once and if I catch you shaking around Mingus again I'll fix you for keeps, you cheap hussy!"

"Cheap? I turn more tricks than you do!"

"Sure, at *your* price you have to, stupid! I can model for a living and make more than you! Grow some and maybe in a year or two you can retire!"

"Okay, skyscraper!" sneers Nancy.

"That's right, baby," Cindy says. "The latest style this year—tall mama!"

"Where's Pepe?" Sally asks.

"I sent him to the other place to get my man some money. Put your clothes on, girls. Let's have some breakfast."

My boy was thinking, "So this is the house of the famous Cindy, rich, white and an heiress! No wonder they call her *Madam* Perkins!" He was still seeing Nancy's body in his mind. He liked her size—petite. Cindy was five feet eleven and when she wore high heels she was taller than he was and it made him feel funny. He could tell Nancy liked him. What if he took her out of Cindy's place? Tim Mark could get him connections for a high-class call girl, he'd said. Well, then, why not?

Cindy wanted him to stay in the Laurel Canyon house and she ordered a piano sent in. During the next week she explained to him all about the business—the discreet operation here and the open house on the other side of town. The girls didn't like to work over there—cops would come in and trick with them and bust them afterwards. She offered to put as much of the business in his hands as he wanted, but with a new baby grand at his disposal he was more interested in music than in all these bodies. And it was good—he felt tight with Cindy, tight enough to permit him to ball Nancy if he wanted to, he thought, only he was wrong about that.

Cindy came home one afternoon and found him looking guilty and Nancy running upstairs to rearrange herself. She didn't say much, she just looked at him, shy and
hurt. "I'm no chippy, Mingus." She threw the contents of
her purse at his feet. Mingus looked at her coldly. "Neither
am I and I can't be bought." He walked to the piano and
began to play furiously with plans in his head for cutting
out and taking Nancy with him. Maybe she didn't have a
million or a Cadillac or a yearly allowance but she didn't
get high and she wasn't glamour-seeking and she said
she'd go anywhere with him and make it. While he sat at
the piano composing a song called "Devil Woman" and
turning these plans over in his mind, Cindy came and laid
her head on his shoulder. "I'm sorry, baby. You can do anything you feel like doing." She kissed him forgivingly.

All that afternoon Cindy sat around watching him
write, fixing coffee and keeping out of the way. "Where's
Nancy?" my boy asked later. "I sent her on an errand,"
she answered sweetly.

The phone rang. "It's for you," Cindy sang out. "Some
woman. Maybe it's your *wife*."

It was Nancy and she was crying. "Baby, I got busted
out here on the west side. Please do something."

"Don't worry, I'll have you out in no time," my boy
said.

"I hope so, 'cause this is my third offense. Cindy sent
me over here to turn a special trick. It sure was funny, the
guy came in and just said which one is Nancy, come with
me, and he was a cop. Please help me, I'm already yours,
you know that. I gotta go, honey. 'Bye."

Charles turned to Cindy. "You bitch! You framed her.
I'm gonna fix you, mama."

"Why don't you do that, you dirty bastard," she answered smiling. "Go get your little tramp and see how long *that* lasts!"

My boy went downtown and bailed the girl out, but then he said good-bye and he knew he wasn't going to see her any more. He felt he'd had a very narrow escape from getting into a kind of life he didn't want to live. But he was lonely and sad as he drove toward the empty apartment on Vermont Street, feeling so blue and alone he hated to put the key in the lock. And as he opened the door he saw with a rush of joy and relief that Barbara and his son Charles had come back home.

ON A SUNDAY AFTERNOON in August, before their second son Eugene had begun to walk, Mingus said, "Barbara, find somebody to stay with the baby and get Charles dressed and ready—I got to make it out to a session at Billy Berg's this afternoon and I'm gonna take you and him."

"Oh, honey, he's too young to enjoy anything like that."

"No, he isn't, and I want his opinion. I gotta call Buddy Collette. . . . Hello, Buddy? Can you make a gig out to Billy Berg's today? Here's your chance to show me what you're talking about with that Merle Johnson small lay mouthpiece and soft reed, 'cause Charlie Parker's going to be there with his old out-of-tune self like you say. . . . Yeah, I heard him with strings. Sounded to me like the strings were out of tune and Bird was bending notes playing jazz regardless of those overpaid motherfuckers— and not one black violin player on the session! Come on out, I want to see you cut him so musicians will start talking about *you*, 'cause I know if you play like you played as a kid, with balls, Buddy, that's what's gonna happen. Later, Buddy."

"Daddy, Daddy!"

"Hey, boy. You and Mama are coming with me to hear some music. I want your opinion today. You remember all the records I played for you, don't you? You remember Buddy?"

"Yes, Daddy."

"You like Duke Ellington?"

"Yes, Daddy. Duke, Duke!"

"That's all I want to know. When I'm up on the stand today playing with Buddy and Bird—that's Charlie Parker, the man with the same kind of horn as Buddy—you come up and stand by the one you like as much as Duke Ellington."

"All right, Daddy."

"Ready, Barbara?"

"Coming."

ND NOW, ladies and gentlemen, the final set for this afternoon. Stan Levy, drums, from Dizzy Gillespie's group. Dodo Marmarosa, piano. Lucky Thompson, tenor sax."

"Who's he, Buddy?"

"Cat cut from Basie's."

"Buddy Collette, alto sax. Charlie Parker, a gentleman from Dizzy's group also. And Charles Mingus on bass. And please will all you people give Miles Davis a hand —Miles is just in from New York. Come on now, everybody—Miles Davis! Give him a good California welcome!"

"Okay, Bird. Something everybody knows."

" 'Billy's Bounce'?"

"Don't know that, Bird."

"It's just the blues in F. Buddy, gone. . . . Take four, Dodo. . . . Blow, Miles."

"I done blew, motherfucker. Now you got it, cocksucker. Blow, Lucky."

". . . Miles, why's his head so swollen? . . . He sounds like a sub-tone Don Byas."

"What was that, country-boy bass-player? Cool it and keep some time behind me!"

"Keep your own time, Lucky, before I start playing your solos back at you."

"What? Dig this cat! With a bass? Come on, I want to hear that."

"Move over and share the mike, big head, so you won't be embarrassed. I'll ape you. Dodo, Stan, lay out. Stroll."

"Whewhee! This motherfucker can play! What was that tag you added to my solo?"

"Kiddle lid."

"How the hell you play that sound like you laughing and talking?"

"Bird, you hear this country boy?"

"Yeah, Lucky, did you? The same way we make dah ooh dah down on chromatics from your C to C sharp to B to C natural, B flat to B natural, and so forth. He just added a quarter tone glissando, put his heart in it."

"The other night I heard a cat play bass the way Adolphus Allbrook used to. It don't supposed to be possible but they do it."

"Bird, you putting me on? That's the second time I heard about Adolphus Allbrook. Jimmy Blanton told me he carved a wooden pick with one hand, kept playing with the other, finished his pick, and played more than a guitar with it."

"Stone genius, Mingus."

"I'd sure like to meet him."

"Yeah, he's great. A scientist too—physics major. Teaches judo at the police department. Mastered the harp in two years."

"When are you motherfuckers going to stop talking and start playing, instead of just Dodo and Stan over there jacking off?"

"Miles, you're so vulgar."

"I want to hear Bird blow, not all this dumb-ass conversation."

"So gone. One, two, one, two, three, four."

"Yeah, Bird. Play, baby! Go, man!"

"Hooray!"

"Ladies and gentlemen, will you all shut up and just listen to this motherfucker blowing!"

"Miles! Careful, man, you can't say that."

"Schitt, man, I put my hand over the mike on 'motherfucker.' Remember Monk calling the club owner in Detroit a motherfucker seven times on the mike 'cause he didn't have a good piano?"

"He had it next night though. If he'd called him 'sir' he'd of had the same old clunker."

"Who's this Buddy Collette, Mingus?"

"My best friend. He used to really play but Whitey scared him white inside. He likes to sound white. He can read fly-schitt scattered on a fly-swatter though."

"And that ain't jazz."

"So tell *him*, Lucky."

"I will. First I'll cut him in his own bag."

"Don't try, Lucky, you'll bleed to death. Everybody in the studio clique tried it. He plays flute, clarinet, everything—just like the white man says you're supposed to play and a little fuller."

"Cat named Paul Desmond up in Frisco plays like that. You heard him?"

"Who's that little boy holding onto Bird's pants leg?"

"That's my son."

"Duke Ellington, Daddy! Duke Ellington, Daddy!"

"What's he mean?"

"He's telling me he digs Bird. Look at old Bird smiling from cheek to cheek. He's sure a beautiful person."

"Go on, Dodo! Man, that ofay sure can play! And that drummer too. What's his name?"

"Stan Levy. He's a Jew. You know them Jew boys got the soul and gone."

"Gone. Take it out."

"Hooray! Yeah!!"

"How about 'April in Paris,' Bird?"

"Sure thing. Sure thing."

"Ming, listen to this!"

"*God dog!* Sounds like millions of souls all wrapped up in that old ragged horn of his. Scotch tape, rubber bands and chewing gum and they sáy he squeaks. Haw! Squeak, Bird! He's just holding it listening to it sing."

"Look, he's got your little boy in a trance. He can't even move."

"Sshhh, Lucky! Now I heard him. He's the cat I been hearing in my dreams."

"Let's catch a smoke outside, Mingus."

"I wonder if Buddy still thinks Merle Johnson mouthpieces give a bigger sound. Some teacher's been telling him that colored cats don't get big sounds with open lay mouthpieces."

"Haw haw, Mingus! It takes effort is what they mean. Work. They don't like to sweat. The white man ain't satisfied till they take all the human element out. Like Bird— he made it this far and they give him horns with soft action. He says, 'What for? Too late.' He likes working. He plays an old Conn with a number thirty open lay mouthpiece. I remember some kid telling Bird he heard Negroes used trick mouthpieces to make things easier. Bird reached in his case, said, 'Here, try this Berg Larsen, son.' The kid put it on his horn and blew. Wheeee! Nothing came out but air. He turned red and blue in the face. Not a sound came forth. Bird said, 'Give it here, let's see what's wrong with it. Oh, the reed's too soft.' He took out a fifty-cent piece and held the reed to it and burned around it with a cigarette lighter—burned it down almost to the stem. Then he tried it out. 'Plays beautiful,' Bird said. 'Still a little soft but it will do.' If that kid had tried to blow a reed that stiff he'd passed out or died before he got it to play. You know who that was? A kid named Lee Konitz. Ask him when you meet him if you ever get to New York. . . . Say, you wanna play with my band, Mingus?"

"No. You wanna play with my trio, Lucky?"

"Ho ho! Mingus, ain't nobody heard of you."

"I'm glad, man. That's why I make three bills a week at home in sunny funny California."

"Three? Who you with?"

"Ourselves. 'Pick, Plank and Plunk.' Me and Lucius Lane and Harry Hopewell."

"Lane?"

"Guitar. The greatest."

"Oh, yeah? You heard of Barney Kessel?"

"Yeah, and Kessel heard of Lane. Lucky, why don't you and Miles rehearse with us? Maybe we can incorporate. We got a *bad* book. Can't too many trumpet players play it. Carl George says he has trouble. He says it's too much movement."

"You heard Diz?"

"Just on records with Bird. Sounds like he's kinda into Bartok. But fuck all that dumb schitt, Lucky. Come and play some of our simple west-coast colored no-name music. We're rehearsing tomorrow at Britt Woodman's. He's with Boyd Rayburn now. Some of the sidemen said no colored could possibly play the trombone parts, so I'm the funny cat that got Britt an audition."

"Boyd's a real straight cat though."

"Yeah, but I can't stand people looking over my shoulder and Harry Babson was standing behind breathing over me so I fucked up Boyd's music. But I told Boyd since he needed a trombone player to give Britt a chance and not judge all blacks by me."

"Want to go inside and hear Ray Brown?"

"If that's the kid with Diz I heard him on the radio the other night—he plays Pettiford pretty well, but I wonder what *he* can do on his own with all that technique. I know when a player is still using standard bass tricks. Bill Hadnot, one of the greatest bass players on earth— and he may not ever be heard—called me to check if I was playing with Bird and Diz. I turned on my radio and wham!—there I was, at least the way I played around 'thirty-nine. It turned out to be Ray. But Ray stays too close to Oscar's ideas. He's thinking bass, which shouldn't be. It's thinking *notes*, sounds you hear, same as a horn. If a cat could *hum* good ideas I'd dig that. Have you ever heard an alto sound like Bird?"

"Not even Buster Smith."

"Well, you watch and see if Bird's sound don't become more or less the pattern for alto, all over the world for anyone who hears it. . . . Lucky, I'd better leave. I have to drive my wife and boy home and then out to Venice for the gig."

"Okay, Mingus. We'll talk about forming a group one of these days. See ya."

"Barbara, ready?"

"Yes, if you can get Charles to stop sticking his head in Bird's alto."

"Hey, boy! Come on."

"Bird, Daddy! Duke Ellington. Bird! Bird!"

"Yeah, I know, son. Bird true is something else."

19

THE TRIO HAD BEEN WORKING fairly regularly at clubs owned by Mr. and Mrs. Bart Morgan. On a Sunday evening in December Charles walked into the Venice place.

"Hey, Lucius! Harry here yet? I got some new arrangements for us."

"Not yet. But Nesa wants to see you in the kitchen. Watch out, Mingus. Her husband won't be in tonight and she's got on a tight red dress cut down to the titties, hanging just right to make a man think wrong and no drawers on, showing pure ass. She said send *you* in and tell anyone else she's busy. Careful, friend."

HELLO, NESA. Not many cars in the parking lot tonight."

"Oh, Sundays are sometimes like this."

"How's your husband?"

"Bart left town for a few days—went up to Salinas to his truck farm. Cigarette?"

"No, I usually smoke a pipe. Besides, it's almost time to hit, I should warm up. What did you want to see me about?"

"Did you know your piano player made a pass at me? I don't want no nigger putting his hands on me unless I say so, you hear me?"

"You called me in to say that?! Look, Nesa, no insults, I don't need it that bad. I quit."

"Where are you going? Come back here! Get away from that door. Look at me, boy, I'm not playing! I'll scream rape if you don't do exactly as I say! . . . That's better. Now listen. My husband hasn't touched me in years."

"So leave him."

"Not on your life. Bart's got more kinds of action than anybody this side of the Mississippi and I helped him get to where he is. Now listen to me, I could make you famous overnight, you know that?"

"Can I go to work now?"

"You still think I'm playing? You want me to scream rape?"

"No."

"John! John, come in here!"

"Yes, Miz Morgan."

"If anybody asks for me out front say I'm in the office making out payroll and I don't want to be bothered. I'm taking this boy in there with me for protection. I've got to open the safe and I don't want nobody coming in touching my husband's money. Give him your forty-five."

"Yes, Miz Morgan. The band s'posed to start 'bout now."

"You tell Hopewell to play piano for a while. And Hickey Lorraine's at the bar—he's got his horn, he'll sit in. Come with me, Mingus."

HAT'S THAT you're doing, Nesa?"

"Locking the door, can't you see? Now. Here— how does this look?"

"Too damn good but I've seen them before."

"Big as this? What does that do to you?"

"Scares me."

"Why?"

"If I *don't* respond you'll scream rape, and if I *do*, your husband'll catch us someday. 'Cause if I did it to you once you'd want it again."

"My husband knows I want you."

"Oh, Lord! I never thought I'd die this way, this far from the South. I'm married. I got sons."

"That's why I want you. You ain't about to talk. You in trouble right now with your wife and I know it. Look. Go on, look. You ever seen a nicer one than this? Come here. I knew that would get you. You hard as a rock. How you open these britches? Come on, I can't wait! Here— the couch opens up—"

"Nesa, I'm sorry, I can't. I still don't dig that nigger-calling stuff and all those 'boys' you give me."

"You know something, Charlie? This is the first time I used that word. I know I used it because I was afraid I was going to lose something I ain't never had and may not ever get a chance at again. I was afraid. You're the first black man I ever looked at twice. Well . . . once on the beach I saw one looked like he had the blue balls he was so big down there in his suit. Help me, I ain't got nothing on but this satin dress—I can't hardly pull this damn thing off— There. Now you get them britches off while I get this couch open. Here, Charles, bend over here and see what's stickin' this thing together. I—hooo! You sweet son of a bitch! Oh! Oh, my Lord! It's been so long! I thought you tore it open! What's all that wet back there, am I bleeding?"

"No, baby, that's flax seed, I used that waveset on the desk."

"Oh, sweet darling baby, hit it like that again for big red hot mama! Go on, work it up to me. I don't care if they shoot us, I'm gettin' this good ass this evening. Big ball daddy, give me more that stuff!"

"Aaah, you don't like it, Nesa!"

"Give it back!"

"Why? You don't like it. I'm a dirty nigger. Why don't you let me call Hickey in here? He's white."

"You think I'm suddenly a tramp because I'm finally asking for that pretty black thing? Here, lie down in these crazy pillows. I'm going to call the bar, see how many people's out there. Hello, who's that—Lucius? How many people out there? I figured. You go on and play without Mingus awhile, he's busy. . . . Now look, you done got all soft. I bet I could make it stand straight up without nary touching it."

"I don't doubt that. Show it. Spread your legs and play with it. Put your hands all in it."

"Boy, you sure are uninhibited."

"If you say 'boy' one more time you just gonna have to have me shot."

"Cholly, relax—all I meant was 'oh boy!' Did you

166

know I was Miss Basin Street in New Orleans? When I danced all the men saved themselves till I come on stage and brought my big fine self out and dangled and squeezed like this, squirming like I was giving up every drop. Some nights I'd strip buck naked and take the draperies and hide it—like this, give me that top sheet. Ho! Baby! 'I'm Comin' With You Tonight!' That was my song. Old Bart sat out there one night and bought me body and soul. You don't see many twenty-eight-year-old bodies this fine that's been through what I have, ain't a blemish on my body nowhere and that cream color ain't no make-up. Where else you gonna see five dimples on one woman? In my finale I used to show it all from behind, like this. In New Orleans you can do about anything long as you don't bring your man on stage with you. I'd bend down shaking my hips, parting my legs, with my bare ass to the audience except for my long net stockings and I'd look back between my legs. All the fellas had their hands on their cocks. You could feel the tension in the whole room."

"Cocks? You call a joint a cock? What's that, New Orleans talk? Haw haw! Baby, *you* got a cock. This here is a cock-opener, a joint, my ding, dick, pecker, peter, rod, ass-opener."

"You call it what you want but they all had their things out. I'd see 'em about to come and we'd all start to tremble together. People thought it was my dance but I was coming and hoping they'd all lose control."

"I'd sure love to see that act of yours. Why don't you call Lucius and Hickey in and dance for us?"

"Let me get to really relax with you first. Look at this.

Ho, daddy! Yeah, Cholly, shake it at me! Ooh, I love this feeling of knowing I got your eyes!"

"I got you too—go, bitch! Show your ninny! Go on, show it! Shake! Shake! Shake!"

Now I GOTTA GO out front a minute, Cholly, so they don't wonder why we back here so long. You still hard as a bull! What you doing—give me my bag! You son of a bitch! Take it then—take it!"

"Baby, you said Bart had too much money, will he miss these few bills? If you want a man and got to hide with him something's got to compensate. This will remind you you have to give up something too, dig? You play, you pay. I don't play, I say I'm falling in love with you. I never had so much woman as you in my life."

"Oh, Cholly, I'm sorry, I didn't think you was serious."

"I didn't either. But you make it so good I'm afraid to really fuck you 'cause you might break my heart."

"I'm sorry, Cholly."

"I know you're using me, Nesa, and I'm letting you 'cause I like your spirit as well as the rest of you. My wife's already left me several times to go to her mother's but even when she's home we can't make it much 'cause she says it hurts."

"I'm sorry, Cholly."

"Now you been sorry three times. Damn, you sure got some fine titty. Firm, full, round femininity titty. Damn, just my size!"

"Oh my Lord, where'd you learn to suck titty like that—oooh, nibble the blossoms and lick the buds. Swhew! Swhew! How many places can a man be at once!"

"Ha! You southern fine ass whore, I got it all up some good juicy tight cunt! You bitch, I'll kill you!"

ESA! NESA! Wake up! We don't want to be here like this—what if Bart showed? Nesa, it's me, Mingus, come on, get dressed."

"Cholly Mingus, I hate you 'cause you hate me, you tried to kill me fucking! Take me, anything I got, just don't fuck me like that! I wanted love and you wouldn't even come. I saw you just before I blacked out—your face looked like Satan. I know I pulled a dirty Southern thing on you but I tried to change when I realized I didn't even know why I called you names. Don't worry, you cured me for life. All men are created equal and Cholly will prove it with his proud ass."

"So you're human. I didn't know. You weren't so nice when you forced me to come in here with you talking about niggers. How could anyone change so fast?"

"Maybe a few minutes out of my life before, I remember asking myself what does 'nigger' mean—those people, laborers, poor ass white trash, that used to come in to our first bar, they'd say 'this old nigger,' 'that old nigger.' But I always did learn fast and I just learned in a matter of moments that it's not the white man who has the superiority complex, it's the black man. Cholly, if you could fuck me the same way you did but with love, I'd follow on your heels. Bart knows a woman can't live without it. I told him I had a yen for you. He didn't feel good about it, but his mind's troubled with all these petty little hoods trying to figure out how to pull the big man down, he don't have time or energy left."

"I sure don't understand *that*."

"And you never will. But Bart'll do anything to keep him and me together, he's a lonely man, he just needs understanding company and I been with him since I was eighteen. . . . Oh, Cholly, I sort of felt those times we talked in the kitchen you liked my looks but you was so polite I couldn't get a move out of you. So tonight I took a couple of shots of bourbon and decided to tease you. I saw Lucius telling you what I said but you came in looking so cool I got mad. . . . Here, let me fix that. I never yet seen a man that I couldn't tell if he had a woman or not by the way he wore his tie. Now why you brushing up against me so gently all of a sudden? Oh, Cholly, I wish I could figure this old life out. . . ."

HAT DID I TELL YOU, Mingus? I knew you could get that Southern cunt."

"Down, Lucius, what gave you that idea?"

"Hah! I peeped you through that office window at intermission and saw you laying on the couch from the waist down!"

"Please, man, that wasn't me, but don't tell Harry or anybody."

"I won't tell nobody and you better not tell your wife like you done before."

"If she keeps going back to Mama maybe I won't care any more. I guess you never should be honest with a woman. I broke down and told her how I rubbed off lipstick afterwards and washed a hundred times. I *had* to tell her what I did—I thought it would make her go find out what's wrong with herself. How can a woman be so small it hurts if she's had a nine-pound child? Don't make sense."

"Cool, Mingus. Here comes Nesa."

"Boys, we closing for tonight, looks like the people all spent their money for Christmas. Cholly, I want you and Lucius to help me plan something for the club New Year's Eve. You want Hickey with you?"

"Sure, fine, Nesa. Hey, Hickey, come here—you got. eyes to gig with us New Year's?"

"Eyes, Ming."

"I like you boys, like to keep you on, but if that Harry Hopewell sneaks one more feel you all gonna have to get another piano player. You tell him that."

"Sure, Nesa. . . . Well, I'm splitting, I'm beat. Night all."

"Later, Lucius."

"I been thinking, Cholly, maybe you and Hickey better come with me tonight and see some of our clubs out on Route Sixty-six going towards Mexico and we just might go on to Tijuana."

"Nesa, I gotta get home. Barbara wasn't speaking to me when I left and I couldn't tell if she was packing or unpacking."

"What time you usually get home?"

"Three-thirty, four."

"Tonight you'll be home at eleven and take Hickey with you. My bartender will call you. Let your wife answer. He'll give her a message about you supposed to meet Bart at one of his road clubs. I'll pick up my friend Georgie May and wait for you down the road apiece. John will give the address to your wife."

"How about *my* wife?"

"John'll call her too, Hickey. Now you boys pack up and go home. See you later."

ESA GOT IT all figured out, Mingus. If she didn't get your buns yet she sure wants them. You better be thinking what to do with all that money she's got—she'd probably give you one of her clubs if you was to ask."

"I ain't interested, Hickey. And if Barbara's home and speaking I might not be going anywhere tonight, you'll have to take care of Nesa and her girlfriend alone."

"Slow down, Mingus. That speedometer been reading nearly one hundred, man!"

EY, LOOKS LIKE somebody's moving, Mingus. Isn't that furniture coming out of your house?"

"That's Barbara's father, he's carrying out the crib! . . . What's up, Pop?"

"Oh, I don't know, son, these women can't seem to make up their minds—first she's staying, then she's going. Just like her mother—left me for eleven months one time. Let's go inside, they're in there packing."

"Wait out here for me, Hickey. . . . Barbara, you leaving again?"

"Now Charles, just a few weeks rest away from each other and Barbara will be back to you."

"You know, Mrs. Parks, you two women consider yourself such prizes. Your husband told me you left him for nearly a year one time. Suppose he hadn't been there when you went back?"

"Then I'd went back to my mother again, the same as Barbara can always do."

"Well, since your daughter isn't speaking, tell her for me that if even *God* rejected me for that long, I'd be looking for the Devil or anything else to come and love me long before the expected date of return."

"Charles, you're a dangerous man! You hit me."

"Barbara, if I really *hit* you you'd still be lying on the floor and how many times did you hit me with your unforgiving tongue? Here, I was going to mail this letter to you if you'd already gone."

"Now, son, this—"

"Stay out of this, Lillian Parks—let the kids decide. Barbara, I'm just your old dad. Do you really know what you want to do?"

"I have to get away for a while, Father."

"Barbara, I'm telling you in front of everybody, I do love you. But the letter doesn't quite say that, it only says what you make me feel when you leave. Here, take it, read it. I'll wait outside with Hickey."

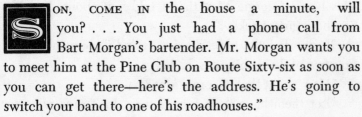

ON, COME IN the house a minute, will you? . . . You just had a phone call from Bart Morgan's bartender. Mr. Morgan wants you to meet him at the Pine Club on Route Sixty-six as soon as you can get there—here's the address. He's going to switch your band to one of his roadhouses."

"Charles, I've read your letter. It's just what I expected, excuses. I don't want to see you again. I'm suing you for support and I'm getting a court order to keep you away from Mother's house except one day a week to see the boys."

"Thanks for reading my letter all wrong. I hoped you'd feel something. I guess we'll never understand each other. . . . Well, I guess that's it. Good-bye, folks, I gotta go meet Mr. Morgan. You'll be leaving the keys, Barbara?"

"I'm keeping the keys."

"So I'll change the lock. Pops, take care of my sons. I'll send all I can to support them. And teach them how to defend themselves. Charles the Third's already got a good left jab, hook, and right hand cross."

"Eugene's going to be an athlete too, son. You should have seen him with a football today."

"Good-bye, Pops."

"So long, son."

THERE'S A SIGN, Mingus—Lovie Pine Lodge—is that it?'"

"Yeah, there's Nesa and her girlfriend out front. Looks like we're going straight on to Mexico."

"Hi, boys! Park your car, we'll use mine, it's bigger. This here's Georgie May that I told you about. You like Southern girls, Hickey?"

"I sure do but I hope she don't mind if we want to pick up a few of them chiquitas, ha ha!"

"How about that, Georgie May?"

"Let them have their fun. If they don't save none for me Ah'll pick up one of them, what you call it, chihuahua men."

"That southern dialect you got there is too much, Georgie May. Makes me feel ill at ease, don't it you, Mingus?"

"Yeah. Drop it, Georgie."

"You all just about know where you can kiss me if you make me mad. Ah ain't about to change, ah loves little ole me."

"I'm tired, Hickey. Let me lay out in the back seat with Nesa a while and you drive."

"Okay, I'm dying to see what this baby will do."

"Cool it, don't do past seventy. After you drive through customs keep straight on down the main road and pull up at The Hacienda, that's the best one there. Five dollars a day and you couldn't do no better at the Ritz Carlton in New York City."

HEY, SOME SUITE! And look out there, dig that big ole blue swimming pool!"

"You ain't seen nothing. Wait'll we jump in, twenty Mexican whores'll turn up nude and be all over you and me and Nesa and Georgie May too. That's right!"

"You joking?"

"No, and I'm gonna take 'em all on tonight."

"Yeah, Mingus? I got twenty says no."

"Make it fifty, Hickey, and I'll show you how to take ten to fifteen yourself."

"Naw, I can only make five, six, seven at the most after resting some."

"No resting allowed. Send for some tequila, lime and salt."

"How about some good old Mexico grass?"

"That's for sissies—makes it too easy. Twenty-five or thirty with pot."

"Aw, man, you're crazy!"

"Nesa, me and Hickey's going down to the pool. Why don't you two get into something revealing and we can have a real party when we get the girls up here. I'm hitting it, Hickey."

"Go ahead, I'll wait and see what happens. I don't see nobody around."

ASPLASH! SLURPLOP!

"Me, *señor!*"

KPLUNK!

"No! Me, sir!"

SPLATT!

"You like fooke?"

"Seventeen, eighteen, nineteen, twenty!"

SPLASHOOSH!

"Two dollars, sir!"

"Hey, Hickey—that you? What'd I tell you?"

"I don't believe this—where do they all come from?"

"Come on in. We need a few more."

"Okay if you say so, Mingus."

KASPLOOSH! FLOPP! SPLASH!

"Me Frenchy, *señor!*"

"That's twenty-four . . . twenty-five . . ."

"You like me? Ten dollar for my leetle sister, mister, she's thirteen jeers, no children, big chi-chis. Fifteen dollar for my cousin. She's seventeen jeers old. Ten dollar for my mother's sister. She's twenty jeers. My mother she cost you five dollar, she's twenty-five jeers old right now."

"All of you get some clothes on and come to suite seventeen—*diecisiete*—you savvy? Party. *Mucho pesos.*"

"*Sí, señor.* We come, fooke everybody. Party. *Sí.* You pay."

"*Sí.* Suite seventeen. Come on, Hickey, let's hurry back and lock up our bread before they pile in there. . . . Nesa, it's us, open up! . . . We got over twenty coming. Let's lock everything loose in the other room."

"We did that already, baby."

BLAM BLAM!

"Well, here we go!"

"*Señor*, it's me with my sister, cousin, aunt, and my mother. See, they all good fookes. Forty-five pesos."

"You're crazy, kid—I want a discount if I'm taking your whole family!"

"Oh, *sí.* Ten dollar?"

"Aw, come on, what are you doing here, anyway. We didn't ask for any boys around."

"Okay, eight dollar and one for me. I peemp for them. See? They're bashful."

"All right, here it is, and beat it. No boys allowed. . . . Come on, mama. You and me. Give me some of that tequila."

"*Señorita*, you want fooke her?"

"How?"

"Any way you like. Like this? See? Or you want I sooke you?"

"Go on, Nesa, let her."

"Not yet, Georgie, I ain't in the mood."

BLAM! BLAM!

"Get the door, Nesa. Yeah, *mamacita*—show it!"

"Here—rubber. No rubber, no fooke. *Nene*—baby—understand?"

"Work then, *mamacita*. Go head on! Little sister, come here to old Ming. You . . . owee! Mama get me just right!"

BLAM BLAM!

"There's the door again. . . . Seven more!"

"This Ming ain't kidding! He invited the all of Mexico up here!"

"Vasserlean, mister?"

"Little—then don't hurt too much up tight. Come on, mama—give me a little chops. Yeah, little sister, here it comes!"

"Aiee! You stretch my peenchee! I make good fooke for you—two more dollar, please."

"I make good fooke for you free, please. You make it good, I work for you."

"Ha ha, *chica!* But this ain't serious, I just want to get my nuts off a few times."

"A few times, Mingus?"

"Ho, you, Hickey! In this white man's society what else have I got, if God don't dig me? Me, myself and I. And I came out from between thighs, not lies. . . . How many is that so far?"

"Seventeen. You stone crazy, man!"

"No, man. Give me the tequila and lime. What's *your* name, baby?"

"Chita. I hear about chew! *Mucho toro*. You no fooke after Chita. I finish you good, no, yes?"

"Ha! Nesa, pay her twice! Yeah! I dig her confidence! Give me the bottle. Whoowhee!"

HAT'S THE MATTER, Hickey? Why you look at me like that?"

"Man, there's something wrong with you. What you did in two and a half hours ain't possible."

"Ha ha! I'll do that when I'm sixty, ninety, one hundred, when I'm dead! And if Nesa and them don't hurry and get back I'll jack off from just remembering it all—I never saw so many pretty different-shaped asses and titties. . . . Hey, Nesa! Come here, baby. Yeah, this is what I been waiting on!"

"Cholly, you all right? You not passing out?"

"Not me, baby, I been waiting for you. There's more of these left."

"Daddy, you and Hickey do that thing to Georgie May you told me about."

"Why you care?"

"I just want to see. Maybe I might want to try it myself."

"Georgie May, get your butt up here, Nesa wants to watch. Come on, Hickey."

"Man, you crazy? Let me rest."

"Then you're it, Nesa! Georgie, give her head, pull up her dress and eat on your knees. Get her! Come on, baby, don't fight, you want to see it so bad. I'll hold her, Georgie. There, I got her. Just kiss her thighs, she'll open up."

"Oh! Cholly! Georgie! Don't you kill me now!"

"Now bend up, Georgie—here's what Nesa's wanting to see. Swheew! You got her and I got you!"

"YES, OPERATOR, PERSON TO PERSON. Morgan, Nesa Morgan, N-E-S-A, on Baja Avenue, about the eight hundred block I guess. Maybe it's in her husband's name, Bart. Yeah, got it, thanks. . . . Nesa? Yeah, it's me, I'm in Frisco. I know, I'm sorry, baby, I should have let you know, I just had to cut out, I just had to get away. I'm not letting you down, baby, I'm sending Shifty Henry in my place—he'll get a good group together. Your customers don't listen anyway, they just watch, we're clowns to them. . . . Just a minute, operator, that's a fast three minutes! Yeah, Nesa. Hear that, operator? Reverse the charges. So give me all my quarters back." CLANK. CLANK. CLANK. "Thanks. What, Nesa? Sure I miss you—you know I got to miss you. No, I don't know what I'm gonna do—just walk around, I guess, and find out what's going on and try to sit in and maybe get a gig. No, I'll be okay, sugar, I got a couple of cousins up here if things get tough—Darcy Jones and Billy Bones. What? Well, Billy's not my *blood* cousin but we're real tight—it's an old family connection. What do you mean, the numbers? Never heard of it. No kidding, *millions?* Oh, come on, Nesa, you got some imagination!

Sure, I'll watch out, I promise. No girls, I'll save it. Yeah, I'll be at the Hotel Franklin on Post Street. Love you, Nesa, hear me? Later."

S O MY MAN WAS in San Francisco again, in search of he didn't know what. He could imagine his mother-in-law's comments, too, when he couldn't send money home, though he was living on canned spinach and mayonnaise. He wanted to make it alone without help from women or anyone else and he didn't want to have to go back to work for Nesa. Even if Bart looked the other way, to work in his clubs and take care of his household chores too just didn't appeal.

Well, Popeye ate spinach and mayonnaise was mainly eggs. With economical eating habits like this he could survive, stretch what money he had and even pay for a room. He left the hotel and moved to Mrs. Raleigh's rooming house where Oscar Pettiford was laid up with a broken arm he got playing baseball—about the worst thing that could happen to a bass player.

He tried to get a job driving a Yellow Cab but he was a few months under twenty-five, the minimum age. Working as a substitute mailman helped for a while and at night he walked around to any club where there was music going and sat in when he was invited.

Luckily he met a great piano player named Harry Zone who asked him to join his all-white band and got him in the union. He didn't know there were two separate locals—Local Twelve for whites and the Jim Crow union for Negroes and Chinese. Harry Zone went to Local

Twelve headquarters with him, and they thought my boy was Mexican, therefore "white," and let him in. One of his own race turned him out. A delegate in the black union walked in on the job and said Charles didn't belong there. He lost his tiddy, his first good gig in Frisco. But Harry Zone's attitude gave his faith in the humanity of some white-skinned people a little boost, to about the same extent as the black delegate's Tomism filled him with scorn.

Zone was a Jew, and he told Mingus he'd known there was a colored union but said nothing because he wanted to break the color bar. He was hoping Ralph Burns, a union official who thought of himself as a liberal, would go along with the mixed groups because he was a Jew too. Harry said Burns ought to know how it feels to arrive in a town and connect with a bandleader who wants you and get yourself a good hime and then be put down by the very people who are put down themselves because they don't think Christ quite made it as God!

Since he was all paid up with his union dues my boy was permitted to work at The Silver Rail with Harry until his salary draws were repaid, then he had to pack his bass and pack his ass off the sacred white bandstand. They cancelled his Local Twelve membership and gave him an ex-slave's card good only for the few clubs in the colored section of town and for the all-black bands that sometimes got together to play ballroom dates, though the union officials liked to hold out these jobs for themselves. Of course, my boy was allowed to sit in free just about anywhere. There was no law against giving it away, it was just that Class A club jobs, the only kind that paid good money, were reserved for a special breed called whites.

Soon even Mrs. Raleigh's rooming house was beyond his means. His artist friend Farwell Taylor offered his studio and when my boy hesitated to accept this charity, he opened the piano and said, "Charles, move in, sit down, compose, and someday pay me."

So my boy worked, studied and meditated, and though it seemed this was the lowest ebb of his life it was a time of development. Farwell and he worked through their karma together and established a mystic understanding between them that was to last through the years.

Finally he felt he needed to go back to Los Angeles to see his sons and try a life there again, so he returned to the apartment on Vermont Street where he and Barbara had lived.

He hadn't seen Britt Woodman in a long time—Britt had been on the road with Lionel Hampton. One afternoon he phoned and said Hampton was making a movie and did Charles want to ride along in the big publicity parade down Hollywood Boulevard with the Goodman and Hampton bands? It was the last day of filming and out at the studio in Culver City while the rest of the band were packing their instruments Joe Comfort asked Mingus to play with Cholly Harris, the other bassist. Hamp dug the sound and rolled his vibes over and began to blow with Harris and my boy. Charles realized that Joe had set him up for what amounted to an audition, since he was giving his notice. The minute they finished Hamp said, "Look here, gates, you want to play in my band?" Joe Comfort had tilted him right into the spot.

Mingus went home and scored "Mingus Fingers" for big band and twelve other tunes as well. Hamp used

"Fingers" at every performance after that, and to my boy's surprise, at his first recording session with the band for Decca, Hamp called the tune. It was his first original composition and arrangement recorded by a major band.

21

THERE WAS A MAN NAMED Fats Navarro who was born in Key West, Florida, in 1923. He was a jazz trumpet player, one of the best in the world. He and my boy met for the first time on a cold winter night in 1947 in Grand Central Station in New York City. Lionel Hampton's band had just got off the train from Chicago and Benny Bailey gaily said good-bye and split: he was leaving for Paris, France. The guys all stood around in their overcoats by the clock, waiting for the new man joining the band. A big, fat fellow walked up carrying a trumpet case and asked in the oddest high squeaky voice "This the Hampton crew?" and Britt Woodman introduced Fats Navarro.

Charles felt embarrassed as the band walked out. There were strangers, women and children, all around, and the guys were laughing too loudly and joking and words like motherfucker and cocksucker echoed through the station. They took the shuttle to Times Square and another subway to Pennsylvania Station and boarded the train for Washington, D.C. It was my boy's first trip to the Apple, but all he saw of it was underground.

Next day they rehearsed at the Palace Theatre in

Washington. Hampton had a nine-brass book. The trumpets were Wendell Cully, Duke Garrett, Walter Williams and the high-note player they all called "Whistler." Navarro just sat there placidly with his horn on his lap waiting for his solos while the rest of the band played arrangements. When Hamp pointed to him, Fats stood up and played, and played, and played! played! played! One of the other trumpet players became resentful of this new star in their midst and started muttering, "Schitt, this guy can't even read!" Fats laughed, grabbed the musician's part, eyed it and said, "Schitt, you ain't got nothin' to read here!" And he sight-read from the score impeccably for the entire last show.

Fats was featured all that week in Washington and then they went on the road. The trumpet player whose part Fats had read with such scornful ease couldn't forget what had happened. He was a man who carried a gun and he was convinced he had been insulted. He was lipping a lot about how he would kill Fats one of these days.

They traveled by bus. The small instruments were in the luggage racks, the basses lay cushioned in the back row. Seats were assigned by seniority and the one next to my boy was vacant and was given to Fats Navarro. Mingus and he hadn't talked much up to now. The first night out the whole band was tired and they settled down to rest as the bus headed west. Later Mingus woke up feeling uneasy. It was past twelve midnight and everything was still, the men were sleeping, but the seat beside Mingus was empty. He heard a voice in the dark, someone pleading. "No . . . nooo . . . noooo . . ." Then a familiar little high-pitched voice squeaked, "Don't *ever* say you gonna cut or shoot somebody 'less you do it, hear? Now if you don't be quiet I might cut you too deep so hold still while I makes you bleed a little 'cause when Theodore Navarro says *he's* gonna cut you that's what he's gonna do." My boy felt the others waking and listening too but nobody made a sound.

Later Fats came quietly back to his seat. After a silence he said, "That wasn't no way to treat a new member, that was old-fashioned jealousy schitt. Me and Miles and Dizzy and little Benny Harris played together and didn't never have no old-fashioned jealousy schitt. Why should any old member of the band be so uncourteous as to uncourteously threaten a new member?"

Nothing was said afterwards about the cat who got scratched and nothing more was heard from him about shooting Fats.

The band played thirty or forty one-nighters in a row, usually arriving in a town just in time to check into their dingy hotel rooms and wash up. Fats and my boy liked to talk to each other and began to room together. It was cheaper that way anyhow.

So this bus rolled on and on across the country, sometimes by day and sometimes at night. And in the crummy hotel rooms with big old-fashioned brass beds that sagged under Fats's enormous weight like hammocks they began a dialogue that continued off and on until the time it had to end.

OU LIKE ALL KINDS OF MUSIC, Mingus? I was born in Key West, Florida. My family's Cuban. You play Cuban music?"

"I'm not hip to that, Fats. I know some Mexican tunes."

"Hang out with me and I'll take you to some of the joints. You can sit in, blow some. Do you play any other than bass?"

"I try my best not to but I get my chops up on piano sometimes when I'm scoring long enough. I love to hear it on piano."

"Who'd you work with before, Mingus?"

"Illinois Jacquet . . . Alvino Rey . . ."

"Yeah? I played with Jacquet too. You play with Diz or Bird when they was in California? See, I knowed of you before you knowed of me. Talk to Jacquet or someone else —you ain't so undiscovered. Miles played once with you. He used to tell about the band you guys had."

"He did? He hardly said a word except with his horn. How cool can you get when a cat don't even say hello. That's the system, Fats, the system that keeps the blacks apart."

"I see what you mean—so busy worrying how to make a dime with your horn, ain't got time to make a race. Gotta go downtown and see the man, ain't got time to shake your hand. So we play jazz in its place."

"Where's the place, Fats?"

"Right in their faces. They know we know where it's at. Aw, they own us, Mingus. If they don't own us, they push us off the scene. Jazz is big business to the white man and you can't move without him. We just work-ants. He owns the magazines, agencies, record companies and all the joints that sell jazz to the public. If you won't sell out and you try to fight they won't hire you and they give a bad picture of you with that false publicity."

"Sell out, Fats? To who? Look at Ellington, Armstrong,

Basie—look at Hamp. All big famous band leaders. You can't tell me that agents and bookers own guys like that!"

"Mingus, you a nice guy from California, I don't want to disillusion you. But I been through all that schitt and I had to learn to do some other things to get along. I learned better than to try to make it just with my music out on these dirty gang-mob streets 'cause I still love playing better than money. Jazz ain't supposed to make nobody no millions but that's where it's at. Them that shouldn't is raking it in but the purest are out in the street with me and Bird and it rains all over us, man. I was better off when nobody knew my name except musicians. You can bet it ain't jazz no more when the underworld moves in and runs it strictly for geetz and even close out the colored agents. They shut you up and cheat you on the count of your record sales and if you go along they tell the world you a real genius. But if you don't play they put out the word you're a troublemaker, like they did me. Then if some honest club owner tries to get hold of you to book you, they tell you're not available or you don't draw or you'll tear up the joint like you was a gorilla. And you won't hear nothin' about it except by accident. But if you behave, boy, you'll get booked—except for less than the white cats that copy your playing and likely either the agent or owner'll pocket the difference."

"But Fats, I know a lot of guys with managers taking a fair cut—fifteen, twenty, maybe thirty per cent."

"Who told you that? Mingus, *King Spook* don't even own fifty per cent of himself! His agent gets fifty-one, forty-nine goes to a corporation set up in his name that he don't control and he draws five hundred a week and don't say *nothing*—but he's famous, Mingus, hear, he's famous!"

"Nobody didn't hold no gun on King Spook to sign no contract like that."

"You sure about that? One time he got uppity and they kicked him out of the syndicate joints. He had to break up his band out in California. He tried to buck it on his own with nobody but his old lady to help him beat the system. Mingus, that's the biggest gun in the world to stick in a man's ribs—*hunger*. So he sold out again. Now he's got a club named after him but it ain't his. Oh, it's a hard wrinkle, Mingus. Haw haw! I'm thinking when Peggy Lee be appearing in some east side club. Her biggest applause come when she says, 'Now I'm going to do the great Billie Holiday,' and Billie be out on the street and they all be saying she's a junkie. They had Billie so hung up they wouldn't pay the right way, they just put a little money in her hand every night after work, just enough so she come back tomorrow. They drives ya to it, Mingus. They got you down and they don't let you up."

"If you're right, why don't some of the big Negro businessmen step into the picture?"

" 'Cause they ain't caught on it's a diamond mine and they too busy scufflin' in their own corn patch and maybe scared. You breaking into Whitey's private vault when you start telling Negroes to wake up and move in where they belong and it ain't safe, Mingus. When the day comes the black man says I want mine, then hide your family and get yourself some guns. 'Cause there ain't no better business for Whitey to be in than Jim Crow business."

"I guess you got something here, Fats. I notice you and

me staying in hotels like this one for twice what the white
man pays."

"Well, if things don't change, Cholly, do like I tell you,
get yourself some heat, guns, cannons, and be willing to
die like *they* was. That's all I heared when I was a kid,
how bad they was and not afraid to die—to arms, to arms,
and all that schitt, give me liberty or give me death! Show
me where that atomic power button is and I'll give them
cocksuckers some liberty!"

"You said money shouldn't matter to musicians, Fats.
What if we all gave up on fame and fortune and played
'cause we love to, like the jazzmen before us—at private
sessions for people that listened and respected the players?
Then people would know that jazz musicians play for
love."

"I thought you had some children, Mingus. Don't they
need no ends out there in California?"

"I'm going to write a book and when I sell it I'm not
gonna play any more for money. I'll compose and now and
then rent a ballroom and throw a party and pay some great
musicians to play a couple of things and improvise all
night long. That's what jazz originally was, getting away
from the usual tiddy, the hime, the gig."

"But Mingus, how about them crumb-crushers of yours
when their little stomachs get to poppin' and there ain't
nothin' in their jaws but their gums, teeth and tongue,
what you gonna do? Play for money or be a pimp?"

"I tried being a pimp, Fats. I didn't like it."

"Then you gonna play for money."

———

HE TOUR CONTINUED and Fats began to complain that he didn't feel good, he hurt all over and he wanted out. My boy thought it was just an excuse because they were all tired of the strenuous one-nighters. One day on the bus Fats began coughing up blood. When they got to Chicago he quit the band and left for New York. But my boy and he were to meet and talk again many times before the day in July of 1950 when Fats Navarro died in New York City of tuberculosis and narcotics addiction. He was twenty-six years old.

22

BACK TO LOS ANGELES, and my man Mingus Fingers was now working two gigs to support his family—Bobo's on Central Avenue in the heart of the ghetto early in the evening and Bewley's Black Rooster after hours. Both were owned by big, burly Bobo Bewley, who once had been a heavyweight boxer. He enjoyed inviting Mingus and Dan Grissom upstairs to his plush apartment, along with the young Hollywood starlets, extras and models as well as assorted hussies who frequented the place. The word had got around about the new music downtown. It was the place to go.

Bobo used to say with his big smile—which revealed a bright gold tooth when it was wide enough—"What you young fellas got for me this time? *Uhm!* Such nice little white ladies! Redheads or blondes, they all look good to me." And he'd say, "Wonder which one of them has got the things old Bo wants. Come on, girls, show them hundred-dollar bills—or did you boys bring me some of them poor ones this time? Old Bo's going to show you how to make real money without leaving this room or getting off your back. If you tired giving it away, just lay

193

there on your lazy red asses and get rich. Whose money is this in this cute little shoe?"

"Mine, Bo," Mingus says.

"Learning fast, aintcha, boy? Now you bitches throw a little talcum and Black Narcissus on those funky asses and the one who makes the most money at the end of the night gets special attention from the great Bobo Bewley. A little noggin, if you get what I mean."

"Hey, Dan," my boy whispers, "does Bo make that scene?"

"They say he's the greatest. Don't you make it?"

"Not yet, man, I just take from those who give."

Bo says, "Now use your heads, girls, make it easy on yourselves. There's a long back-breaking line at my back door so get your lipsticks out and pretty your chops. Ever work this side of town before, Pat?"

"Yeah, at Taiwan's."

"How 'bout you, red butt?"

"My name's Sandy and I didn't come here to work except on your pretty singer and bass player. But I'll stay awhile if I get twenty dollars a trick for myself."

Bobo laughs. "Sure, half of every trick you turn, baby, which is fifty dollars on the average. These hard heads pay for nice ones like you. Sometimes you can get as much as a bill for a little half-and-half or straight head, but don't hold out on old Bo, you hear me?"

As they walk back downstairs Bo says to Mingus, "Boy, you're too simple. Don't make the same mistake you made cutting out on Cindy. That bitch upstairs could make you four to five thousand a week. Tonight she's doing me a favor splitting for twenties. Maybe she wants kicks with them big black dicks."

"Do any decent ofay chicks exist?"

"Decent? I thought you was waking up. Is it less decent to get paid for what everybody else *gives* away and feels sorry for later? No, sir, that's just *smart*."

"I feel strange around people who don't seem to dig love and do anything for money."

"Haw haw! I like you, boy, you remind me of church, but if Sandy gives you her bread, take it for old Bo's sake. Your kids gotta eat, don't they? They ain't gonna say Daddy, where'd you get this bread."

"Something just don't let me hear that, Bo."

"You may not hear that but everybody around here hear *you*, laying in there on your back thrilling and hollering when them brawds be biting on you all over. Haw haw!"

"Maybe someday I'll overcome that weakness."

"Weakness! Ogh! Oh! Let me get away from this man, you getting too far out there for me! Go play some music."

Bo walks out to the front of the club. Sweets, a famous local pimp on the town tonight with his stable, looks up from his table. "Hey, there, Sweets," says Bo. "I was just talking to Mingus Fingers. He still ain't woke up to the facts of life."

"Yeah, I know," Sweets says. "Give him time."

Charlie Davis is playing a piano intro and just as Dan begins to sing Phil Moore's "Shoo Shoo Baby" Bo screams —"Oh God! That nigger's got a gun!" Shots ring through the room. The lighted juke box shatters. Glass spatters. People scramble under tables and rush toward exits. Before I know it my boy has calmly laid his bass down and is walking toward the gunman. "Man, you crazy?!" Bo shouts. "Get down! He shooting a gun!" The man is aiming right at him but looks frightened and as Mingus yells "I'll kill you! I'll kill you! This is *Bo's* place!" he fires a wild shot and runs for the door. In the confusion outside a voice calls "Halt in the name of the law!" RAT TAT TAT! All is quiet. And another nigger lies dead in front of Bewley's Black Rooster. But as usual it's the wrong man, it's just poor Half Pint, the bootlegger who supplies whiskey to the after-hours joints.

Later in the kitchen Bo tells Mingus the police captured the gunman several blocks away, it's all a mistake and the nabs feel very bad about it so there's no use in making trouble for them. "Yeah, you tell Half Pint that," my boy says bitterly.

"Don't get smart with me, motherfucker," Bo says. "You can be replaced, you know."

"So can you, Bo, and don't threaten me, man. I'm as crazy as you are and I'm starting to get that funny feeling that makes me don't care what happens! So tell me you're kidding 'cause I don't want to have to remember who don't like me!"

"Now wait, Mingus—"

My boy is moving toward the gun Bo keeps on the kitchen shelf. "If you're gonna do me up, Bo, do it now and do it yourself, with your hands! Can't you make room in your mind that people don't have to like the way you do everything?"

"Wait a minute, nut! You misunderstand, son. Wow! Boy, you crazy! You know old Bo ain't got nothing but love in his heart for you! Relax, forget it!"

Mingus walks away from the gun. "Okay, Bo. I love you too, man."

It's over. They walk out front together. A beautiful brunette sitting alone at a table looks very hard at my boy. Earlier in the evening both he and Dan had noticed her giving them cool, unconcerned stares but they weren't sure which one she was unconcerned about.

Smiling, Bo says, "Who's gonna get *that* one?"

"I think she was looking at Dan," my boy says.

"She's sure looking at *you* now."

"Damn, she's got class! . . . Okay, I'll try for it."

Followed by Mingus, Bo walks toward her table and stands looking down at her with his Bill Robinson ear-to-ear grin. Fingering his polka-dot tie, clearing his throat, he says, "Why, *hello!*"

"Hello to you two," says the girl.

Mingus sits down beside her. "Let's not waste time. Were you digging Dan or me?"

"I dig Dan's singing. And your smile."

"Oh, my God. There goes another woman, disappearing from the avenue, gobble, gobble, gobble. Good-bye, little girl, I'm going outside and hustle some customers back in here." And Bo leaves.

"Charles is my name."

"I know. I'm Donna Parker."

"Well, Donna, it's you and me, I guess, or are you too bashful to dispense with the flowers and candy bit?"

"Me, bashful? No, baby, but we do have to wait one more set, don't we? An intermission wouldn't be long enough for me. Did you know that whore Sandy bet me she could get you in the twinkle of an eye?"

"Yeah?"

"I lost a hundred dollars on that bet but I forgive you.

And believe me, daddy, you won't be leaving *me* after twenty minutes and I won't be leaving *you*, unless you kick me out. So be sure what you're saying when you say 'It's you and me.' Because when it's true it doesn't happen in bed first, it's like right now, in our heads, and it could be for keeps. Do you feel it?"

"I hear you and I feel it, and, baby, be sure *you're* for real, I'm tired of games myself."

"Give me the keys to your car and apartment. I'll wait there. Where's your car?"

"Out back. It's the green convertible with—"

"I know which it is, I've been digging you, man, for a long time. Forty-two sixty Vermont Street, Apartment Two. Here's cab fare. Don't waste any more time with Sandy."

"Keep the charity, pretty. The light switch is to the right of the door as you go in or do you know that too? Just about even with that healthy bulge peeking through your blouse at me. And baby, if the phone rings, don't answer."

"Why not?"

"I said don't answer the phone and I mean it."

"Good night now, sweet Mingus Fingers."

"If I'm right not just tonight will be good. You called it and we're going to live it. It's happening."

Bobo smiles and bows her out the door. "Good night, Madam. Call again." He comes back to Charles. "My boy, I've seen them come and go, come and go, yours and Dan's, Dan's and yours, but damn if I can see how you'd let a queen like that get away!"

"Too much lady for me, I guess," Mingus says.

Back on the stand, Mingus tells Dan, "Donna said to say good night. She dug your singing."

"Donna—is that her name? Did she leave any other message?"

"Nope."

"Schitt. Well, forget it. Wanta come with me and Fannie after work? She's got a crazy chick with her, dig over there. We can have a little daisy eyes, you know, all four hold hands."

"No eyes tonight, Dan."

"Aha! I knew it! This cat's done stole my chick Donna! Wow, my *friend!*"

"Aw, come on, do they all belong to you? No, man, I just don't dig evil Fannie Fong—she is *really* crazy. Crazy!"

"Man, you could be right. This Hong Kong chick told me she's gonna leave her mark on every nigger singer that balls her."

"Sure, like the brawd that cut Duke and Herb Jeffries. It's always on the right cheek—wham!—she just ups and surprises a cat for no reason, no warning, and leaves a famous face hanging open!"

"I guess I ain't famous enough, I been knowing this one two years and she ain't cut me yet."

"Better stop laughing and keep your fingers crossed if that DJ keeps playing your record five times a day. And don't be coming up with no patches on your face talking about poison ivy."

Bo strolls by the bandstand. "When you motherfuckers gonna play some music and stop using my time for your escort bureau?"

"Oh, Bobo Bewley!" says Charlie Davis. "Must you be so uncouth!"

"Yeah, Bo," my boy says, "you running all the decent customers out with your loud dirty mouth."

"Fuck 'em! I run my place the way I see fit."

"That's not what them cops told you," Dan says jokingly, "when they was back there counting the take and giving you your share. Seems I heard one of them saying 'We don't want any schitt outta you, nigger!' Now cool, Bo, before I quit and go work back down the street at the Downtown Cafe and you know where I go, the crowd follows."

"Make some noise with them damn horns and things, you halfass punks," Bobo says.

"Why, certainly, Mr. Bewley. One two three four, la la . . . Hey, Dan, you swing on them snares!"

"Just sweeping brushes—nothing to it."

"Take one, Mingus."

"Gone, Charlie."

"Blow, Fingers!" Dan shouts. Then he whispers, "Mingus, you oughta make this chain thing tonight, you'll learn something, that Fannie can think of so many things!"

"Some other time."

"How about you?" Dan asks the guitar player.

"No, man," says Lucius Lane. "I'm going steady, I might get married."

"Who, Mitzi?! You wouldn't marry an ofay brawd, would you? Them bitches don't mean no spook no good."

"I dig Mitzi," Lucius says.

My boy frowns at Dan. "Yeah, Lucius, she's nice, Dan's sore 'cause he couldn't make her."

Dan whispers, "That bitch was laying her head in my lap long before Lucius met her."

"Aw, lay off, Dan."

"Yeah! Bo's got some pictures of her doing me and him upstairs two years ago!"

"Gonna show 'em to Lucius?"

"Man, you crazy?"

"That's right, give 'em a chance, they want to get married."

"Sure, okay, reverend. Take it out, Charlie. I'm now going to sing 'Diane', key of A flat."

Mingus says, "I think you mean the relative minor B natural. Haw! One two three four . . ."

"I'm in heaven when I see you smile. . . . Smile for me, my Diane. . . ."

INGUS DIALED his own number, Kimball two-one two-one. When there was no answer he thought to himself, "Donna's her name and she just might be all right!" My boy hadn't seen the best of human nature lately and he felt he might be losing faith in the entire human race but this new woman who had come to him out of nowhere and with such seeming honesty made him wonder again if there could be such a thing as frank, true, down-to-earth emotions and if two people's dreams, misery and hope could be totaled up in five minutes and labeled love, even "till death do us part," all in one night.

Lee-Marie, Manuela and Barbara, all different stories and different kinds of lives, they'd all been beautiful but so was Donna and she was a white woman. Not a better woman, just someone life was easier for—she'd never been subjected to the galling rules America inflicts on Negroes.

Donna. Who is she, what is she, what's she doing alone over here with us black folks? She's not a whore and she doesn't seem like the nympho kind that comes exploring Central Avenue's smalltime Harlem possibilities. Well, whatever, he would soon know.

As he pulled up in front of his house in the cab he saw his neighbor Jake Baines standing in the shadows. Jake had been a high school track star, a potential great athlete, and a beautiful trumpet player, but his greatness had seemed to fade after he caught his wife and only true love in bed with a friend he trusted. He still lived with Bess but he was changed and very subdued. From time to time he and Charles talked and confided in each other. Both had failed in their marriages and it seemed to bring them closer.

Jake stood quietly while Mingus paid the cab, then he walked over. "Hi ya, ball spot!" Mingus had an idea he'd seen Donna arriving and had eyes. Before in such cases my boy hadn't cared and likely as not would tell him to hang around or wait on the porch and later call him in, for the girls were often ready for more than one man alone felt like supplying.

This time Mingus didn't extend the usual invitation but merely nodded—"What's happening, Jake?"—and passed on by. Jake followed a few steps and called after him in surprise. "Mingus! Hey! What's going on?" A screen door slammed and his wife Bess was on their back porch screaming: "Yes, Jake, yes, go with Mingus! Still getting even, Jake? I'll give you something to get even with! Last time

Mingus left you alone with one of his tramps I told him to come over here with me, what do you think of that!"

"Did she ball?" Jake asked softly.

"*She's* talking, man," my boy replied.

"If you two were as true to your women as you are to each other you'd be able to keep your wives!" Bess yelled. "Go on, Jake, get your leftovers but don't come back 'cause I'll get Mingus in here one way or the other!"

"That's all right with me, Bess," Jake said.

My boy tried to make a joke. "Not me, man, I don't want you throwing me all over your house."

Bess began to cry. "Well, if it's not Mingus it'll be some of those other guys you always accuse me of!"

"Okay, okay, Bess," Jake said, "I'm not going in. I'm sorry."

My man was relieved. He didn't want to have to explain to Jake that tonight he had a different kind of woman who might be staying awhile. As he turned away he heard Bess spitting out her jealousy—"White tramp trash!"

The door to his apartment opened and the scent of his Indian incense and rich perfume streamed toward the angry outdoors and seemed to say "Silence, you fools! This is a night of love." The deep strains of Debussy's *Images* filled the air. Donna could have chosen any music to play but she had instinctively found his soul. He looked back at Bess's tearful face and Jake, grim and sad, and he felt superior. Never could a woman like Bess know how to set an ancient scene for love with music and frankincense as Donna was doing.

"Good night, Jake, 'night, Bess, I'm sorry," Mingus said.

"Good night, ball spot," Jake answered.

HO WAS DONNA? Could this be a bad woman's mouth, so dry and trembling, warm and soft? These pillows of hair that knead so well in his hands. . . . Mingus wanted to shut out all reality, all sounds—the slamming of a screen door, the drip of a faucet, screech of a brake, the unpleasant radio in the next apartment and even the lure of perfume and incense and leave this earth in her eyes. Donna must know the importance of honesty—hadn't she been the first to say for keeps, not just for tonight? "Darling Donna, I'm so tired of this stupid, faithless existence. Tell me the truth, tell me why you're here, tell me all you are."

"I knew you'd be like this, Charles," she said. "I have coffee ready, so come and sit down and I'll tell you everything important, everything."

Mingus let her go and said lightly, "Just give me a minute to get into something more stove-side like."

"Sure, baby—sugar and milk?"

"Please."

"Oh, hey!"

"What are you looking at?" my boy asked, self-conscious.

"You."

"I haven't always been this heavy. Two hundred twelve. I used to weigh a hundred and sixty-seven. All the chicks looked more than twice."

"Then stay heavy, I don't want them to look more than once."

"Donna, let me bring you the pants to those pajama tops. It'll make it easier to listen if you want to talk."

She crossed her legs and dropped a napkin across her lap. "Does this help any?"

"Pin the top together."

"How's that?"

"I'm cool. Now talk."

"Well, I'm twenty-two years old, I was born in Virginia, both of my parents are still there, this is my natural hair color."

"And it's beautiful, too. Rich and brown like chestnuts. Continue. About your parents. Are they straight?"

"They're still in the South. When a white person prefers the South, it's the ways of the South he likes. My parents came to the coast for my wedding but they were still in the South."

"Are you still in the South?"

"In some ways. For instance, I'm proud. But of the right things, I think, not stupidly proud. There was a little girl named Piggy that they raised me with. I'm proud I knew it was wrong when she told me I shouldn't play with her little colored friends—especially the boys. Even poor Piggy was brainwashed on that."

"I've lived that story."

"I know you must have. Anyway, there was a man who lived out here who was a business associate of my father's and Papa would always tell me to be nice to him. He seemed to be such a wonderful person. Finally I married him and he turned out to be in the South, just like my parents, the South I married to leave. He stopped me from everything I wanted to do. Would you believe that my parents told him I liked to hang around with the colored help? When Piggy came out here and worked for me he decided in his head we were perverted and hired a detective to watch us. The detective was her boyfriend and he shot her because of what my husband said! She didn't die, she's all right, but look what the South did to her!"

"The South follows Southerners everywhere."

"Didn't you wonder, Charles, how I knew so much about you, where you live and all? I know, for instance, that you carried mail last Christmas holidays."

"I'm not ashamed of it. Did you see me? I don't remember seeing you."

"You didn't. My husband insulted you when you delivered a letter. I was listening and watching."

"I remember that cat—Parker! Brent Parker! I wanted him to sign for a registered letter and he said 'Leave it in the box, boy, like the regular nigger does.' I told him to shut up and sign and he said if he had me down South I'd dance for him. There I was, Jim-Crowed in music and Jim-Crowed delivering mail while the whole world was preparing for a season of love and feasting to celebrate the birth of Christ. I tried to kick the screen open and he slammed the door and said he was getting his pistol. But I got him later and he never knew it was me. In February, when I wasn't working, I started waiting for him night after night."

"He said a gang of Negroes beat him up in the Hollywood Hills."

"The gang was me. I pulled my cap over my face and opened his car door for him. Wham! The first time he came to I told him I'd just found him there. 'Some *niggers* held me up!' he said so I let him have it again. Every time he'd come to and say the word I'd out him. I threw him in his car and drove him out to Watts. He kept babbling how niggers stole so I took the money out of his wallet and stuck it back in his shirt with a note saying 'Don't use the word nigger again.' I signed it 'Black Plague.' "

"Oh, Charles, I guess I shouldn't laugh."

"Why not laugh? . . . So what's happening now with your marriage to that fine gentleman?"

"I left him and took my son Malcolm, but he's trying to have my baby taken from me. Malcolm's with Brent's mother now—she's a nice person. But he won't give me anything and I have to get some money or go to work soon. I've been doing some modeling but it's not enough."

"Why the show of money tonight at the club—betting the hundred and all?"

"To impress you. After the scene with the letter I asked Piggy to find out about you. She told me you were a crazy bass player at Bobo's and I began reading about you in the papers. Piggy thought you were carrying mail for a front for Internal Revenue or something."

My boy laughed. "Yeah, and when I'm down at the unemployment that's a front too."

"If you need money, I still have some, Mingus."

"Never mind that. I can make it with the gig. Besides, I took a little money from Sandy tonight. Here's the hundred you lost on me."

"No, daddy, here's two. Now we have five and it belongs to both of us."

"Come here and leave that napkin where it falls."

". . . Hold me, Charles. Teach me to love you. Let me love you for every cruel thing the world has done to you."

"From now on?"

"Now on."

23

I NEVER REALIZED there were so many places to go and yet so few places to stop and relax. You know what I mean. Here's a man and a woman with something bringing them together, maybe not love but something deep that makes each try to hold on to his understanding of the other so as to build a perfect friendship.

A trip. A stop for coffee. And a black and white couple meet with barriers of hate that the world's greatest lovers couldn't overcome. Not only the hard stares at a stoplight, or a truckdriver's grimace, or Mingus and Donna sitting ignored at a La Cienega drive-in till a girl in white boots and red uniform throws a tray against the car and refuses to serve a nigger with a white tramp. Not only the booted racist's smile of surprise and relief when Donna lies, explaining she isn't white, and the insulting reply: "I'm sorry, sir—then may I have your orders?" Or the fact that Mingus says, "Yes, dear, kiss my pretty black ass!" when he could have controlled himself, or that he didn't knock down the fellow who came running to protect the snob Donna was now beating with her shoe heel. Or that they drove away—*ran* away it was—with Donna in tears and

Mingus harshly hoping the *Communists* would straighten out all this kind of schitt! Or that Donna said, "You shouldn't have cursed at her, honey," and Mingus replied, "To hell with you too, you stupid white bitch!" and it was their first fight.

It was every one of these things, and a thousand more.

Deaf with rage, he couldn't even hear her crying. "No, Charles, not us too! Don't let them put *us* against each other, I couldn't stand that!" He couldn't hear a word until she said, "Darling, I'm going to get us out of this city, out of this country, and I'm not waiting for any divorce! We need money now, lots of it, so we can live somewhere else and you, can make it like the man you are—Europe's not like this, it can't be, we'll go there."

He began to understand what she was trying to say but he didn't help her though she was pleading. "I can't make enough money modeling and I can't even sell this car, Brent still owns it. We need money for lawyers so I can get Malcolm and a property settlement and we can go away and live in peace the way we want, don't you *see?*"

Still he wouldn't answer and she went on—"Baby, I'd do *anything* to get enough money so we can be together. You know what I'm talking about. I'm going to sell myself. Sandy or Bobo or someone like that can help us find a connection."

Finally he said, "Donna, no. You'd get caught. And lose your self-respect. And your baby. Yes, what about Malcolm?"

"We'll be careful, we won't be greedy. We won't be in it forever, just long enough to get a little fast money and go from there wherever you say."

At first he was stunned. Nothing like this had ever entered my boy's mind. But he'd been out of work since the Black Rooster closed and it was a drag having a girl like Donna and no bread. He told himself, "We must not really be in love. If we were we'd marry and make it somehow, nothing would matter. Sure she's beautiful, too beautiful for the dumps Bobo has. I wouldn't want to hurt her. I dig everything about her and I miss her when we're not together. But . . ."

Billie Holiday. Charles remembered when he had written a song for her—"Eclipse"—and, how did it happen?—she'd given him a madam's phone number. Mama something?—a madam up in Laurel Canyon. Billie told him, "When you get one of them real nice ones, Mama will fix you up right. But watch her, she likes those pretty girls as much and more than you do."

"Yeah!" he thought, suddenly excited. "Donna's for the big league, she'd be a million dollar call girl!"

Now he remembered Mama Clara's full name and he stopped the car and went in to call this famous madam who said immediately, "Bring her on out and let me have a look at her. If she's what you say she'll go home with a thousand before the night's over."

It was a sudden plunge to pimpdom for my man. Things were happening too fast and this was no game, it was the real thing. There was a sad, tight, crying feeling deep inside him but he had no tears to let go. He feared that he was now a full-fledged devil waiting to be cast into hell-fire.

He went back to Donna and told her but he lied and said Mama just wanted to take a look at her and might not have any actual johns. Maybe she could work as a hostess, serving drinks like a French maid and all, and pick up a few bucks.

Then they sat down in Mama Clara's place. Donna said two words and Mama sensed that she was shy and not too sure of her own mind. So Mama went right to work telling her she was the most beautiful girl she'd ever seen and that there was a big, famous white movie star she'd been describing a make-believe girl to, just to kid him along, and how Donna fit this very description. Donna blushed when Mama said, "Any man would spend a thousand for a few hours with a beautiful new young girl like you. I'm gonna call him right now and tell him you just passing through town and you'll be right up to make him feel good."

Things were all arranged by Mama. Mingus and Donna were driven near a mansion in the hills. Dropping Donna off two blocks away, Mama's chauffeur said, "He's not over a coupla hours. I'll know when to pick you up by his lights upstairs. Act like you never saw him before, he feels safe when he's not treated like a star. You'll get a least a thousand. Half goes to Mom."

My boy felt lower than he had ever felt in his life as he sat waiting in the dark limousine. Donna returning with sudden tears was comforted as best he could, for his own eyes were not dry.

She decided to go to her apartment and get some clothes to take with her to Mama's. There was no thought of turning back now and there was nothing to say on the way home for it was too late to tell Donna he loved her and hadn't really known till now. She kissed Charles's eyes and mouth and cried. "I love you, Charles! You! You! You! Come in with me, I want to be with you every minute, as much as possible. Come up and help me choose some things to wear." And she kept repeating, "Mingus, don't feel bad," and asking for kisses and telling him of their stronger love for each other, swearing she hadn't done anything she didn't want to do. Anyway, it would soon be over. "After Christmas, we'll be on a boat to Paris," she said. "Oh, Charles, somehow I love you more."

He refused to take the five hundred dollars, telling her to put it in the bank—it was for her attorney and her baby. She cried again and insisted that he didn't want her now that she was a whore and that was why he wouldn't take the money.

I'm the only one besides my man who knows how he felt—cheap, low, still in love with a woman yet hating her for giving in to his cautious turning out. So ashamed he couldn't even look at her as he folded the money in his shirt pocket as Timmy had taught him to do. Was this the way a pimp felt, turning out his first girl and finding out he loved her? It couldn't be. Pimps are usually pretty calm people, cool but lively, full of laughs and jokes and some are even intellectuals. Surely they could never feel like this. To be a pimp, one would have to lose all feelings, all sensitivity, all love. One would have to die! Kill himself! Kill all feeling for others in order to live with himself. Not to think. To keep going because you're already going. *Mingus* couldn't be this . . . a pimp.

OBO'S BLACK ROOSTER reopened and Mingus went back to work. Soon after, he told Donna about a girl named Pam who sold cigarettes at a Hollywood club where C. P. Johnson's band was playing. She was more beautiful than Hedy Lamarr but dumb as all hell. One of the musicians, Rivelle, had introduced her to my boy and she started coming to the Rooster after hours. In the course of a week she was in love with Mingus and convinced that he loved her.

He was sure he could turn her out and then Donna could stop hustling. He bet Donna that in three nights he'd have the girl out and Donna, joking and acting rather flattered and proud, said it was a bet and that she would stay away from the gig and from his apartment until his mission was accomplished.

The first night of the bet he began by telling Pam how he wished he could buy all the nice things for her that other women have. "You're the prettiest woman around, Pam," he said, "and you're almost ragged." She dropped her head and smiled. She wasn't as dumb as he thought, she'd heard that part. He said to himself, "All right, bitch, you've heard that part but from now on it's you and me."

He dropped the economic angle and adopted the romantic approach. He drove her around before she went to work and sat in the car in front of the club as if he couldn't bear to leave her. He held her and stroked her hair and teased—"Here we love each other and you go off to work and leave me and I have to wait all night for my turn!"—kissing between her fingers with the tip of his tongue. Almost swooning, Pam said, "Oh, it's nearly *eight!* Kiss me, Mingus, I don't *want* to leave! You don't really love me, Mingus, like I love you!" And she left, looking back, pouting and smiling, and went into the club where for a long time she had walked around every evening selling smokes, looking pretty, ignoring passes, and waiting for a guy like Mingus.

Later she waited at a dark corner table at Bobo's Black Rooster until Mingus came to sit with her at intermission, his hand gently caressing the base of her neck. He spoke casually of needing bread and she said eagerly, "I haven't much money but you know you can have it. Here, I know it's not enough." And carelessly brushing the few bills to the floor as if they were nothing he said as Bobo would say, "Thank you ma'am, thank you ma'am."

On the second night Mingus made his move. "Oh yeah, I meant to ask you, Pam. How many men were there besides Rivelle? 'Cause I know you were with him. You don't have to tell me—he's colored, so to get to him I know it took you four besides. Let's see. The first one you really loved virgin style. You weren't really for it but you did it when he came on strong. Then he cut out. So you try again for love—this time it's for real, you say. But you find you still don't know a man from a pair of pants. The third one's a bad guy who gets around, who knows life and he'll show you what the others didn't 'cause after they got the body they didn't know what to do. You start to think you must be bad too, so you want a guy like you, no flowers, no candy, just 'Come here, pretty sexy little Pam, let's make it.' But this hip guy, he's got friends of all kinds and they get high, which means you casually meet a guy at one of the parties. Funny, you never even looked twice at a colored cat before. This one's handsome and even hipper than your hip Casanova. You're intrigued. He's gentle, human, cool, and slips you his phone number. You can't wait to get home to phone him. Oh! This is it! You've heard such tales about Negro men—once you have one you'll never want anything else. You've seen their muscles when they're digging up the streets. They're made for a bad woman like you. The phone answers and he says, 'Baby, I knew it was you, hurry on over!' You don't waste a second getting back to him. His front door buzzer is still vibrating as you stand clinging to him in his animal-like grip. You feel glad you're so bad. There isn't time for words as bare shoulders feel wet feverish lips. If you don't find love this time there's no other chance. So superstition, fear and longing drive you to your knees to shower worship on a black man who found you just in time to save you from a breakdown for a reason plain as the nose on your face— there are too many white women for the white man to take time to love them all carefully. Your story's the same as every ofay girl's I've met over this way. But pretty soon your black Casanova gives you weird stories of how he excuses himself to live a vice life dealing pot—he's a Negro, he has a *right* to sell drugs 'cause Whitey makes it impossible for a black to make enough honest bread. Just the same it scares you away when you accidentally run on a hypo and he explains that now and then he deals a little H or C. But now you take notice of an even handsomer Negro right where you've been working—one of the musicians, Larry Rivelle. It's exciting when you give him the eye and he responds. He comes over, so well-mannered. 'Pack of Luckies, please.' And with his change and matches you give his hand a little squeeze. He's got it. He's got it, phone number and all. He calls, says meet him at the Rooster. This one comes on different, asks you for money and things you've just heard of but with him you'd do them. But the day he asked you to sell your body you told him you were through. So here we sit. You know what all that means to me, Pam? It means you're a chippy who's had at least five men besides me which is five hundred dollars per man you laid up on your back and *wasted*. Stop that crying stuff! Love! You mean that's *not* love. I don't see you coming 'round me with no wedding bells. You like it out there in the streets chippying from one man to another. What proof have I got that you won't be out laying with some dirty cat first chance you get out of my sight? Go on, tramp, and I don't care any more. Stay a slut!"

Well, he said three nights but it only took two. Pam dropped her head and said, "Mingus, if that's what you want me to do to prove I love you, I'll do it. You're my pimp."

But who could stand it? The girl died right in front of him. Died? She was murdered.

He told her, "Pam—I was just kidding. Don't ever do that for any man. Don't let them break you. There's more to life than you think. At least tonight there is."

It was like giving a bottle to a crying baby or freedom to a slave or pardoning a condemned man. Pam looked up with her stupid, beautiful smile and believed him. "Oh, Mingus, you don't know what you just showed me. You've just shown me there's God, whether you know it or not. I'll always remember you and this night forever. I think love is knowing the other's wish before he speaks, and you knew. I want to love and be loved and I sure hope that will be with you. You've made things seem so easy now."

So Mingus told her she was just about the most beautiful woman he'd ever known but to let her stay with him would be to say, "Continue to chippy with me until the real thing comes along." "Not that I *don't* want you," he said, "but I don't know what I want, except not to hurt you or anyone else ever again and tonight's not too soon to begin. Get out. Get away from me as fast as you can before I change my mind. Stop looking at me and get out of my face before I grab and kiss you all back up in hell where one part of me is and the other heckles me so. Move, Pam."

Pam with tears moves toward Mingus to put her arms around him. He screams, "Cut! Fool! Get as far away from me as you can!" He takes her out, hails a cab, opens the door and pushes her in. "Don't let me see you near Central Avenue again! The next time I see you, be behind a baby carriage or I'll kill you, bitch! Just move, move away from here!" And he slams the door.

INGUS IS CONFRONTED by the local pimps and chippies. "What happened, Mingus?" Sweets Mallory asks. "One of your girls hung you up or something?"

"Nothing, man," Mingus says and walks away.

MY MAN HAD AVOIDED WORKING in any of the Morgans' clubs for some time now, knowing how it would be between Nesa and him if he did. He couldn't help feeling that there was something wrong with such an arrangement—anyway it was confusing and uncomfortable. But Nesa remained his friend. She tried to do things for him and sometimes offered money or presents but he didn't really want to take anything, though he liked her. Then one day, okay, okay, she gave him a car. "Cholly, you take it. I wouldn't give it to you if I didn't want to. Take it, daddy, it's just a little old Ford. It's half paid for. You can keep up the payments. If you can't, I will."

"Nesa, baby, why is it all the nice people like you belong to somebody or something they can't leave?"

"You know how it is. But look how you've changed me, Cholly. I don't even sound Southern like I used to, because I don't want to offend you. Come on, drive down to your rehearsal in your new car, I'll follow."

"I don't want you seen on Central Avenue with me, Nesa. The white cops'll think you're a whore, check you out, and cause trouble with Bart."

"Fuck 'em, Cholly, nobody's gonna bother *me*. I know somebody can shut 'em right up no matter what I do, outside of committing murder with a lot of witnesses."

"All right, come on, baby, I'll show you off to all the pimps."

T HERE'S THE CLUB over there, baby."

"I thought you said you had a cooperative group. The sign says 'Lucky Thompson's Stars of Swing.'"

"What? Wow! Lucky really got some ego! There's Buddy standing out front with Bobo. . . . Hey, Bo! This is my former employer, Mrs. Bart Morgan."

"Nesa!"

"Lewis K. Bewley! Cholly, this is the 'Bo' you been talking about? Bart and him are old friends."

"Nesa, what you doing with this chile, trying to get him shot?"

"I've decided to be his manager. Don't you tell on me now."

"Well, since you're his manager I guess you'll pay for the new sign. Buddy here say this one won't do. I hired Britt, John Anderson, Buddy, Givons, Oscar and Mingus and they tell me they adding a man I never heard of He goes to my sign makers and tells them he's the leader and look at this sign we got! I never heard of no Lucky Thompson and I'll be damned if I'm paying twenty-five dollars for a new sign."

"Here, Charles, pay the man."

"Ah hah! Ah hah! Boy, you better hide when you with

this woman, her old man may have you erased—your *mama* won't even know you was here."

"Oh, Bo, you heard Nesa say she's managing me."

"All right, now how's this new sign gonna be done?"

" 'Stars of Swing,' real big, and all the names in alphabetical order. Huh, Buddy?"

"Maybe we should put Lucky's name first."

"He hasn't even got any music in the book. Man, he's got some head!"

"He'll change like you done, Mingus, soon as he sees hats don't come that size."

"He thinks we're country boys!"

"Ha ha! Guess he don't realize you're from the Big Town—what you call it?—Watts. Buddy, take Nesa on into the bar, them bulls is pulling by here looking at her fine self. Cholly, come with me, we'll phone the sign makers. . . . Boy, you know that lady owns Venice? Is ya gettin' that? Whooohwhee! She is one fine tasty bitch—a small package but everything there. I *know* you ain't gettin' that. They really from the *deep* South. They own thirty, forty clubs, hotels, the whole works. You got yourself some manager! And a pretty little new yella Ford out there."

"Why not? I been working steady."

"Yeah, nigger, and you come out wid Boss Morgan's wife. Well, least you getting some bread to fill your children's mouths. . . . Hello, Honkey? Make me another sign. Get it here as soon as you can. Talk to Cholly here, he'll tell you how he wants it, hear me now? . . ."

OW LUCKY, we *told* you it was a corporation group. Man, don't cry, you breaking my heart! Schitt!— your name's first on the new sign!"

"Oh, you cats! I've told my wife. You don't know how I struggled in New York. I got a name, you guys are just locals."

"More people know us here than you, Lucky. Come on, I'll prove it to you. Just ask people in the club what's our names, come on. . . . Pardon us, we're in the band—you know us?"

"Oh, Mingus, don't be silly! You and Buddy been around here long enough!"

"Do you know this gentleman?"

"I've seen him somewhere. Are you a musician?"

"He plays tenor."

"Oh! You're Bumps Meyers! No? Well, I'm sorry, I guess I don't know him."

"Ha! Try another table, Lucky?"

"Aw, man, fuck these farmers."

"That was no farmer, that was De Lawd Himself— Rex Ingram. Now how about those white ladies?"

"Crazy, they'll know me from the Basie band. Pardon me, lady—"

"Why, Lucky Thompson!"

"Haw haw! I'd like to introduce you to my friends."

"Oh, we know Mingus and Buddy. We saw you play with them and Bird one Sunday. I'm Nancy and this is Sally. We've heard a lot about your new group, Mingus."

"It's not mine. We're a corporation, or trying to be."

"Is Lucky with you?"

"Yes."

"No, I don't think I'm gonna make it. You cats are too good for me. I'd be embarrased to play with such a famous group."

"I oughta kick your ass, Lucky, if you're going to hang us at the last minute. Somebody's gotta shrink your head before it busts. Mine's busted, so I'll take the job."

"You're the one's too hip."

"Okay, we'll make it better without you, Lucky. You never tried to play with us or even with yourself so get your horn off the stand and leave so we can get our little group together."

"Oh! I've never been so humiliated in my life!"

"Damn, Lucky! Do you have to cry? You talk to him, Buddy—I'm tired. One minute I want to bust him, the next I feel sorry for him. See you on the bandstand. . . . Hi, Britt. Lucky's left. Guess you'll have to switch back to tenor parts."

"Fine, ball spot. I like the tenor range. I can play the alto parts when Buddy's on clarinet. I like that sound better."

"Tell the truth, I do too. We're more together. . . . Hey, John, you high, man?—wipe your eyes. Hey, Oscar, ready to go? Hi ya, Bo, 'bout time?"

"I ain't rushin' ya. Just get up and play."

25

MY MAN'S REPUTATION AS A PIMP is growing. The others in the district greet him buddy-buddy style now but his ego's no better off, especially when one day Bobo walks over and says, "Mingus, where's your girl Donna? Some of the boys tell me they been seeing her with that halfass pimp John Clark. Now listen to what old Bo's telling you—you got her, you keep her! Though there's an old saying that the first man to turn a chippy never gets to hold onto her."

Mingus tries to look unconcerned. "Thanks, Bo. If Donna's gone, she's gone, there's ten to take her place. I'll check, anyway."

"You can check right now. I see her outside—and ain't that him with her? . . . Come back here, Mingus! Dan! Charlie Davis! Stop my man! Oh, my God, that nigger's got a knife out on Ming! Whew! That boy sure can hit—there goes another one sleeping on old Bo's front walk. Dan, go out there and get Ming—look at him shaking that nigger, helping pick up his money, trying to bring him to! Get him and his bitch on in here before the cops come!"

Donna clings to Mingus's arm as they walk inside. "Honey, why did you just walk up and hit someone before you said anything to me?"

"Honey, why did you just walk up and hit someone before you said anything to me?"

"Take it easy, boy," Bo says. "You'll get old Bo closed down. First laying out them sailors, then mixing in a customers' fight, now this. I know you mean well trying to look out for me and all but I'd have to let you close before I'd let you shut off my bread and butter."

"Crazy," my boy says. "I close now."

"Schitt, nigger, I didn't mean that! . . . All right, you called it. Here's your money for a half week's work. Get me another bass player and I'll pay you your two weeks' notice. I don't know what's got into you, boy, goin' against old Bo. I don't want to see you no more, get your business straight with your girl and get out of here." Bo looks at Donna. "What you done to this man? Damn! You got a golden cunt with diamonds in it or something? Out there lollygagging with them halfass third-rate pimps!" He turns back to Charles. "Mingus, watch your step, I don't want you hitting on me 'cause I'll have to kill you or have you killed and nobody'll know the difference. But you better call Mama Clara on this broad of yours before she gets out of hand."

"I'll get you a bass player now, Bo," Mingus says. "I need a rest. Too much is happening."

"Okay, Mingus. Old Bo trusts you when you talk like that, so here's the two weeks for your vacation. Take it easy now, don't let these brawds upset you. You still got a job when you rest up."

"Thanks, Bo. Come on, Donna, we're going to my place. We got some talking to do."

ELLO, MAMA CLARA? This is Mingus."

"Boy, what kind of girl is that you brought me? My girls get anywhere from five bills to a thousand a night depending on how hard they wants to work. But when a chick comes up here turning one or two tricks and going home, ain't doing my business no good—'specially when I done told my best johns about her and them calling and she ain't here. Straighten her out. She can't be spending no hour with them fifty dollar tricks! Is she getting her kicks or something? She's gotta move! Teach her what's happening."

"Okay, Mama."

"Now you were talking about New York. You know I got that good connection for you, the best, on the East Side. I can't have no girl making me look bad when she gets there. You all come on out here, I don't want to talk on no phone like this."

"Okay, Mama, I'll bring her up in a little while." Mingus hangs up the phone and turns to Donna. "I've decided I might take you to New York with me. But first of all what's this about you and some pimp named John Clark?"

"Nothing, baby."

"Donna, if we can't be honest we can't have two minutes together that makes sense. If you think we can still make it even though we've goofed, if you love me, let's get it out."

"Now I know I love you, Charles. Everyone tried to make me think you're a blow-top. I was afraid to tell you—I thought you'd beat me. Now you come on so cool. Forgive me, I'm sorry."

225

"Next time don't hide anything, baby. What happened?"

"I don't know who planned it. Mama told me this man John Clark is an important connection. He's a faggot, anyway a gate-swinger, and he has this wealthy woman who wants a young girl who would live with her, like a companion, when she's in California. I was supposed to pretend to be a lesbian and hit on her sort of casually and never let on it's a set-up. They said they'd pay me five thousand a month for seeing her a few days a week. They were trying to get her favor for something else, buying wholesale from them for her chain stores or something."

"Don't tell me the rest."

"I will some day. And I think you're right, it's time to get out of here. But, Mingus—my son Malcolm—"

"Yes, your son. When did you see him last?"

"Oh, Mingus, I'm such a phony. You see, I know now I don't really want Malcolm. He's Brent's now. Baby, Charles, I love you. I want to go away with you alone, can we?"

ELLO, GRACE? This is Charles. How's Mom? Tell her I'm leaving for San Francisco for a while."

"Mingus, you said New York!"

"That's later, Donna. . . . Hello, Mom? Yes, ma'am, I'll take care of myself."

"Shall I wear this, daddy?"

"Your choice, sexy. . . . You did, Mom? *Lee-Marie?* How did she look? Ah, she'll always look that way till she's ninety. . . . Cool, Donna, we haven't got time for that now."

"No? It sure responds to my touch!"

"That's right, San Francisco, Mom. No, I'm not going up to see her, Mom, I didn't even know she was there. Yeah, I heard Spendell retired but I didn't know he had a joint in Sausalito. . . . Okay, Mom, I love you too. Let me speak to Grace again. . . . Damn, Donna, stop that! Let's see how *you* like it, bitch! . . . Grace, could you look out for my apartment and my car?"

"You tore them, daddy. I'll take them down for you. Charles, she can have my car too. Let me talk to her."

"Here, bend over. You started this, I'm going to let you really feel it."

"Hi, Grace, this is Donna. . . . Oh, daddy! . . . Yes, we're on our way. Listen, we may send for the cars later— oh! Daddy, Grace can tell—she's laughing—Grace, we'll leave the keys with Jake and Bess. Yes, we were, Grace, I'm sorry, it just got so good—you know how we are."

"Donna, I'll be back in a second. I'm going over to speak to Jake."

"You come back here, right *here,* and finish what you started before we go, hear me, Charles?"

EY, JAKE, wake up! What's the matter—your doorbell ain't working."

"I don't know, just ain't working. Don't bother me too much, rent control and all that. What's up, ball spot pig?"

"Jake, we've had it here, we're going to New York."

"Oh, Mingus! You and Barbara and the kids?"

"No, Bess, my wife's mother took care of that. They're in Pasadena someplace and I got orders from the police to stay away. So the best thing for my sons is for me to go where I can better myself so I can see them through school and whatever. First San Francisco, then look out, N.Y.C.!"

"Ball spot, know who we saw out in Southgate not long ago? Lee-Marie! Man, she sure is the most beautiful woman in the world."

"Damn you, Jake! Schitt! Things get going again, I'm about to live again, and oh, what's the use. My sister, my mother, now you! Lee-Marie, Lee-Marie, Lee-Marie!"

"I didn't mean to hurt you, ball spot—"

"Oh, shut up, Jake!"

"Why? I thought Charles would want—"

"Shut up, dear, brilliant husband! Here, now, Charles, no tears, they hurt us and don't help you. Charles, face it, whenever any of us see her we think of you, we see you way back in her sad dark eyes. Why don't you try to talk to her?"

"I don't think I'd even recognize her it's been so long."

"I could help you, ball spot. If you see Gene Tierney looking her best and with a crazy sun-tan, it's Lee-Marie Spendell. She's the color white folks spend all summer trying to get. Why don't you call her, man?"

"I can't begin that again, Jake, after all these years! She was my wife, and they killed our child, her father hit my child and killed it before it was born! I could see it in her face—the agony—she was letting our child die in her mind. Bess, you want to see the scar of a bullet that was meant to go through my heart? You've seen it, Jake. My body was saved but nothing could save my child or our love. How could a man legally kidnap my wife and erase our marriage with an annulment like we never even happened?"

"Charles, call her, see her. Her father must be sorry now, it's so long ago. She's still unmarried and hardly ever leaves the house."

"My mother just told me that Spendell retired and bought a fish-and-chips place in Sausalito and Lee-Marie's there with him. I guess he don't feel being a waitress is beneath her like being married to me was."

"She gone up there? We heard she and her sister was going to help him get the place organized."

"Bess, you been knowing about Lee-Marie and me all these years I been married to Barbara? Did you tell my wife?"

"There was nothing to tell. Why should I tell Barbara that poor girl's parents had her spayed?"

"What?! What are you saying?"

"Didn't you know that? You were in the hospital. Her mother saw the ring and the Mexico marriage certificate and just went crazy. I don't know how they went about it legally, they had her certified unfit or something. Then they sent her away to relatives, they said, but it was really to an institution. After she came back she was walking around like a dead woman. I remember you graduated from Jordan High that fall and you never stopped dating other girls. But she didn't want to see anybody—or wasn't allowed to. Couple of fellows used to meet her after school. I saw her—she'd let them have her books and just walk home with those same two following."

"What could I do, what could I do? Even after I graduated I used to go and wait outside her school but she was never alone. I'd end up going back to Watts and taking Manuela home."

"Was those chili buns hot, Mingus?"

"Stop, Jake! Charles is talking."

"Like what did they raise her for?—*why* did they keep us apart? I knew she had her cello lessons on Thursday so I used to go over to Southgate and wait in a diner across the street, but her father always came for her in his car. When I tried to speak a few words, she'd just look straight ahead like she was scared to death and rush and get in with her father and drive away . . ."

"What's taking so long, daddy? Hi, Bess, Jake!"

"Hello, Donna."

"Donna, go on back and pack me some drawers in that fortnighter, and get out my suitcase with the music if you can lift it, and get some plane tickets to Frisco tonight."

"Okay. Hurry now."

"We'll take you and Donna to the airport, ball spot."

"Yeah, fine! So anyway, Bess, whenever I got a chance I'd tell her I loved her. And she'd say things like 'I can't have your child now,' over and over. I only thought she meant she couldn't marry me again and I felt she wanted me to get away from her."

"No, Charles, I asked her what was wrong and she told me what happened."

"Oh my God, Bess, are you sure? I knew she lost our child when her father struck her but I didn't know the rest. We lived two months in Mexico and I wrote music for a couple of groups there to get money to come back home but there wasn't enough work and our rent was due. If it wasn't for Lupe Madrid sending me money we'd never got home—and we'd of been better off. They tore us apart and we couldn't see each other or talk on the phone. I didn't even care what was what by the time I got well and went back to school. You and Jake knew all this, Bess?"

"Ball spot, Watts is a small town. Everybody hears everything—like when you got out of the hospital and Spendell had some of his cop pals raid you and Buddy's pad. We all knew it was a frame."

"Yeah. Dot Dawson told us they busted in on him downtown and said they'd lay off if he gave them some pot so he gave them Lipton's tea and catnip mixed up in a bag and that was what they planted on Buddy and me! They was so dumb they didn't know it till they turned us over to the narco squad. There was these dumb nigger Uncle Tom cops standing there holding guns on us and their white superiors took one look at the stuff and threw it on the floor in disgust. 'Where'd you boys buy this trash?' they said."

"Did you press charges?"

"Buddy's father tried to. But what good is it to press charges against cops? Listen, Jake, I want to buy that German Luger from you. I want to see her daddy in Sausalito and afterwards he's going to realize that while we were talking I had a gun pointed at his fat belly, just hoping he'd reach for his again."

"No sale, ball spot."

"Thirty beans."

"No price."

"Fifty."

"No price."

"A hundred dollars."

"Aw, take it, ball spot. Fifty dollars. Thirty for the gun

and twenty for taking care of your apartment and the cars."

"That's cool, I won't have to count on Grace. Damn! It's getting late. Lemme use your phone. . . . Hello, Mama Clara? I'm not going to get over there—Donna and I are flying to San Francisco tonight and see Billy Bones. Yeah, well, I'm going to lay with him for a while and then be on my way. Yeah, I may play a coupla nights someplace. Okay, I'll look up Saunders King at Jack's Tavern. Thanks. Anything to get enough bread to get to New York. Oh, she's definitely going to model—nothing but first class, though. Fine, Mama—I got it—Madam Goose, yeah, Fifth Avenue, apartment 4G. I'll send you a grand if Donna uses this introduction. What? Aw, that's all right, I figured you was just testing her with this john what's-'is-name to see if she loved me. You wasn't kidding? Then I'm leaving just in time. Yeah, I'll tell Billie hello first chance. Yeah, she told me—you want Billie's exact words? On the phone? O.K., Mr. Policeman, If you listening. Billie Holiday said 'Now watch her, Mingus, watch old Mama Clara. She loves white pussy more than you do.' Haw! You do? That is a whole lot of loving, wow ooh wee, baby! When it's right, you and me all night. Talk it, baby. You know what I mean, it's mean. Bless you, too. Save your money for Judgment Day. You'll hear from me. 'Bye. . . . Wow, Jake, that old school is something! Wow! . . . Come on in, Donna."

"Daddy, everything's set, tickets and reservations."

"You sure look good to me, baby. I haven't seen you dressed in a suit in so long. Damn! Come here!"

"See, Jake? You never tell me things like that."

"Your girl Donna sure is pretty, ball spot."

"Yeah! Come here, you beautiful ugly bitch!"

"What you doing, Jake?"

"Taking off my clothes. You all make me want to love my old lady."

"Thank God for favors! But do you have to take off your britches in front of company?"

"Yeah, Jake, we've all seen Gargantua and where in heck did you get those drawers? My daddy used to wear that kind and called them B.V.D.'s."

"You mean this ain't modern?"

"That's funny. Every generation keeps discovering something left over on the top shelf and thinks they come up with something new!"

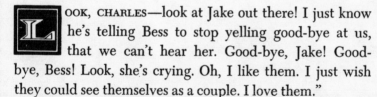OOK, CHARLES—look at Jake out there! I just know he's telling Bess to stop yelling good-bye at us, that we can't hear her. Good-bye, Jake! Good-bye, Bess! Look, she's crying. Oh, I like them. I just wish they could see themselves as a couple. I love them."

"I know what you mean. I think they'd fall in love again if they could forget the past."

"Did you fasten your seatbelt, ma'am? And you, sir? That's fine."

"Look at all these people, Charles. Everyone seems to be on their best behavior, flying. What is there about an airplane that makes nice people nicer?"

"It's a good idea to be nice to the pilot, too—like his wife might have goofed and forgot he was due in last night and we get him this morning but he gets all these love vibrations and decides not to kill himself. He'd have to be stone nuts to crash us up for his problems. Yet everybody's flying around all the time and nobody seems concerned. They sit and take it for granted. They never think the pilot might feel drug, too. If they could stand on the edge of the earth and see it in motion in relation to this plane, they might pray. 'Cause, baby, we're moving so fast the water's scared stiff and can't fall off."

"You're crazy, beautiful Charles."

"I used to do that with a bucket when I was a kid. Tie a string on a bucket full of polliwogs and swing it through the air. Gravity is formed through motion. Those frogs be acting the same when I finished as before the bucket left the ground. Look at all the polliwogs looking like little angels. . . . Well, I guess we're up here now. Here, baby, swing with your menu."

26

THE MAN NAMED WILLIAM BONESS—they called him Billy Bones—was angular and gaunt and stood well over six feet tall. He carried himself at his full, proud height with great elegance. He said he was from the West Indies, spoke with some kind of accent, and looked like a dark-skinned Latin actor playing Gary Cooper playing a swinging bullfighter. He was very careful about his person and always dressed correctly for whatever he was doing— tennis, golf, billiards, squash—and undressed and showered and dressed again when he was through. On the street he wore expensive, proper clothes, appropriate for the San Francisco climate, and walked around in hundred-dollar Stetson shoes. He lived a kingly life, like a man on a continuous vacation with interruptions to see his florists or talk to his chef or instruct his brokers. He was perfectly at home with people of any financial or social position or any color and his attitude was, "We're all at the Top of the Mark together. I can afford it and I assume you can too." He could afford anything because he was the Black Prince of Pimps and he called my boy cousin and he was waiting at the airport in San Francisco.

BILLY! We're over here!"

"Hey, Mingus boy! Is this Donna? Oh, she is *beautiful!* This is my Number One girl, Honey."

"Hello, Donna—Charles has been telling us nothing but you!"

"Come on, get your luggage. You kids'll stay at our apartment, we have plenty of room. Porter! Take this bass to the car, my chauffeur will help you."

"Is that Rolls yours, Billy?"

"Yeah, I don't dig Cadillacs, everybody's got one."

BILLY, I want to rent a piano while I'm here."

"What for? I got a Steinway concert grand at my place. I forgot, you never saw my place on the Hill. I bought a couple apartments, cost over one hundred thousand dollars. I'm the only spook owns property up there."

"The luggage and the instrument are in your motor car, sir. Is there anything else, sir? Thank you very much, sir."

"Oh, nigger, stop tomming to your own people. We out here scuffling just like you."

"Exactly why I am showing my respect for you, sir. I am proud to be of service to my black brothers."

"Man, drop the British accent."

"Excuse me, I am a student from Nigeria. My accent is due to my studies at Oxford. It is my pleasure to serve Mr. Mingus. I have one of your records—'This Subdues

My Passions.' I have seen your picture in the jazz magazine when I was at school in France."

"I'm sorry I was stupid. My name's Billy Bones, I'm Mingus's cousin. You mean he's famous?"

"Oh yes sir, everywhere, I'm sure."

"You hear that, Donna, Honey? You're world famous, poor motherfucker."

OME ON, Honey, let me pull in your coat so Sam can close the door. Mingus, you ever see one of these nice pictures of President Coolidge?"

"A ten-thousand note! Donna, look at this crazy fool!"

"Boy, I'm a respectable real estate owner. I'm passing for Spanish here and so's Honey. Soon's you say 'Spanish' you should see the johns jump. Say 'Puerto Rican' and *nada*—ain't that stupid? It's all the same cunt, and you know what I told you she could do with hers."

"Who could forget?"

"Donna, have you ever heard of the Kama Sutra?"

"I've read about it, yes."

"Roll up that window. I don't want Sam to hear this. . . . Donna, you study with Honey, build your muscles and things like she says. Read her books. You'll have those New York blueblood johns begging for your number once they see you in bed. Honey can pick up a cigarette off the floor, puff on it, and blow the smoke out."

"How do you do it, Honey?"

"It's actually a study of the harem girls for cleanliness —tightening and loosening the stomach muscles and breath control was used while sitting in a bath of goat's milk. Later this sucking trick became popular in the harems. Look, I'll show you, I have no pants on anyway. The driver can't see with Chazz and Billy in front of us. Give me your cigarette, Billy. Hold my dress up, Donna. Now watch. . . ."

SMOPOCK!!

"Haw haw! That's the craziest thing I've ever seen or heard of in my life!"

"Yeah, Billy! But if I look again Donna might get the wrong idea."

"Strictly business. You pay, you play. I'll let Honey sleep with you both to teach you what's really happening."

"Oh, I don't doubt Honey can show us something about muscles and all that, but Donna and me making love, we can come together sixty different ways, you dig? But if you want Honey to freak with us, crazy, she'll enjoy it too. . . . You know, in L.A. I was trying to get Donna a girl that we were both going to do up. But the girl, this kid, her name was Pam, had too much heart. I just couldn't make myself turn her, for all the money in the world I couldn't do it. Can you understand that, Billy?"

"I hear you, cousin Charles."

THIS IS THE FUNNIEST city in the world to me. Like your chauffeur just passed that cable car on the left. If it was L.A. twenty cops would be all over us with guns out, shooting."

"It's San Francisco, Charles, the hippest. New York was meant to be like this but somehow lost it after the thirties. New York's cold, like a dying animal with no-

where to go but Central Park where the outdoors helps it
remember New York isn't the only place in the world. The
animal drinks that green into his soul, then goes back to
the streets again and the tombstones with neon epitaphs
flashing his life before him, as cold as the stone around
him. He's aware he's no longer dying, he's long been dead.
New York's his graveyard. He's a walking shadow of a
man, lonely and tall as those windowpaned tombstones
that haunt him into leaving his bed on Harlem's skid
row, the lure that leads him downtown to see if it too has
fallen with his dreams, the impulse impossible to resist, to
look up and see if it is all still there, higher than any moun-
tain with its sudden daring sweep into the sky. How else
should a city with the standards of hell be built? With
grass and trees, on the ground, where heaven can be seen
by a small child just learning to walk or by a man six feet
tall? No, New York is an idea built high into the sky by
those who own and run it, so they can look down and not
see its filth and look out and see only space between the
skyscrapers at eye's level with heaven. If a man can accept that city for the hell it is and still go on about his
duties, it's truly God he's found."

"Reverend Billy! Amen!"

"What you're looking for, my cousin, is the peace that
men go into the mountains to find. It's easier there. But I
felt this same peace around you when I met you as a
young boy seventeen years of age. You could have con-
verted me then. You had all my buddies in fear of their
souls, talking about God that time in Sacramento. And
when you finished you told them they actually were all
saved anyway."

"They were. Some are still saved, some are not."

"Remember Marty, the club owner up there? He ain't stopped drinking since you talked to him. He asked you to tell him why he was still out in the streets."

"He was a beautiful person."

"Yeah, boy, but what's your answer now that you're a man and the shoes of my buddies you preached to are fitting you pretty well? What kind of a preacher would you make, with the biggest pimps and whores all coming to you to be saved? I'll back you in a church right now if you can still sell it the same way."

"I'm not a worthy salesman, Billy. Besides, God's free, no collection plates. That's when it goes off. It's better people give their money away on the streets."

"Yes, Jesus. . . . Well, here we are home. Sam, take the bags upstairs and ask your wife to unpack them. You'll have our best guest suite, kids. Stay with us as long as you like, days, months—what's the difference when you're crazy with beauty?"

C HAZZ, you still eat like you used to? I got two cooks. Remember Jimmy, from the Shanghai in Chinatown? Jimmy Ho. His whole family works for me, his wife and daughter are maids and his son Win is my busboy. Wait till you taste Jimmy's down home Chinese style food. Weekends I have caterers from all nations for a few friends I invite by. Last week I had the best Pakistan cook this side of India. Saturday you and Donna'll eat Siwash cooking—American Indian—fish, duck, Chippewa quail, wildfowl, Utes' boss herbs and vegetables.

Both Utes and Chippewas burn bear meat, venison, wild turkey, quail, guinea hens, rattlesnake, possum. Sunday will be unbelievable. Seafood steamed in Indian herbs, jellyfish, eels, raw squid and fish mixed up with octopus and prawns in a paella—sound good? . . . Come on with me, Chazz, I got an idea—I bet we catch Honey and Donna playing around. Honey teaches all my girls and from Donna's face in the car she couldn't wait to get started learning some of that muscle control. . . . Ha! What'd I tell you, Cholly?"

"Billy! Isn't fair sneaking in like that!"

"Bitch! You couldn't wait. Donna's tired but you managed to get your fingers in her. . . . Here, Cholly, have a little coke, then go rest you up. After dinner we'll send for more girls if Donna and Honey feeling like balling alone. I think they still gonna need us—ain't but one bitch with much joint as a man. Dolly Markle, know her? She's something, all right, real freak. Hell of a nice lady otherwise, and when I'm loving her it shrinks all back up where it belongs. What you doing, sniffing on fingers? Here, use this glass tube or one of those plastic straws. Go slow right down the row on that glass tray, up each nostril till you get where you're looking to go. . . . Honey, cool! Come over here!"

"Oh Billy, you sound jealous. I'm just trying to show her how to do it."

"Then why you all wet down there?"

"I'm sure not wet. Check me, daddy. Feel my muscle development."

"I'll do that later. Honey, you feel like putting on a show tonight? Get some of them lesbian trick-turners over

here. I know a couple of johns in town who'll pay.
. . . How's that for some real uncut shit, Chazz, pure
sugar cane? . . . Come in here in the closet, kids. Watch
while I pull open these drapes."

"Hey, that's your living room downstairs!"

"Yeah, and it's my personal photography studio. From
these controls right here I can shoot you from every angle
in the room. Honey's had ten- to fifty-thousand-a-night
parties down there. Important johns. A rich, retired police
commissioner, famous movie stars—why, I've got pictures
of some of your most prominent government officials,
senators here and in Washington, doing the oddest things
to each other and my girls. And I'm sitting up here by
myself unseen, just watching and shooting away on the
All-American male whores. With Chicago and here in-
cluded I'm the only black pimp that's made over five million dollars a year in hustling alone. My other businesses
don't even count, they're for my income tax reports. One
of the johns tried to have me busted a year or 'so ago. I
don't blackmail or anything, Cholly. He just received by
registered mail a reel of film of himself and one of his
friends. I don't even bother to send a copy, I sent an
original print with my attorneys' address. That means just
what it implies—if anything happens to me, five honest
white lawyers that only know my legitimate business have
access to my property, films and sound tracks and all. I'm
not invincible, but as long as they keep buying pussy from
my friends all over America and just about the world, I
get pictures like this. So what can this ex-police commissioner do to me? I get a reel sent to me by a madam in
New York with his head in between all kinds of legs, from

blond to black. Before he'd get me I could have handbills
out on him with pictures he'd posed for and some he didn't
know about. I'd print them up and have them dropped
over every major city in the U.S. by plane. Sure, I'd be
dead, but so would he. That motherfucker came here as
a recommended john, next thing I know he's trying to
move the Italian pimps in on my rackets. You know
Cousin Darcy, Cholly. To start with, he got their license
plate numbers and checked the make and model of their
cars, then stole cars like theirs and sold or dumped them,
after switching the stolen plates to the mobs' shorts. Right
away the cops were all over their asses for hot cars. Then
me and Cousin Darcy up and kidnaps their girls and
divides the bitches with some of the heavy boys. The
bitches need the change. Most of those motherfuckers
keep their old ladies doped out on main line and believe
me, they're glad to get away to some soul brothers."

"Billy, what's that face bowl doing so low to your toilet
floor?"

"Haw haw! It's a bidet. They're to wash asses in. It's
an antique idea in France. I have all that specially made.
Dig the marble effect."

"Classy."

"You see the toilet?"

"Yeah, it looks different. Deeper."

"The white man don't think of us when he builds *anything*. I'm tired of holding myself to keep from dangling
in the bowl. And I had my urinal built in the floor like I
saw in Paris. I guess Frenchmen and us are the only ones
got joints worthwhile to think about when we start con-
tracting toilets in this white man's world."

ILLY WAS RIGHT, Donna. Mingus has a good woman. Now we can get those clothes on, no? I mean, all right, yes?"

"You mean you were testing me, Honey?"

"Sí, you are an investment. You heard of Bethlehem Steel? Which you think is bigger business, pussy or steel? Yes, I have to test Billy's girls sometimes. He seldom sleeps with them."

"You mean he has girls working for him that he's never loved?"

"Of course. He has eighteen, nineteen girls always. I fuck more of them than he does. He romances and courts them, though—he has over three hundred dollars a day in flower and candy bills. He teaches each girl the language of flowers. By the time they learn it, they're turned out accidentally in one of his apartments. He's always intentionally behind in his bills—he doesn't want his legitimate businesses—his restaurant, for instance—to show a profit. Sometimes he rings up thirty or forty thousand of his hustling dollars on his cash register just to show something to the government for taxes. You think your bass player is a genius? My Billy is the genius. He once got high and read three entire law books in two weeks— he only slept a few hours a day. When he finished he told me 'Reading is just like conversation. Once you realize that, you can remember it all.' Even today someone can start a sentence in any of those volumes and he can just about finish the whole chapter by heart. Oh, I have a lot to tell you about Billy, Donna. For instance, how he turned out an heiress who was visiting here on vacation—what's wrong?"

"Are you sure she was an *heiress?* If she was just a girl with a rich father, you can bet prostitution is preferable. I ought to know."

"You mean—?"

"My father and my ex-husband are two of the richest men in the South, I guess. Last year my husband inherited his thirtieth million. You'd never know it, the petty way he handles money."

"My Lord! Does Mingus know?"

"I did tell him, but Mingus hears what he wants to. Before Mingus I was watched by private detectives, the whole scene. We've had the works too—telephone threats, notes in my mailbox, cutting up his car-top in front of my apartment. . . ."

"You should change your name when you go to New York, for his protection."

"I've done that. I'm not using my husband's or my father's name any more."

"Ha ha! *Ai frijoles!* You tink dey know?

"Honey, you're a bitch with dat phoney hacksent!"

"Tee ha! I like yours too."

27

"THAT'S TOO MUCH HEATER, Chazz, too bulky, you give yourself away. Leave that dumb Luger there and take a look at these."

"What are they, fountain pens?"

"Nitro shells."

"Man! You trying to kill me, Billy?"

"No, the safety's on. Now if you want somebody, I'll get him for you with this while he's asleep."

"What's that?"

"Something from your home, boy. Africa, mother-fucker! Hey, don't touch! These were used in primitive rituals thousands of years ago. Steel cobra fangs mounted on ebony."

"Looks like my bass finger board."

"Would you like me to get Spendell for you, Cousin Charles?"

"No, thanks. I leave that to God, even though that halfass two-bit bank guard once shot me over his daughter."

"And you didn't kill the motherfucker there and then? Better not tell Cousin Darcy—*he* don't mind playing God. What did you do to his daughter, turn her out?"

"Nothing like that, I married her. He had it annulled."

"So what do you want me to do? Darcy's out of jail, shall I call him? Just in case the old man pulls a gun on you again. Where you gonna see her?"

"I'm going to his place first and do him the honor of letting him tell me I have his permission to see her. Here's the address."

"Hello, Minnie, Darcy there? . . . Hey, Dar, can you get on over to a place called Spendell's in Sausalito?—it's a fish joint down by the water. I've got Mingus with me, he's got business with Spendell. Keep an eye on the old man and don't even see us when we come in. No, just watch him, don't let him go after no gun. He shot your cousin Charles in cold blood. See you there. So long. . . . Darcy's dying to see you, Chazz, said Aunt Lois was just over. Okay, we'll get a cab, ready? We won't take the chauffeur for this little scene."

WHY, HELLO, Charlie!"

"Hello, Mr. Spendell."

"This is funny. A minute ago I almost took that guy at the shuffleboard to be you!"

"That happens to be my cousin Darcy, and this is my cousin Billy Boness."

"Oh, yes! Oh! Yes!"

"We want to talk to you."

"Why, sure, sure, Charlie. . . ."

"Hello, Darcy."

"Hey, Billy. Hey, Cholly, how in hell are you? I told Billy we look like twins, how in hell did you expect him to miss it?"

"Give us a beer, Spendell. Make it off the shelf. Lager."

"Sure, Charlie. Patty! Come on out. Patty, serve these gentlemen."

"Oh!"

"Patty! Come back here! You hate me that much you hiding? Did it ever occur to you that I loved Lee-Marie? What did I do to you people? Answer me!"

"Son! Son! Don't get excited."

"It's too late for 'son.' You killed *my* son, your grandson, and you had my wife spayed! Didn't you bother to ask your daughter would her husband mind if you had her tubes tied? Patty, what did you tell your people about us —long before Lee-Marie and I eloped? Are you the Virgin Mary or something?"

"I told them what I saw! You know I saw you, you were undressing Lee-Marie under her coat!"

"Could you see under her coat?"

"No, but I know you were fooling around with her there!"

"You know *what?* Give me your gun, Darcy! I oughta kill both these—"

"Mingus, Mingus! Find out what you want to know! Nobody hurts you, nobody gets hurt. Understand? Find out now so you can get well."

"All right, Billy. I want to know, Spendell, what Patty told you she saw when Lee-Marie was only twelve years old? Tell us what your filthy mind imagined, Patty!"

"I did see what you did!"

"Go on, Patty, what did we do?"

"You took her outside the picture show and you did it to her!"

"What did I do to her?"

"You funked!"

"*Funked!* Oh, my God. And where did I do this?"

"I don't know. In the lobby. Someplace. In the alley?"

"How old were *you,* Patty?"

"Nine."

"You dirty little whore!"

"Look out, Mingus!"

"God damn, you fast, Darcy!"

"Help!! Police!!"

"Shut that bitch up! Drag the old man in the back there. . . ."

"You sure hit that motherfucker, Darcy!"

"Charles!"

"Lee-Marie—you here? Tell Patty to stop that screaming!"

"What happened—what's wrong?"

"Your father reached for his gun and my cousin busted him."

"Don't let those men hurt Patty, Charles!"

"Look at all the suffering, all these years, because of your little sister's dirty mind and your hot-headed father! Your life and the child we'd of had, a bullet in my shoulder, even my wife Barbara and my sons suffering from one lie from a misguided little nine-year-old and two people living in misery to this day!"

"Where is my father?"

"Darcy dragged him in the kitchen. Patty, stay out here, don't open your mouth again, don't move, don't even think! I'll kill you myself if you do one thing more! Your dad's gun here will shoot him, you, all of us, understand?"

ATHER! FATHER! Wet this cloth for me, please, Charles."

"He's all right, Lee-Marie, don't worry."

"He's too heavy to fall like this at his age. Are *you* all right, Charles?"

"I guess so. You won't need what you're looking for, Mr. Spendell, I have it here."

"Give me Father's gun, Charles—give it to me. Thank you."

"Daughter, this man is no good. He cursed your sister —called her a whore!"

"No, I'm the whore, Papa, remember? Chippy, slut, you name it, I've been called it by the great, virtuous, self-righteous John B. Spendell!"

"My baby daughter—oh, my Lord, what have I done?"

"Would I make as good a whore as your friend Donna, Charles? Would I?"

"Answer her, cousin. Why don't you tell her where it really is?"

"Billy, please . . ."

"Little fat boy, listen to me. You stand around, let people make you look like a fool. This girl is in your corner. I'll tell you, pretty girl, Darcy and me makes millions. With that bass player you won't know coming from going. Your father and my cousin Charles, they're the same kind of phonies. Tell her you're going to New York with Donna, why don't you, Charles? My hat's off to you, Lee-Marie! Are you going with that dreamer or coming with me?"

"Billy, I left my Luger at your place but if you keep coming on like this you're gonna be dead!"

"Haw haw! You phony-ass punk."

"All right. Lee-Marie, you have your father's gun. I'll count three. Spendell goes first, then Darcy, then Billy. I'm counting. One, two, three—kill them, Lee-Marie, kill them all!"

CLICK. CLICK. CLICK. CLICKCLICKCLICK.

"Oh, Charles! Charles!"

"It's all right, baby, come here."

"Whoohwhee! This motherfucker's crazy, Billy!"

"He ain't crazy. His bitch is crazy."

"Gimme that gun!"

"Don't touch my woman, Darcy! I took the clip out when I took it away from Spendell. Are we cousins again?"

"*She* didn't know that gun was empty!"

"Mr. Spendell, tell whoever you've been saving your daughter for she's not making that scene. She's coming with me. Help him up, Darcy."

"Lee-Marie, you're not my daughter, you're no part of our family any more. You're dead."

"You're finally acknowledging my death, father?"

"Where's your belongings, Lee-Marie?"

"Just across the street."

"Go help her get 'em, Darcy. We'll wait in the cab. Good-bye, Mr. Spendell. Come on, Chazz. . . . Chazz, this is the right thing for you to do. Donna will be glad to have Lee-Marie around, you'll see. Confidentially, I had an old lady just like that once. Her name was Willie, same as mine. I won a hundred grand on a bet one night. A few of the better local pimps and I was all betting whose old lady would obey her old man no matter what he told her to do. They did everything and anything that was humanly possible to do to human beings. The girls all came through and they decided to call it a draw. I said no and told them to follow me out to a farmer's I knew. We rented the barn. Slim's old lady straddled a horse's belly and we tied her legs and we swung his joint in. Mack's old lady started sucking another horse's joint. Slim's old lady got down, sucked her horse's nuts. Mack's old lady licked around her horse's ass hole. I said, 'Give *me* the money, motherfuckers!'—and pointed at the ground. Willie was down there eating the horse's schitt. She was better for me than any kind of woman I ever had."

"Billy, Lee-Marie wouldn't do that."

"She'd kill for you, wouldn't she? Even her own father. She'd do anything you told her to. I'll take this cab that's coming, Cholly—you wait for her and bring her home."

MY MAN MINGUS SAT IN THE CAB waiting and he was pretty nervous. He wasn't too sure Billy was right about Donna being glad. Lee-Marie came out of the house across the street and walked quickly to the cab and got in with him. She didn't look toward the restaurant window, where Patty and her father stood watching. Darcy put her suitcases with the driver and leaned in the window.

"So long, Cousin Charles, I gotta leave you now."

"Thanks, Darcy, for all your help."

"*Any* time, Chazz, any *thing*."

They drove in silence toward San Francisco and finally Charles said, "Lee-Marie, I guess you know Donna and I have been together since Barbara left with the kids, but somehow I never really stopped loving you."

She took his hand. "Charles, I know a good deal about your life since our last day together. My uncle's on the force, he hears everything that happens. I knew about that wild last semester at Jordan High, and later things like that woman Cindy. But I've always had my knowledge of the you that could never change, though all I could do was love you from a distance. They said if I ever talked to you again I'd be sent away to a sanitarium forever and something very bad would happen to you—I was afraid for you. When I finally went back to school I couldn't study the way I did before—I tried but I couldn't concentrate. I'd stare out windows all the time, just hoping by a miracle you'd pass by. I was a prisoner, I lived dreaming you'd break past our enemy and rescue me. Did you imagine I didn't love you any more! Oh, my parents—carrying on about their daughter daring to be a woman at eighteen! Standing over me, swearing, crying—She couldn't have, she couldn't have! Oh Lord Jesus! Tell me my baby's still a virgin! Then they had my tubes tied—poor, pure ignorance, thinking my desire for you or any man would be killed, saving me to please some future husband they approved of. I don't know what male monstrosity they envisioned—who wouldn't have me if I had ever loved another man! That first summer I begged them to let me go to you and they struck me till I fought back. They sent me to Norwalk for observation, claiming I was sick, depraved, and threatened to have me confined for the rest of my life. Time just stopped, Charles, for me. . . . Two years later at Compton College I saw you with Barbara Jane Parks. I knew you didn't know I'd been through hell. I saw you leave the lunch room and followed. I walked out through a group of girls and there was Barbara showing what was supposed to be *my ring!* I was trying to get enough courage to tell you, Charles, that we should run away. I followed you to the train stop. The train pulled in, it was crowded. I got on anyway and at first I didn't see you but I heard your voice—you were talking about your engagement and suddenly you said, 'Why, Lee-Marie—is it you? I haven't seen you in so long.' From Compton City to the Southgate stop I rode standing in that crowded train with you pressing up against me. You didn't even seem to feel me and I thought you were laughing at my tears and anger. But just as the train stopped I realized that you were hurt, puzzled, frightened—'Lee-Marie,' you said, 'You still love me?' I wanted to kill you! I pounded my fists into your body. What did you *think?* Did you think I waited for you till I was a woman just to see you marry someone else? When I left, you didn't even get off the train. Charles, I was almost of legal age, we could have walked away together like we waited all those years to do. Even my parents couldn't have stopped us then. But no— you called me on the phone and told me you still loved me and asked me to wait for you through a marriage you had to keep your word on! Isn't that strange? I waited—that's stranger. I waited till now. I know I'm attractive, Charles. I could have married many times but everyone knows I'm Mingus's girl except him. So now I'll be Mingus's whore, I'm going to be your million dollar woman, better than the others. And you're going to write a lifetime symphony for me. I don't care as long as we're together physically. No more dreaming. I lived a lie, you lived a lie. But now I'll have you somehow till the day I die."

"Lee-Marie—"

"Don't say a word."

"I won't let you."

"Yes, you will. I won't be without you again. To add a note of happy hope, I hear in Paris—and Africa—it's quite fashionable for a man to have more than one wife."

"Baby, I'm so sorry. I didn't know if I'd ever see you again and Barbara and I had grown to mean a lot to each other. I didn't know how to just drop someone because you suddenly came back from the dead. And loving you brought such pain, I thought I'd surely die if I went through that again. Barbara was in love with me, we both thought our past was done with, and I loved her as much as I knew how."

"I know. It's over now. Please, Mingus, your mouth—open your mouth to mine."

"Baby—oh, Lee-Marie! God damn! God damn! God damn!"

"Charles. . . ."

ILLY, where's Donna?"

"Upstairs. I tried to tell her. No telling how she took it."

"That wasn't your concern, Billy. That was up to me."

"She didn't say nothing. I think she's cool."

"Depends on how you told her and what your reason was."

"Look, cousin, I got *twenty* girls. Like now even Honey don't dig that. You have to go into things like this very sudden. I know this problem."

"I'm sorry, cousin. Hi, Honey—this is my wife Lee-Marie. We're still married in the sight of God, no matter what man's law says. Baby, come upstairs with me. . . ."

EY, sug! Baby! Donna? You asleep?"

"No. . . . Is this Lee-Marie? Hello. You're beautiful."

"*You're* beautiful, Donna. I like you right away. I feel

like we're longtime friends. Nice, real nice. I feel a little strange, like someone's sharing my private dreams. But I think that's the raveling away of convention. It'll go."

"I see what you mean. I'll just sit quiet with the idea. I want what you want and there's only one, so I understand you *and* myself."

"You're both beautiful—in the mind, too."

"Oh, shut up, Mingus, you wouldn't understand, you're a man. Look at the big baby pout, Lee-Marie. Ha! Baby wants mama's titties, all four of them."

"I don't know what I want. There's a million things I used to scheme up to excuse the truth. I know I love you both with all of me, whatever that is. Let's close and lock all the doors—Donna, turn the key in that closet door too. Come here, my babies—um hum, you sure feel good. You want to—no, you all talk awhile, I feel like a shower. Get to know each other."

"Lee-Marie, don't we need showers too?"

"Oh. Oh, yes. Yes, we can all wash each other! . . . I'll beat you two in!"

. . . "Mingus! Come in here! Look what you're missing. Dig this angel! Ha ha! Tee hee! Make the water hotter, steam up that mirror, Billy's probably back there somewhere with a camera. I feel he's watching through every wall."

"Let him! I don't feel shy about anything anymore. Let's press close together, Donna, and make our man jealous!"

"Babies, you're getting better every moment, close up like that. Ummm. Slide and rub all over and against me."

"Mingus, why don't you pretend to be a big, pretty, double-jointed richard and squeeze in between us."

"Come on, babies, bring all the towels. Let's go in the bedroom. Spread them over the bed and just lay out together. Ho hum. What else are big beds for other than a king and his wives?"

EE-MARIE, we need us a new man. Look at him laying up there. We make it twice and he can't make it once."

"I just can't come, babies. Kinda too shocked or something. Like waiting all my life for what I want and when I get it, too scared to enjoy it."

"Let's rape this bastard. Let's, Lee-Marie. Grrrrr. . . . we're going to eat you alive. Yes, kiss and suck his rollers. I dig this heart-shaped head."

"Oh! You, you bitches! Give me some kissings. Um! Oh! Owh! Sawowhee. . . ! No more! Ease me down, babies, easy. Let up a second. Whewaah!"

"Cholly! Cholly! Hey in there! Cousin Cholly!"

"Don't stop, don't stop. Forget *him*. Daddy's right here."

"It's me, Billy—in the closet! Let me in, you got the door locked."

"Schitt. Open the door for the cat, Donna."

"I don't dig him, Charles."

"Me neither."

"You mean we agree on everything, Lee-Marie? No wonder we came like that—wow! Throw me my slip."

"Where's mine? It was here someplace."

"Use my housecoat—over there."

"Ooooh, it's beautiful!"

"Wait till you see what's in that box, the one on top. It's for both of us."

"Oh, a coat. Some kind of fur."

"Yeah, some kind of fur, some kind of ten fucking thousand dollars kind. It's a loan from Honey."

"Donna, open the door for God Almighty pimp gangster Billy Bones! No, let me do the honors. . . . Enter, your *hine ass!*"

"Damn, Cousin Charles, I thought you learned to put business before pleasure."

"Lee-Marie, have a good look at my cousin Billy, he don't even fuck the girls that make all that bread for him, he lets his wife do it."

"Do you fuck Honey, Billy?"

"Mingus, talk to your woman, she got a fresh mouth."

"Aw, Billy, come on in, be human for a while."

"Yeah, teach your cousin Charles how to make five million a year like you. Are you happy with it, Billy?"

"You think everything's funny, huh, Donna? Okay, I'll tell you. I'm not happy with it. Why don't you kids quit and go somewhere and freak off together? Money just gets in the way of love. You don't believe me? Well, if you must find out, get dressed, Donna. Pierre wants to meet you tonight."

"Pierre?"

"Yeah. A lonely john. Honey's convinced him she's your lover, that's how she knows you. If he only knew— the great white man is buying back a white woman from a nigger! Now that gives me a laugh. Ho! Haw! Hello, Honey, what's up, is he still downstairs?"

"Yeah. He wants to see her now. Can't wait."

"Not now—make it hard for him! I know what I'm doing. Donna, get ready. We checked you in at the St. Francis. When he phones there, say you're resting. Stall, make him beg and don't let him come up. Meet him in the lobby. Capture his mind first. If not, you've got nothing but a few pennies and a cold water douche. Now you know Honey's been telling this cat she loves you and she's been keeping you—clothes, car, all that. Act square. Got the jewelry, Honey? Good. Here you are, try this for size."

"Too big."

"How's this?"

"Okay. Have you got your own diamond factory?"

"Now put on this watch. Coupla grand right there. That's one of my ways of banking—the insurance is my vault. This bracelet matches it. Ears pierced?"

"You're weighing me down with junk. I hate diamonds, they're pretentious, like mink."

"Don't wear it, then, just lay it around where he can see it. Now, Donna, if he wants you tonight really bad, use your own judgment but get his mind first, baby, hear me? His mind pays off, not his johnny. Convince this cat he's the first and greatest man in ninety years. Here, take this alum. It'll tighten you up where Mingus and Lee-Marie loosened you. Douche with clear water afterwards or his lips will pucker if he goes down. Honey says you know what money is, with your family and all that. Well, get your most expensive tastes up tonight 'cause you're trying for New York City. You're gonna make it on Park Avenue and Sutton Place. Now that five million you were joking about, that's no joke. Twenty girls, working ten days, off three, two hundred and fifty-two days a year.

Minimum, one thousand dollars a day or they work the eleventh day to make up. Quarter million per year per girl. Most of them are well off today. Some married guys like you're meeting tonight."

"Okay, okay, slow down, Mister Billy Bones! Charles, help me fasten up. I'll just slip into my coat—our coat—your coat—and take the rest in my overnight case. Daddy, Lee-Marie, hurry, hurry, kiss me good-bye."

"Let me see. Nice! Nice, Donna. I have a feeling we got this one. Can't miss. All that woman, and legs, and the way she carry that beautiful head. She's smart, Cholly—temperamental but smart."

"That's all hers and mine, too, Billy."

"And Lee-Marie's, from what I could overhear. You sure ought to be my *true* blood relative, boy—sometimes I think you got the Boness style. Come on in here, let's dig what happening downstairs from my private viewing place. Maybe we can get a few worthwhile shots. . . . That's Lola down there, the big-butted redhead. And Dora—supposed to be a dike. That Lola bitch is getting too smart—talking about going to New York. There's Lily, she and Lola work together. Good hustlers, freak off on anything. Killed a jackass here one night putting on a show for some important clients. Lola got under him, hung her legs over his back. Lily jacked him off and swung the donk's dick in. I got reels of the whole thing. Damn ass fell down to his knees when he came. Lily wouldn't let him rest—started sucking him right away. He let out a holler, kicked over on his back and died."

"I know both those brawds. If that's an example of your ladies, I don't know how you make millions. They were burning up hundred dollar bills one night in Jack's Tavern."

"You that nigger they was telling me about was providing the matches? Look down there, Chazz, ain't that white man something? All that ass out there and he's playing with himself. Look at that Dora—I'm getting rid of her for the parties, she can't think of nothing to do. Beautiful, but not a brain in her head. I'm ashamed of myself. But she's good when they stand in line for ass on weekends."

"Which one is Donna's john—Pierre? He there?"

"The one jacking off."

"What's that guy doing to Lola?"

"Just what you see. She ain't got no mirror back there, he sure ain't looking at his teeth. . . . Well, that's that for a while, I got too many reels of that crap. This ain't even good copy for those young priests—you know they're some of my best customers for this type of films, 'cause they just human and can't marry so they sneak around and buy some trim."

"I can't understand that, Billy. I gave up sex when I was studying yoga. For eight months I forgot it completely."

"Well, most of *them* don't forget it completely. Honey's aunt back in San Juan had a child by one. He took care of the kid, paid for it to be raised, and when it got big enough sent it to school and *it* became a priest."

"How about cats like that looking out for our souls?"

"Not mine, I got mine covered better than that. . . . Remember when I first met you, Cholly? You were sitting backstage with two of the finest chicks I've seen in my life on your lap, and you only about seventeen. When I think of it, seems you usually be with two chicks at a time."

"You got some memory. I find there's less bullschitt with two or more girls, all on their best behavior. They're like so many flowers to me. I dig just about all of them except another man's."

"You're fickle, cousin. I have lots of girls but I don't tell myself I dig them all. But your two brawds are real champs, just like Honey. Listen at that Lee-Marie in there, you hear?—every time she turns over, sighs, coughs, she's calling her man. She won't ever upset you if you want her. She could be in severe pain, you'd never know it. You be good to those ladies. It's rare, cousin, that much honesty gets all in one man's house. If you told Lee-Marie you felt like some extra trim she'd either get you some or give you so much you'd forget you had a joint. What you dig is each other's minds, the other is just little surface diminuendos. Listen at her, she's asleep in there, but you heard that little sigh? Listen. There. See? She saying 'If you love me get your pretty black ass in here to me.' Ha! Ha!"

"All that in one sigh, Billy?"

"Go on in. Don't worry about my cameras, there's none in that room. I'm going and get some sleep. See you tomorrow, Chazz."

"OH, HE'S CONVINCED NOW, daddy! All those dates we had and for three weeks I kept him at arm's length—he was almost out of his mind. Like you told me, Billy, I got his mind first. I outdid Sarah Bernhardt. I told old Pierre I'd given up men so long ago I couldn't remember. He asked if I worked for you, Honey—I was never so insulted! He was sorry and apologized—wanted to make it up to me for thinking such a thing! So Charles, Lee-Marie, we now have two apartments in New York, one on Park Avenue and the other on Seventy-fifth Street just off Fifth. Pierre said it used to belong to a maharajah, it was his private town house in New York. He showed me pictures the agent sent—we'll have the basement with a bar and a games room and garden and the entire first and second floors, a private elevator and two libraries with twenty-foot, hand-carved ceilings!"

"It sounds too magnificent. Tell me, Miss Parker, will you allow your maid and chauffeur to visit your boudoir?"

"*Oui, certainement*—especially my *maid!* Pierre is so convinced that women and I are inseparable I told him I'd have to have another girl if Honey wouldn't come to New York. That takes care of Lee-Marie. Tee hee. So

Mingus and Lee-Marie will live in piss 'n schitt on East
Seventy-fifth Street and I will allow Monsieur Pierre to
visit me at my Park Avenue apartment, by appointment
only. How boot tit, daddy? You'll have your studio in our
basement with your own private bar and a garden for
outdoor balling. If you get tired of Lee-Marie or me we
can stay over a few nights at the Park Avenue Palace till
you finish work that's bugging you or fucking one of those
little rich girls you'll be bumping into. And if you can't
make it then send for your mamas and we'll turn her on.
Hear that, daddy? Ha! You! You! Ma te du da de, ra ta *ta!*
New York City, here we comeommome! Mister Charles
Mingus and his harry um yum yum yum!"

"Ha ha! *Some* big plans! Now let old Professor Billy
Bones tell you children where it really is. Pierre knows
you're lying, Donna."

"Oh?!!"

"He's no fool. When I said convince him I meant convince him you love him, make him sincerely believe he's
the first man to cause you to make it sexually."

"Billy, I saw that man's life change right before me as
I gradually went into my act. He was just a weak old discouraged man thinking all he knew how to do was make
money, a tired man trying, hoping to keep his hard up,
until I began my speech: 'Oh! Oh no! Pierre! Pierre! For
the first time in my *life*—' And his face slowly grew bold,
strong, convinced, his balls came down and dangled, his
penis grew out of hiding where his wife must have sent it
in his youth when she shamed his erection back up into
his mind and shrunk his balls. No, Billy, this man did not
lie."

"Did he jack off, Donna?"

"Of course not."

"He lied. He'd rather see you and Honey or Lee-Marie licking each other's groins while he plays with himself, that's been his kicks for forty years. Ten of those years I've seen him with his girls that he hires as 'business advisors' at unbelievable salaries above board and laying it under the table very heavy too, till they finally leave the country with their real man or lesbian friend or whatever. Donna, I'm trying to show you something. If you leave your ego out of this you'll learn. Donna, Pierre is crazy, everybody who lives a lie is crazy, and you were crazy last night with Pierre when you lied to yourself. Until now everything you've said and done has been honest. You really weren't bad or good before last night. If you was my old lady I'd kick your ass. You see what I'm getting at? Mingus is no pimp. Not yet. He's no musician yet either. But he's one thing—true to himself. See, Pierre isn't just a john or a trick, Pierre is a system and every man who chooses Pierre's system knows in front that it includes his kind of wife to go out in public with and your kind of woman to milk his dick and his pockets. So up until last night you been *gambling*. But last night while you were playing a sure thing you became a phony like Pierre in those few moments when you chose to love the same things that Pierre loves."

"Money, Billy?"

"No, my dear. Last night the devil inside you sold your soul to another devil in Pierre for love of the kind of power money can't buy. Last night you *came* different than ever in your life. Tell me you didn't come."

"How did you know, Billy?"

" 'Cause I fucked another devil once like you did. You didn't think of Mingus or use your fingers like Honey told you to do, I knew it the moment you spoke. You dreamed and existed in no-man's-land last night with all the money, riches, in the world stacked up in one room in the tiny corner of hell in your mind. You and Pierre married the same spirit of evil last night. Mingus, do you understand this? What would you do? Prove it! Look at these—I have here twenty one-thousand-dollar bills. Now jack off. Don't think about no woman—or even the warmth of your hand. Come from looking at this paper. Not even what this paper can buy for you 'cause that would include, subconsciously, a woman."

"Keep your bread, Billy. It's very clear to me."

"See, Donna, you're fucking with your soul. Pierre wants you to think you've convinced him. You think for one moment Pierre believed you weren't informed *all* about him? He wanted to be sure your con was his protection, that you'd never expose him, that you want some of what he has so much that you'd live a lie and convince yourself that lie is true. Those people own the backbone and some of everything else in this country—even this chump Mingus's profession, which might be said to make whores out of musicians. . . . Now, Mingus, here's how to save yourself from depending on what rich punks think and critics say about jazz, true jazz, your work. By my reckoning a good jazz musician has got to turn to pimpdom in order to be free and keep his soul straight. Jelly Roll Morton had seven girls I know of and that's the way he bought the time to write and study and incidentally got diamonds in his teeth and probably his asshole. He was saying, 'White man, you hate and fight and kill for riches, I get it from fucking. Who's better?' That's what Jelly talked when we hung out and I want you to do like-wise. . . . Now you, Donna—you're a product of the system too. You might be pretending or believing you're like *us*—from the streets, born from scuffling parents—but your family's got money, your real sympathies could be with them. Like looking at a yacht you own could mean one thing to you and another to me. Maybe you could get your kicks just looking at it and knowing what it symbolized, where I'd have to ride that yacht and look at the creations of the earth in order to enjoy it. You better make up your mind before you go to New York with Mingus and Lee-Marie whether *they're* still your tradi-tional enemies or are your true foes now the people like Pierre and his wife who own this country? Do I need to tell you you're against Pierre if you're with Mingus, a victim of the system Pierre upholds?—and that now, even as his courtesan or almost priceless concubine, you'll be one of Pierre's slaves too?—the same as a streetwalking whore is for the cheapest male slave-labor. . . . I'm all too familiar with the place you're going, my friends. Your proud cousin Billy Bones was given a floater out of that jungle you intend to conquer, Charles. I had most of the uptown districts in the numbers racket—eight legit clubs, four hotels. But it wasn't that easy for anyone that dared to come up against Dutch Schultz or the Mafia during the gang war days. Hits were a dime a dozen in Harlem. Some bad black boys went down, Chazz. Your cousin Darcy and I and two much older brothers in Chicago invented the numbers—it came from an idea in the brain of the black

man 'way before us. San Francisco wasn't worth a black
con man's time then, so I show myself for the first time in
the Great Apple. You should have seen what Dutch sent
to take the numbers away from us—big fucking ugly
gorillas with their jaws hanging down and hair all over
their bodies. They spoke in German and I translate for
Darcy and he laughs. Then one of the gorillas calls me a
smart nigger in Italian and Darcy starts translating him to
me in Spanish and I laugh. Somehow it got awful funny.
Think about anger and hate and feel the tremendous
tension and fear involved. We got to laughing so hard
they were scared trembling stiff—pure hate can't understand laughter. I reached for my files and papers and one
of them went for his gun and couldn't barely move. They
were all paralyzed. We could have shot them dead—two
little black men stopping hoodlums with laughter! Darcy
and I both said, 'Tell Dutch you got the whole thing.' We
quit altogether. If they wanted the numbers bad enough
to kill for it they could have it—and the Mafia already
planning on taking from Dutch, and him too dumb to see
it! I knew I could make it in something else, I wasn't going
to be an employee of theirs in our own invention. I decided to finish law school and work my legitimate business
concerns. We learned from our white brothers to invest
our rackets money in slum joints for the elite. After-hours
clubs thrived on white celebrities and society folks and
those slummers weren't mistreated—the ex-slaves stood
off to the side in awe, watching the wealthy visitors like
they was gods arriving for inspection. Crimes were ten to
one in Brooklyn and the Bronx compared to Harlem—
man, we policed the district ourself for muggers 'cause we

knew it would kill business. But the white press ran night life business out of Harlem with propaganda that still lasts today—that in every shadow there's a big black nigger with a knife or gun ready to rape or stick up white folks. The only whores I knew then were the ones I read about in the newspapers but when I got run out of my legitimate businesses I took to a little light pimping till I could get my breath. I was caught before I got started good and kicked out of New York on a floater, which ruined my ever getting admitted to the bar. So now I'm a real pimp—just like that big time playboy from Santo Domingo. The only difference being he can have dinner at the White House. He's a nice boy but a lightweight. We meet in Spain and different parts of the world now and then—we know girls that come to this country and work the whorehouses like gold mines till their visas is up. . . . The system ran me out of a lot of things and they try to run me out of even life. They can't. I got a brain that teaches me to be the best no matter what I do. So have you, so use this knowledge or get out now. And I speak to your woman, Donna, as I speak to one of us. If she don't like or understand everything you start out to do, explain it again and again and don't move on your ideas till both of you know where you're going, if it's the moon or a flophouse. Don't go with no woman who's guessing. If she understands and still don't want to go with you then cut her loose and go your way because I do believe men like you are needed for the battle or the world will be taken over by a bunch of clock-punching, cocksucking robots. . . . Now there's two things you can do for me, cousin. If you ever get a little famous in the music business, tell them black men that a black brother named Billy Bones started the numbers and got run out and no black man should play the numbers now, 'cause the white man took what wasn't his and owns the toms who run it for them. Tell them to get rid of the toms and bosses or start something of their own. Like I'm working on a new thing—everybody likes games of chance and the numbers ain't the only idea in the world—it's called the Pyramid Club. I'll get going one of these years and by the time they catch on I'll clean up a few million and have it stashed in Swiss banks. When I start my game they won't be able to get blacks to play numbers. Number two you can do for me is tell every white man you meet what those columnists did to keep the white trade downtown and the control of Harlem business out of black hands. Take these news clippings and my notes and pictures of the elite's daughters living it up with Harlem pimps so you'll have all the proof you need when they try to get you. You're going to need this protection the first time you open your mouth. Just put it in a vault or give it to your attorney and let 'em know you have it. I'm from the streets. I know what it is to start from nothing and rise to millions. The real dangerous people are those who never came up from the streets 'cause they're basically cowards, they pay for everything— from good clean fucking to dirty killing. I'm sure killing *themselves* would be more preferable to them than braving the morn of that awakening day when they have to go to work and fight their own wars, cook their own food or fuck their own horrible women. Right now they buy all that from you and me."

"Billy, you told me you studied law by a correspondence course. What formal education did you have?"

"I'm on the record as a college man, but I conned that. When we first came to the States from Santo Domingo and I was still living in Florida with my mother, my sister went out to some little college in New Mexico that had a Spanish-speaking faculty. Later, I figured that would be a good college for me to hold a degree from, far away from New York and not too well known. I wrote her to send me all the records she had and when I noticed on her diploma the name Marian W. Boness—W was for Wanda and she was always called by that name—I just believed I could work something. I wrote the Registrar from New York using another name, saying I was thinking of employing a young man who went to school there—Marion W. Boness, the Marion spelled with an O. They answered saying no such person had attended that school. I wrote back saying there must be some mistake and I told them the W was for William and gave my sister's date of birth in Santo Domingo. The next letter from the Registrar had a copy of the school and college records of this fella Marion William Boness, Marion spelled with an O, and they apologized for the clerical error. I was now a college graduate whose grades indubitably showed him to be an asset to the New York offices of Con, Incorporated. Then I picked out a few of my sister's classmates in the graduation yearbook and started to track them down and telephone them. I convinced the first fella that he not only remembered me but he met my family and dated my sister. When I got around to it I took a trip to New Mexico and looked up a couple of the fellas and girls, like for old times' sake, and said we ought to form an alumni club and keep track of each other. I told them how drug I was I got

left out of the yearbook because I graduated in absentia.
One of the girls I met was a Puerto Riqueña named Joan
—she was studying to be a schoolteacher—ha! I had a
date with her and was driving her home in my rented
open convertible when she said just for fun she'd show
me Lovers' Lane. We parked and when I reached for the
glove compartment to get my smokes she fell back against
the door, bent her knees and spread her legs so fast I
cracked up laughing."

"*Chingale tu madre*, Billy!"

"Shut up, Honey. And this Joan is trembling, biting
her lips, saying, 'Oh, Billy, no, you'll give me a baby! I'm
getting married, I couldn't do that to my poor husband-to-
be . . .' So I take my gray suede glove and brush it down
into her thighs slowly toward her ass. Before I even get
there, her drawers are being wiggled off. This hot bitch is
a nymph. '*Besame cula*,' she says and done peed or comed
all over herself, I don't know which. Her wet drawers
brush the back of my hand. I dig where she's at so I pats
her pubis and with the other hand I reach into my freak
night-bag on my back seat, leave it all cocked open after
retrieving my douzzie out, and I slap this big black French
douzzie jumbo dummy bull's dick in her face, hair and
under her chin. I throw it between her legs, saying, 'Fuck
yourself, you hot-ass bitch, I wanna watch.' My pants and
shorts are off in a flash. Standing, I pee all over her hair,
face, eyes. She gets more frantic, rips open her blouse. So
I yank down the front of her brassiere and floods all down
and over her big firm titties. Her nipples quiver up hard
like a joint. I hear this gushing, splashing sound. This
whore is got my five-inch round, fourteen-inch long douz-

zie jugging in and out her cunt and it's larger and wider than any small Italian salami you ever seen. This bitch is up on her knees reaching for my dick, piss and all, guzzling it in her throat. I don't even feel no teeth, all smooth lips and tongue. She starts crying, 'What have you did to me? I never yet done these things in my life! I swear I'm not like thees before weeth some won hells!' She was coming, squirting like a man all over the man's car. I snatch her dress up and reach back to my night case for my Brazilian horsewhip and bring it down full force, cutting into the flesh of her big fine fat trembling bare ass. She lunges forward from the shock. I bring it down again hard as I can into her butt. A few seconds go by. I bring my whip down a third time and this time she meets my whipping with her jelly rolls and I know she's mine, and with my cock opening, split fitting, cunt holing, ass popping, jaw breaking dick fitter throbbing deep inside her mouth, I comed with my whip lashing fast and hard twenty or thirty times on her frantic, shaking, wiggling, seething hot hips. . . . You think I'd ever let that beautiful freak go? Not in this life!"

"You son on a beach! I cut your nuts if you leaved me! Who taught me, Billy?—you're the freak!"

"Honey, I said I loved you."

"Yes! *I* didn't make you take me to New York! For ten years, Mingus, I'm his woman. Him whipping me now sounds horrible. If I knew he would do that tonight would I go to bed with him? I wouldn't. The whips he does depends on the way I feel—*tengo que estar de ganas.* They're part of my life—when he do it those two, three times a year—*madre mia! Ai yo yo!*"

"Anyway, that was another story, back to what we were talking about. I wasn't trying to impress you with my knowledge of the rackets, Mingus. But I want you to know what you're getting into, 'cause if you get busted they'll hit you harder than Capone 'cause you're black like me and got white girls. Living on Manhattan's East Side, they gonna think you got money even if you ain't. Don't hang out with pimps, black or white. You get categorized. White pimps are jealous. They put the finger on you to the cops or some hood who might think you dumb enough to pay off. I tell you one good way to handle something like that. A big fella—'bout my size but twice my weight—was following me, trying to put the arm on me and he jumped me right downtown in a crowd of people. I put on my glasses and I'm yelling help and just slapping at him with my newspaper—rolled up like this one, see?—every time he steps in on me. Women are pleading to him, 'Let this man go! He's not hurting you!' Somehow he falls down between two parked cars. I walk off and throw my paper away and buy me another at the stand across the street and roll it up the same way. Then I go back over. People are saying things to the police like 'He hit his head on the bumper' and 'He had it coming to him—that big bully attacked that man!' The ambulance came. Names were taken and all. I had my innocent little paper folded under my arm. I got ten witnesses for myself and went my way around the corner right past my bloody old paper in the trash basket. Here, you read it."

"Ouch! Damn! My foot! There's a lead pipe in here!"

"Haw haw! And that's the advantage, Cholly, of keeping up on current events. . . . All right, so you'll be in

New York in a few days. Suppose Pierre finds out Honey
set him up with Donna for a half-yaller nigger bass player.
He's not gonna want that big money coming *your* way. He
may have her watched for a few weeks so don't be seen
with her for a while. Don't phone one apartment from the
other, use pay phones. You can't be too careful. I can help
you get some fair contacts, but as long as Donna's with
Pierre that's all you need. It would be better, Chazz, for
you to stay in a hotel for a few weeks, or better still let
them go on to New York before you. Let Pierre see Lee-
Marie, Donna. Say she's staying with you, waiting on her
cousin Charles to arrive. I bet he tries to get you to propo-
sition her. If he does, that's it. You got his drawers and
socks then, Cholly. White john's biggest charge is to see a
white-on-white woman and a beige-on-black woman kissing each other and rubbing cunts together. And then they
want to see a black man loving their white woman, pant-
ing like his biggest dream is coming true, while they play
with themselves."

"That's what I like about your Billy Bones, Mingus.
He speaks with such finesse on the art of sex."

"Well, he just cancelled our trip."

"Why, Cholly?"

"No eyes, Billy—I don't put on no show no kind of way
for my enemy's encampment."

"Then find somebody else. Get Mama Goose to send
over a white girl and send for me—he'd die if he saw me
work on one of his women. They love to see old-fashioned
Southern-style boys doing it, looking around scared the
white man might hang him any second. They been doing
that for years down South for kicks. The white man asks,

'Is you hard, nigger?' Sam supposed to say, 'Nawsuh.'
'Then why ain't you hard, nigger? Ain't our white women
prettier than them dirt-black women you got?' 'Yes, suh!
But I ain't hard 'caze I ain't lookin'.' 'Then how you know
they pretty, nigger?' ' 'Caze my maw looked once and told
me so. Now can I go, suh, please?' 'Let that nigger go, he's
a good one. Just don't you put your peter in none of them
white pussies.' 'Yes, suh, boss!' . . . All right, Cholly?"

"What you do, you do, Billy, but I'm out of anything
like that."

"All right, girls, get packing. Cholly will stay here with
Honey and me till you get in tight and set up right with
Pierre."

"Donna, while you're furnishing that apartment include a Steinway grand and a good upright at the other
place."

"Yes, Massa Charles."

30

"HEY, DARLING! Over here, Mingus! Charles!"

"Porter, no cab, my wives are here to meet me."

"What, sir?"

"Over there—the car."

"Hey! Hold us, daddy!"

"We missed you—love you so much, love you!"

"I missed you two. You're like a fantastic dream of the supremely greatest beauties gathered for a contest from throughout the entire universe—"

"Yes, aren't we? This is our chauffeur, Percy. This is Mr. Mingus."

"Hi, Percy—and the judges are unseen. Through a voice in the clouds a message is relayed to me: 'Would Mr. Mingus step forward and receive his prize! Chazz Mingus, you have created a single ideal love out of the perfect opposites, Lee-Marie and Donna. We award you first prize for conjuring *Donnalee*, for that shall be their name!'"

"Ha ha! Crazy as ever, our Charles, isn't he, Donna?"

"Yes, he is, our dear husband. Everything in the car? Let's go, Percy."

"But why does Donna's name come first—why not Leedonna?"

"Oh, stop—*I'm* the one who should be jealous—Charles and I were getting married until you came along! But now I dig this more. I may even have a child for all of us. Charles, we have to tell you something—last night we tried to ball. Lee-Marie loved me, I made love to her, we tried everything. We got gradually high, me on vodka and her on scotch. Still nothing. We kept hearing noises in the apartment that were never there before. The lights were low. Then we began to feel you were actually with us, saying 'Wait, babies, wait on old Ming—' and suddenly a funny spark of light ran across the floor. It was like a bluish soap-bubble shining and we both saw a single tiny face in the bubble. It looked like you—with crosses or plus-signs in place of your eyes! Lee-Marie was scared and so was I, but we thought it could be a reflection from the candlelight. We got down close to look and there were now *two* faces in the bubble—mine and hers. They came slowly together and dissolved to someone else—no one we'd ever seen before, like a man and a woman in one—we couldn't decide which. Then your face appeared again, and this time your eyes were closed. I don't know about Lee-Marie but I began to pray to God or Someone to forgive me. We ran to the light switches and our fingers each pressed one of the buttons—click! the exact same instant, but the lights didn't scare the bubble away. It turned yellowish, greenish, purple, and bright in the center like a crystal ball, then it gradually got dull like a tiny colored balloon and sort of sputtered across the floor. We couldn't move—I just held my breath and prayed to the flaming

candles to go on burning for me for Christ's sake. . . .
Mingus, don't be a witch anymore, please!"

"Why didn't you go out and buy a mouse trap?"

"Oh, Mingus, a mouse with two faces?"

"And then it just went poof without a sound!"

"No, with a pow kind of sound."

"I didn't hear that, Lee-Marie."

"I did."

"Well, I don't know what it means, Donnalee. But last
night I couldn't go to sleep, I kept falling off into those
funny fast naps that come over me. So I just laid there
thinking how I loved you both. That's when I decided to
think of you as one—I could see you both in my mind's
eye."

"Donna! I told you it was *his eye!* The size and shape
of a large, dark grape, only crystal-like, transparent, and I
swear it made noise. Like the pouring of fresh soda in a
large glass—crackling and popping like seltzer bubbles
around ice cubes but about ten times as loud."

"Daddy, don't scare us like that. Send *all* your image
next time or don't come. But I'd like it to happen when
we're all together. Some day we'll have a séance or try it
with a Ouija board."

D ONNA AND LEE-MARIE took my boy to the house on
Seventy-fifth Street and showed him his own private quarters, which were just as Donna had
described—a ground floor studio with a bar and games
room and garden, and the grand piano. They left him
alone, telling him take a rest, and went off upstairs, teasingly promising "a big surprise" later. He unpacked, show-

ered and changed, and tried out the piano, playing aimlessly for a while, feeling happy. Then he put on his black Burberry topcoat that he bought because it was just like Billy's, and went out looking for Central Park, which turned out to be not more than a few yards away. He took his first walk in the place which would become a refuge and escape in all his New York years.

The story Donnalee had told was on his mind. He believed it had been a real experience and that he'd been there in some unexplainable way and he thought about it.

I COULD ALWAYS hypnotize people. Even when I lost sight of God, I could hypnotize with music—they'd come running and screaming down the aisles and jumping out of bleachers. Like when I was with Hamp. He has a taste of the power too. It's easy with music, but I believe he could control those same masses of people without it. Of course, we're nowhere as good as Jesus Christ was or even Buddha or Amenhotep. Swami Vivikananda is closer to my league and I'm not even out for the team this season. But I know I was born with something mystic. I should restudy the dangers involved. Are these my hands the right hands to have this gift? I've seen enough to scare me. Like the time someone in the band needed a draw and Hamp refused. On stage—not even looking at him any different than usual—I concentrated on him, I wouldn't let him go. Now are you going to tell me he couldn't get the band swinging because I played bad, one bass? Not so. I actually played better. Even with electric amps, Buckner's piano, loud drums and open brass sections, it cut right through to Hamp. He came over to me and said something like, "Lighten up, gates, take it easy. You and me together." He was smiling, clicking his sticks together, being a showman. I said nothing, I just *thought*. Then Hamp said, "You the weirdest cat I know, standing there looking innocent yet putting your thoughts over the whole band into my head. Okay, okay, I understand you. Morris Lane gets the hundred dollars." So I came to understand I had this power to use when necessary and began to develop it. It's always been there but it's coming back stronger now that I know what side I'm on. I wonder if I could hypnotize all the prostitutes of the world so they'd run into the streets nude to rape every man in sight! Their foulery will enter the homes of our leaders, the madmen plotting to conquer the world or destroy it and whose wives are also women forgotten about. I'll spread it from country to country—Russia's women, France's, Germany's, Japan's—there won't be enough cops to arrest them and even the policewomen will join in. Then when my entranced women pounce upon the leaders of government, the world will know where it is—that Hitler could only have an erection when elated crowds or his girl Eva yelled *Heil, Hitler!* and that Napoleon was a faggot and Mussolini an M6-plus junkie. Goering was an H16 stone junkie twenty-four hours a day. Kings and royalty practiced perversion and cocaine-sniffing and arrested paupers for what they did themselves ten-fold. It's time to know what our leaders are that lead us to die for their way of escaping life. Whores, off with the clothes of our leaders! Today! All over the world! If they run cut off where their balls should be. Save this sick world, oh ye priceless whores!

31

"WHERE WERE YOU, Charles darling?—you disappeared on us!"

"Walking in the park, baby."

"Surprise! Surprise!"

"What's going on? Hey, Lee-Marie, why didn't you tell me? Who's all these people?"

"It's a party for you, daddy, we called everybody you'd want to meet and the whole town's coming. Here's Teddy Cohen. This is Charles Mingus."

"Yep! I've heard about you, Mingus, let me tell you!"

"Hey, Teddy, it's good to meet you first thing!"

"Man, you're too much and what a place you got here! You're real party style—and look at this Lee-Marie of yours—beautiful! Whoah! Whoah! Who's *that*?"

"That's Donna."

"Fix me up, Charlie?"

"No, Teddy."

"Oh, I *see*. Wow! Whoah! Mingus, dig the ass on the one standing next to her! Look at those tits! The tall one, kind of elegant—who's that, Lee-Marie?"

"Her name's Jane Anderson and the other one's her

roommate—they're college girls. They both live just around on Park. Where's Allen Eager? He wants to meet Charles."

"Eager? I heard about him in Watts. I like the way he blows tenor."

"Where the hell's Watts?"

"You never heard of Watts, California?"

"Sorry, Mingus, I'm an Apple man—greatest city in the world. Have you noticed the foul air? Hudson, East, Harlem Rivers, all full of filthy sewage, beautiful lakes of schitt. Think of all that schitt out there! Fifteen million people going to the bathroom. Condoms, old diaphragms, abortions, all of it down the toilet. I see it all from my boat. Sometimes my rudder gets stuck so I get down in there to fix it. Wham! All clogged up. Old douche bags. Kotex. Rubbers. Dead cats. Dogs. Garbage. Anything they don't want, flush, splash, right in the river! And the air! Kiyaa! Whew! Cachew! Yep, greatest city in the world. . . . So you're from Watts, Charles Mingus. Is Lee-Marie from there too?"

"Yeah, near there, Teddy Cohen."

"By the way, I've changed my name. Cohen is out—I can't fight these clubs with a name like Cohen. Call me Teddy Charles."

"Oh, gonna pass high."

"No, just stop starving. I want to save up enough money so I can be buried where I choose, right here where they kill you. Hey, there's that child Jane—whatever her name is—coming this way!"

"Who's the slick with them?"

"He's an ex-orator, an unemployed actor, manages a strip joint down in the Village. Wait'll you hear this cat's

284

line. These chicks must have loot. I can tell by the hungry look on his face."

"Hello, Teddy. I've seen this man before but I just can't seem to . . ."

"This is Charles Mingus—it's his apartment. Mingus, meet Johnny Crane."

"Ah, yes. These two young ladies are your fans. Jane, you're right, it *is* Charlie Mingus. Jane Anderson."

"I love your music, Mr. Mingus. This is my roommate, Diana Taylor."

"Hello, Charles, I recognized you too."

"I'm not really Mingus, I'm Pettiford passing for Safransky. Where did you hear me play, Jane?"

"In Paris last year."

"No, you didn't. I wasn't there."

"I heard your records in discotheques. And saw your picture in jazz papers."

"Well, that won't happen to me here unless I pay for it or get some critic to double as my manager. In fact, a bass player can copy my style and play it back in my face and if he's white he's gonna become a wealthy man on my ideas. He can be a nice guy too but I can't really like him 'cause I know he's messing with my bread."

"Don't be bitter, Charles."

"Bitter? How could a kid like you know anything about it, Jane?"

"Anyway, I do know your work and I love your composing—my favorite is 'Revelations.' And once I heard a tape of a tone poem where you recited 'The Chill of Death.' David Brookman played it for me."

"Baby, I wish I had that one myself."

"Excuse me, ladies, I have to take Mingus away for a moment, we'll be right back. . . . Mingus, how about that girl Jane, have you noticed?"

"Noticed what, Teddy?"

"Take a look."

"I'm looking."

"You dig her, don't you?"

"Aw, Teddy, what is it?"

"Well, it's in my mind that Jane is—a white Lee-Marie! Don't you see it? Sure you do!"

"Now wait a minute, man. Lee-Marie's my old lady."

"Don't get mad, man."

"You're looking into my reason to live."

"Okay but you've got *two* chicks, right? I saw it when that Donna looked at you. She's your side chick, girl, wife, right?"

"Donna, come over here! This is Teddy Charles. He says you're my wife 'cause he saw you look at me."

"Can't I look at what's mine? Daddy, it's time you met all the guests. Will you introduce him, Teddy?"

"With pleasure. Ladies and gentlemen, I'd like to pay a tribute to our guest of honor—a toast to one of the greatest bass players in the world of jazz—Charles Mingus!"

"Boo, Teddy Charles! Mingus is a composer, a very good composer. Most people don't know the real Mingus music. Ask my friend Diana—we played 'Revelations' for music class at school and the professor thought it was a piece by some classical composer he'd forgotten!"

"Donna, where are you going? Donna, wait. . . . What's the matter?"

"Godammit, Mingus, I don't like her!"

"Donna! Sit. Don't move. Just set. Donna, is it possible you're *jealous?*"

"Hello, Mingus."

"Hey! You're Allen Eager—you sure play, I dig you!"

"Dig *you*, motherfucker. This is Thelonius Monk."

"Yeah, it's me—thought I'd look in just to keep the party right, not all white."

"Thanks, T. . . . Hey, aren't you Baby Lawrence?"

"My pleasure, Mingus. Welcome to New York."

"Look, Monk's already dancing, showing off for Baby Lawrence!"

"I'm Ulanov from *Metronome*. Welcome to the city."

"Thanks for coming, Mr. Ulanov."

"This is our feature editor, Bill Coss."

"Hi, Bill—I've read some of your liner notes."

"Hello, Mingus. I'm Bobby Gladen and this is Anchovies."

"Charles."

"What is it, Lee-Marie?"

"Can we be alone for a minute?"

"Not now, baby—later."

INGUS, you got some place to relax in this house? Diana says she's tired, wants to lay down. Confidentially, I think I can make a little bed eyes if I cool it with her and her friend. Maybe we all can—Lee-Marie, Donna, you know, a little daisy chainerooney. I'd like to watch if nothing else."

"I don't think so, Teddy. Especially my two. What

gives you that idea? And Jane and Diana don't look like sluts either."

"Whoah! Whoah! Gets pretty lonely up there at those girls' schools. Would I love a party scene with them educated ladies!"

"Teddy, your opinion of American womanhood is more debased than mine. Is it possible that these tramps adopt masks of prudery for me and bare their naked selves to you?"

"Well, there's some that's got and some that ain't."

"Daddy, here's the key to our private elevator. I want you to come upstairs a minute, I have to talk to you about something important. Second landing."

"Be right up, Donna."

OWEE, Donna, this is something else! This brass bed looks big enough for a party! Wowee! Oh, well, I guess it don't take too much to gas a man from Watts."

"Mingus, listen. You know you've got us, Lee-Marie and me. We love you. That's why I've sent Lee-Marie to tell that girl you've been with all evening that you're waiting for her up here. I want you to fuck her, fuck her and laugh in her face because I don't like that bitch. Put your pretty black dick in her virgin ass—suck her big breasts—enjoy yourself. That's our present to you. If you don't, I'm leaving you. Because if you don't fuck her tonight you will when I don't know it and then we'll lose our honest thing with each other just like everyone else in the world."

"Why—thanks, Donna, but you've got it wrong. I—"

"Oh, excuse me—I'm sorry—I thought—"

"That's all right, come in, Jane, we're waiting for you. I'm Donna. You've met Charles, I've noticed. You better be careful, he's horrible. He rapes people. Why are you getting up, Mr. Mingus? Jane's seen men lying down before, I'm sure—her brother or maybe her father. Well, are you coming in, Jane?"

"Well, if . . ."

"Oh, sit down, girl, you're too obvious! I'm leaving. Mingus, come outside a minute. . . . Mingus, don't love her like you would me or Lee-Marie, you hear? If you do, I'll feel it downstairs and come up and break these doors down! Teddy! What're you doing up here?"

"Whoah! Whoah! I got a sleepy girl here named Diana. Which way do we go?"

"Take any room you like—except this one, Mingus will be busy in there. Goodbye, daddy, I'm going back and be a hostess. Remember what I said."

"I love you, Donna."

"I adore you, Mingus."

ANE! Hey, wake up! Did you doze off?"

"Oh, sorry! Guess I'm a little high. Why are we up here?"

"If you're high let's go back downstairs for coffee."

"I'm not really high. I'd like some sparkling burgundy."

"I'll order some. Here's a phone with some buttons."

"Don't turn on the light, Mingus."

"Hello? Are you the bar? Send a bottle of sparkling

burgundy up to the second floor, please. The double doors."

"Aren't the candles pretty, flickering on the ceiling and in all those mirrors? This looks like the Royal Suite at the George Cinq. . . . Mingus?"

"Oh. . . . Your things, let me take them. Here's a hanger."

"Oh, your quiet, so gentle hands, Mingus . . . your musical touch. Yes, touch my face with your fingers. Umm . . . like that. Umhum! . . . like that . . . where are you going?"

"Shower. Come on in. Beats a midnight swim this time of year."

TAP TAP.

"It's the waiter, sir, you ordered wine?"

"Just leave it out there."

"Yes, sir."

"Ooooh, Mingus, there's too much steam, I can't see, where are you? Oooh! Where's the rest of you?"

"Feel, baby. Come on in. I feel for you and you feel for me. Yeah! Hoooh, Jane baby!"

"Mingus, don't hurt me."

"That's impossible. Oooh, Jane—the *biggest, softest* in life. . . ."

"Oh, that's good, but—no—don't hurt—"

"Just calming you down, baby, so nature can take its course."

"Promise no pain?"

"Only good ones. Come closer, baby, right here. Where's that soap? Yeah, lay your head back, right on my shoulder."

"Soap me, wash all over! Ooooh, my stomach's ticklish . . . . Isn't someone pounding on the door?"

"Yeah. . . . Who is it? What do you want?!"

"It's me, Teddy! Let me in!"

"What? Man, you crazy!"

"What's on this tray out here? There's food. We're hungry."

"Help yourself but leave the wine. 'Bye, Teddy."

"Hey, great!—salmon, ham, caviar. . . . Mingus! Whoah! Whoah! You got a seal in there or something?"

"GOOD-BYE, TEDDY! . . . You all right, baby?"

"It doesn't hurt, Mingus. I feel all loose and good."

"Come under. Let's rinse the soap off. Now turn around."

"Oooh, hold me close! But this will never fit, Mingus— you'll kill me!"

"Come on. Bring a couple of those big towels for the bed. Aaaah . . . it's good to stretch out like there isn't a man living in the world that's able to do anyone any harm. . . ."

JANE. . . . How old are you?"

"*Toooo* late, Mingus, you forgot to ask forty-five minutes ago. I'm old enough to know better and this is better than anything that's been near me. Don't take me this far and start feeling guilty. I thought it would be like this since long ago, before I was eighteen. I'm twenty now. Does that make some great difference?"

"Damn! I wonder who that is, ringing up here. . . . Yeah?"

"Hello. Can you hear me, daddy? It's Donna. Hope I didn't interrupt?"

"Yeah, baby. What's all that noise down there?"

"Monk and Baby Lawrence are having a dance contest."

"I recognize Baby's sound—he makes the pitch of each tap sound like a musical note."

"Pierre just called. Says he's lonely, wouldn't you know it? I'm going to the other place. I'll try to get rid of him—I'll wear a Kotex with tomato paste and if he's not like some johns I've known he'll go home early. If I can lose him, why not meet me later at Trader Vic's?"

"Remember what Billy said about being seen together."

"That's all cool now. Pierre's seen Lee-Marie. He thinks she's mine and you're the fool."

"Haw haw! Look, Donna, I need a car to take the lady home."

"The Ferrari's out front."

"Oh, yeah, Miles got one of them ferries."

"Daddy, if you can't pronounce it I doubt if you can drive it. Take the Cadillac, the driver's waiting. And if you've finished fucking that little snob bitch up there come down and spend some time with your other guests. I'll call later, honey."

"Later, Donna. . . . Jane, baby, take your time getting dressed, I'll be waiting for you downstairs."

TEDDY, been having fun?"

"Nothing man, nothing at all. I'm going back down to the party. After I got her all buttered up and everything she just conks out. Blah! I know plenty of chicks. Why do I have to get hooked up with one like this? Yech!"

"Teddy, I hear you out there, is that a nice way to talk? Come back in here! I'm wide awake now."

"I hate to be a drag, Teddy, but the girls have to go back to school tonight."

"What? Oh no! Just when she's all woke up?"

"They'll be back next weekend, Jane says."

"Oh, hell, all right, next week it'll be."

"I'll go down and mingle a little then we'll take the girls to Grand Central, wherever that is. You better get Diana up."

EY, COLEMAN HAWKINS! When did you make the scene?"

"A while ago. Heard you got in, couldn't miss this for nothing! You really got some wild schitt here. Where'd you get this buffalo meat from, they still shooting 'em out in Watts? . . . There's Roy Eldrige. Hi, Roy!"

"Yeah, Bean?"

"Here's that California boy I told you about, Cholly Mingus. You know, your man Tatum'll be falling by, I told him where you were abiding. He laughed, said you ought to spend all that energy on music."

"You mean Tatum's coming?! Lawrd! Let's go somewhere and clean my ears out. With all that piano over there I know he's going to get some of it."

"I knew it. Can't be nobody but some Dizzy walking up from behind pinching ass."

"Hello, Mingus."

"Bird! Yardbird!"

"Good to see you here, Mingus. I often spoke to Miles as to why you didn't come sooner."

"Oh, I'm not ready yet, Bird, just visiting. Going to come around and listen to all you cats."

"You sit in anytime, Mingus."

"Soon as I hear whatcha doing."

"Mingus, who invited all those white folks?"

"I guess my white old lady, Dizzy."

"I don't see nothin' over there but critics."

"Man, that's a lot of talent, don't you dig it? I see Leonard Feather, he's a piano player. There's Bill Coss and Gene Lees—they sing, I heard. Barry Ulanov must play drums or something, dig, with that *Metronome* beat. Martin Williams can play everything, I can tell by the way he writes. Put Marshall Stearns on bass and let Whitney Balliett score and John Wilson conduct. Let all them other young up-and-coming critics dance. How would you like to review that schitt for the *Amsterdam News?*"

"Especially would I love to hear Gene Lees sing. Ka badga dougee! Sing, Gene Lees! Right on stage in New York City so I can be there at your grand opening and compliment you backstage, dig?"

"Thank God you didn't make him sing right now 'cause here's Art. Hey, Art!"

"Oh-oh! Ladies and gentlemen, your attention please! God is in the house. On your knees as Art Tatum walks by. That's what Fats Waller said, Mingus."

"Yeah, some white man heard Fats say that. They always hear something else. What Fats said was, 'Oh, my God, Art Tatum's in the house!' Fats had a left hand, too. He wouldn't be calling Art God."

"Why not? Art's definitely related to The Man."

"Yeah, Bird, but related don't make him *The*. But here's His baddest piano-playing son walking up right now. Remember the gardener in the New Testament, after the Crucifixion? In this century, the gardener is a piano player. . . . Hey, Art!"

"How're you doing there, Mingus? Can you still play, boy?"

"Yeah, Art, but I'd rather listen tonight, for future reference. I hear on this coast people pay attention. . . . Bird's taking his horn out."

"Come on, Bird, let's see what you got to say tonight!"

" 'Lover.' One, two, one, two, three, four. . . ."

DAMN, DIZ! You ever heard any schitt like that in your life?! Art backing up Bird with left-hand solos, playing a counterline with his right and somehow keeping the rhythm striding at the same time. Bird's laying out now, look at his big moonface smiling down at Art. Uh oh. Art looked up. There goes Bird. Art ain't comped him yet. Don't seem to be draggin' Bird none. Listen at them motherfuckers. Dig the critics over there still talking to each other. Don't hear a thing."

"Like the time Duke and Art played opposite each other, next door to Birdland. Played their asses off—it should of made headlines in all the papers. Instead, the one review made a joke about the Cuban bass-player's funny-sounding name."

"Go ahead, Bird! Get 'em, Art! Man, Bird's got another sax hidden there somewhere and two extra hands. Got to be. Listen to that big sound! Like two cats playing in unison."

"Yeah, Hawk, big like your sound."

"There it goes—a million birds chirping, singing, flapping their wings high up in the sky! Hear it, Mingus? Chirp da la da la! Hear it coming down?"

"Yeah, Diz, that million-bird sound reminds me of the music I heard the day I was born!"

"You high, Mingus?"

"No, why?"

"Then don't ever get high, or you'll leave this earth! Ha ha ha!"

"Yeah, Bird! Yeah, Art! That's tellin' all those ofays to shut up! Too much! Oh, my God! Too frompin' much! Yeah! Lord, oh Lord! Now they finished. There go the critics, blinkin' eyes, clappin' hands, tryin' to act like they was listening. And get Bird, playing as he walks off! Ha ha! Shuffle off to Buffalo! Ha ha! Ho ho!"

"Charles . . ."

"Yeah, Jane baby? Excuse me, all you fellas."

"No, go ahead, Mingus—Diana and I are going home to pack, it's just around the corner. Come when you're ready."

"Okay, baby."

"Ming, is she like that one in San Francisco? Is her hair the same color all over as her head?"

"All right man, that's enough, you got it."

"Mingus?"

"Yes, Lee-Marie?"

"Will you come in the library for a moment now?"

"Sure. Excuse me, Diz. . . . Hawk. . . . See ya. . . . Something wrong, baby?"

"Donna just called. Pierre has something special planned tonight, Donna and me. Without you. I'm sorry. It's your welcome party—we three should be together. Everything's so confused—what am I to do?"

"Do? Relax. Everything's just beautiful. Do what you want to do."

"But Mingus—I hate to leave. I love you."

"I don't think you do, Lee-Marie, you love an idea. I only began to see what I'm doing to you and Donna and myself after you left San Francisco. Listening to Billy talk big, almost like a saint, I got suspicious. What does this all mean?"

"What it means to you, Charles."

"It means nothing to me, nothing at all. It's all so much pretense. This money in my shirt pocket? Nineteen thousand seven hundred and ninety-eight dollars. It wasn't a loan—Billy *gave* it to me and they gave you and Donna clothes. Why? Because Billy and I are tight like family? I don't think so anymore. It's because he wants company on that train he's on. When I was a child I was knocked unconscious by a fall. A boy lay bleeding on the floor. I was that child yet I was not that child. I was someone else in the same room, yet the family couldn't see me. I was a kind of wise man as old as time. It was entirely up to me whether I let that boy lie there and walked off into infinity or breathed my conscious life into him again. And now I can see you and everything around you as clear and as plain as I saw that day when I knew where people were going and could think myself there or ride in their car beside them without their seeing me."

"I don't understand you."

"Yes, you do."

"Telephone, ma'am. It's Miss Donna."

"I'll take that!"

"Yes, sir."

"Hello, Donna, she's not coming. Yeah, she told me and you can tell him she's not available—she's gone, just gone, left. Tell him if that's what he wants to go to Harlem and find it. . . . I'm sorry but that's what I do mean. You're both quitting, if I'm concerned in this. I'm glad she hasn't made that scene yet. Tonight or any big money night won't bug us from now on. . . . You say love, Donna? I hope to God I can really love before it's too late. Can you get away from him? . . . Yes, she's with me here but she's not coming, I told you. . . . All right, hang on."

"Hello, Donna. Yes. . . . Yes. Yes, I will."

"Lee-Marie, don't go! You're no whore. You lied to me, I saw it all in my trance the night of your visitation."

"Yes, Donna, he's feeling sorry for himself but he'll be cool. . . . Yes, in about twenty minutes. It's all right— he knows we love him. 'Bye. . . . Can I go, Charles? Tell me I can go. Because I'm going."

"Why? Why? It's not for *me* anymore—I don't want you to!"

"Well, then, for your music. You'd die punching a clock, if it kept you away from that."

"I don't think so anymore. I'll have *more* to say musically, living with the underdogs—*beneath* the underdogs— more to write about."

"Why didn't you get a job, then, when Barbara and her parents wanted you to?"

"It was too early to interrupt my studies. I'd never of made up that time."

"You can't stop music, *any* time, Mingus. I could play cello concertos once—now I can barely play in tune."

"Lee-Marie, you only practiced because your parents made you and you stopped first chance you got just like my sisters. If all the money spent on them was spent on a good teacher for me I'd of made it when I was five years old."

"I was no genius, Mingus."

"You didn't try to be. Maybe I am. No one's going to stop me anymore. I've acquired technique now, my mind can *think* through practice with the same and better results as if I'd worked through hours and hours. Now I could work at anything—in a post office or anywhere—and be practicing in my head. The only thing that would suffer would be stamina and toughening my callouses."

"Genius! You want applause?"

"I want reasons why you or Donna should try to make me as rich as Billy Bones. This talent's not going to be wasted pimping."

"Right, Mingus. I'm not as good as you."

"It's getting all twisted, baby."

"I couldn't hold out. I began loving you too early in my life. I used to think I loved music, too. I don't really, I couldn't put it above people. You can. I'm your whore, you can like it or not. You've conditioned me to need you because I've had it your way. Here, let me touch you. There are millions of these but when I lie down I want *this* one in me and you'd better be behind it. I never even considered loving anybody else—except Rags, because he looked like you. But he's not you or I'd be there."

"You say you love me, Lee-Marie, and you can give

this to another man, my enemy, who hates me?"

"Oh oh oh! You're smart, Mr. Mingus. Clever! Dirty! And cold tonight. *You . . . want . . . answers!* All right. It's because I'm *just like you.* Like you were with Jane, a free lover, and I don't want to admit that's what I feel most naturally. Something makes me feel low, sinful, lost, suspecting that it's fatal to the salvation of my soul. But if you tell me *I've* lost my soul for being carnal and for loving you and Donna all the ways I've loved, and *you've* stopped short of sinning because the girl you just finished with takes no pay, then I'm lost and glad of it. There's going to be lots of company up or down—wherever it is—in hell!"

"You're the witch, Lee-Marie, not me. You're the one with all the soul."

"I'm not making fun, Mingus. You judge people and cast them into hell for a slight deviation from the same sins you commit—like live in adultery but take a dime and you're doomed! You think I've lost my soul and yours has just begun to grow. The strain was and is too much. To be with you I had to make a choice and I did. Now I really want as much money as I can get—millions like Billy if I can do it. Then maybe I can buy my way out of all this with you and for you—Europe, I don't care where. I want you, baby, and if it's got to be with Donna and Jane and Jane's *mama!*—I don't care. Don't take this honest thing from me because I'm only selling what's going in the ground to ashes and dust. I'm not selling me. That part's as untouched as before our first trip to Lake Elsinore."

"Come here, listen to me, Lee-Marie . . . Come on, no tears."

"You don't love me, Mingus. You don't love Donna."

"Then why am I not *overjoyed?* My problems would be over. Two whores! How much would you get tonight?"

"A lot, I guess. It's a party, a show. They want to watch."

"Well, fuck it! Let them go to bed and watch their sacks of money!"

"Would you want Donnalee if you had to provide for us with your music? Don't say it, I know the answer. Sure you love us but you haven't made it yet. My father really didn't miss, did he?"

"You're confusing me, but you're the one person I got to level with. I don't know a damn thing, baby. Baby, don't *you* cry now. We both love each other, I'll love you till the day we die. Oh, that dream—that dream when I couldn't wake up. . . ."

"Charles, don't you see—it's all *solved!* You don't have to 'make it.' I don't want you to have to, ever, as long as you have your beautiful and ugly dreams and wake up to what you still believe. And I'm going now and get the money of those people that caused all this! And tonight when I come back you'll tell me about your dream. Now I must get dressed. And you're going to take that girl home. We'll just let this crowd carry on, I don't guess anyone will run off with anything we can't buy —see, Mingus, that's the way I want to feel all my years on this earth!"

"Lee-Marie—"

"Good-bye, darling."

ERE'S OLD CHAZZ! Where you been? Me and the girls been waiting almost an hour. They have to take a later train now."

"Hi, Teddy—sorry, I couldn't help it. Come on. . . . You girls sit back and Teddy and I'll take these seats that unfold."

"Mingus, drop me off at my car on Fifty-second, I have to get out to my boat. I invested too much to lose her if that Hurricane What's-her-name hits here."

"Aren't you going to see us off, Teddy?"

"We'll all be seeing each other next weekend, right?"

"Yeah. Okay, Teddy, but let's stop off for some coffee. Maybe some pig and eggs."

"How about that joint on Fifty-second and Broadway?"

"Crazy! Might as well see Broadway my first night in New York."

ELL, just the three of us now, girls—I'll sit in the middle."

"Could I have a cigarette, Charles?"

"Of course. You too, Jane?"

"Yes. . . . Thanks. I feel so—how can I say it—strange. I can't believe this numb after-feeling. Do you think the numbness is the result of my super-ego protecting me from feeling .I lost myself, because Charles couldn't possibly have my idea of love? Yet somehow, Charles, now I feel an integral part of your creative life. I feel I understand much more deeply the meaning of your art. I remember when I learned to ski and entered my first race—I think there's an analogy here—the eager novice's excitement in

302

sharing and competing with professional performers. Or is it something else entirely—the subconscious fear of destruction in the atomic age that makes us vulnerable to animal urges and primitive appetites in a drive toward survival of the race?"

"Mingus, what Jane means is the threat of the atomic bomb makes her think she'd better get down to making some scenes with a virile-looking bass-player and drop her inhibitions and also her—"

"Excuse me, I'm just closing Percy's window."

"And also her sweaty nylon lace panties. And in her dreams she hopes you're wilder than a wild-dicked animal because she's never left Newport, even in her toilet."

"Oh, Diana! Very funny."

"Well, then, you interpret it another way."

"If that's what I mean, though you put it crudely, then I'm not ashamed."

"Can I say something? Ladies, may I?"

"Of course, Charles."

"Okay. Ha ha! Ha ho ho! Wowoohwee!"

"Mingus, I . . . I . . ."

"I know, baby. Me too."

"You'll write me?"

"Or I'll come up to see you. When can you be visited—off campus?"

"Any time you want. But I'll be back here with you Friday."

"I'll be waiting."

"Diana, I want to show Mingus my private echo chamber in Grand Central Station."

"Go ahead. See you on the train. 'Bye, Mingus."

" 'Bye, Diana, see you. . . . Where you taking me, Jane?"

"It's my secret place, a present my grandmother gave me when I was a child. Hardly anybody knows about it."

"How could there be a secret place in this big room with all these noisy people milling around?"

"We go to the farthest door west on Forty-second Street and then it's just to the right before you reach the big room. . . . See, you press your ear close to the curved wall . . . and you can hear the slightest whisper, the smallest sound, from any part of the room."

"Let me go over there and whisper to you, Jane. . . . Can you hear me?"

"Yeeeessss . . . Minnnguuuussss. . . ."

"Think about next weekend . . . baby."

"Oooh, sooooooelectrifying!"

32

"THAT SOUNDS LIKE the happy ending of a romantic novel, Charles. Hero escapes life of vice and corruption and takes up with new love."

"Nope, the hero didn't escape, Dr. Wallach, I guess endings don't come that easy. He stayed with Donnalee and tried to make a go of it but there wasn't much of a family life any more. From San Francisco it seemed like a perfect set-up but the reality of it in New York had a different meaning. I knew I couldn't make the scene, it was all a fantasy."

"The girl Jane, what happened with her?"

"Didn't too much happen but meeting her changed my life and eventually changed my direction. I thought about her a lot, she was something completely new to me. I'd go see her or she'd come down to New York on weekends. She was always with me in my mind, a sign of what things could be in another kind of existence, but I'd never allow myself to become really hooked with someone like that. Their lives are too different—skiing all over the world, speaking languages, owning things. To her, Black America was famous musicians in a spotlight bowing to thunderous applause. But I had a need for her to understand me and I wrote letters that tried to be colorless.

dear jane, now i've told you how i see the girl jane anderson but what if i ask what does mingus mean to her? could she come up with a true picture of him? i doubt it. i don't want to offend you that's the last thing i want to do but i don't believe you could understand mingus. but inside your body inside your beautiful personal dwelling place where you are really you he is like you, free and beautiful as you are. let's take this mingus and this jane and change him a little but leave her mostly as she is. let's put him at harvard music school bass and all for a fair shake. that would give him a little more edge in the social circles that surround jane. since he wishes to woo her let's give him a crazy little motor boat with just room for two closing out competition and enabling him to court her on his own waters so fittingly called the charles river. let's even move old ming to a fancy address on beacon hill. all this might bring them closer a little closer but even so a million guys have all that and more and grew up knowing jane in the palm beaches and st moritzes of the world. one of these guys can say to jane remember that time in prep school when i had spent my allowance so i borrowed a rolls from the local garage without permission and drove my date to new york, signed my uncle's name to the bill at the plaza and got arrested for car stealing and my father had to come bail us out (in evening clothes of course) and boy did i get a lecture! that's a story jane would understand and find amusing. but if i told her i knew a black kid in pasadena who didn't have wheels for his big date and borrowed some without asking and went to jail for three years and came out destroyed would that amuse jane? jane close as we were lately i don't even remember what you look like. but i can relive our fantasy as you called it as clearly as though you were here. . . .

ANE WAS SO DIFFERENT from me, doctor, that she couldn't even see or understand my problem. She was always inviting me to Southampton, places like that, yacht trips, wanting me to meet her father. It seemed like he owned half of America and I was afraid of what he'd think or say or *do*. Finally I asked her. 'What do you mean, Charles, what will he do?' she said. I'm talking about my color, I told her. She looked very surprised. 'Why, I never even thought of that,' she said. I didn't believe her. Would you, doctor?"

dear jane, if you feel you can't answer this in your own handwriting type a reply. no need to sign your name if you think there might be complications and if you don't i have reason to think there might be. a smart young man came where i was playing one night recently and questioned me about knowing you. dropped little hints about THE FAMILY saying if i took you seriously i should realize it would be safer to forget you. color has nothing to do with it he said ever so subtly but the difference in social level is too too much! i was frightened at first i admit but when i called to

tell you i didn't know what to say. i felt clumsy awk-
ward stumbled and felt stupid and hung up bursting
with anxiety and wondering if i really was a phony
and your money was what i was after. excuse me baby
i know now that's a lot of schitt. fact is i don't even
know what it's like having that much bread so how
could i want it. when i met you newport was a place
i heard of in the movies and yacht was a word i
couldn't even spell till i looked it up.

i want jane to think of me as we both know each other
inside not in terms of her money and social standing
and not in terms of jazz and what they write about
mingus in the newspapers and magazines. jane and i
are real with each other, no axes to grind. so friend of
mine that i also love answer <u>answer</u> to me please. and
fear not to send a picture of yourself and sign it with
any name you choose. let's always speak the truth with
each other. enough truth might clear up a whole lot
of things. yours with love, chazz.

BUT YOU WENT ON LIVING in the same house with—
Donnalee, as you call them, Charles?"

"I couldn't leave, I don't know why, but the closer
they got to each other the further they got from me.
When I played clubs they'd come to hear and leave together before the last set. At home, it got so they slept together in the big Hollywood bed. After we made love
they'd go to sleep and I'd go downstairs to the piano in
my studio and work, I was writing music all the time, all
night. Sometimes they'd do a little copying for me but

the truth is when we weren't in bed it seemed I was always in the way. They were in *business* and always getting dressed to go out or expecting somebody to call or come and even in bed there's only a few sensible things that two women can perform with one man and have it mean anything for everyone involved. Anyway, I always get the bathtub blues when it comes right down to chicks making it with other men. Our love scenes cooled out to almost nothing and the tension was building. One night I finished a score for a television show and was sitting there feeling the letdown and Donna sort of sneered—'Look at the pimp with nothing left to do.' I said, 'Fuck you!—go look under your mattress and find your bread!' Under the mattress of that Hollywood bed was hundreds of bills I'd been putting there—I don't even know how much it was, thousands of dollars, all hers, all theirs, I didn't want it. The next day I looked in the paper and went out and rented a top-floor walk-up over on West Fifty-first Street. I knew I had to find a whole new scene."

"Was that the end of you and Donnalee?"

"No, it still wasn't the end, but I was in search of a way of life, a broader truth than it was possible to find living with two hookers 'cause that's what it had really become—two hookers and me, not a trio love affair. But it was still hard to let go of the beautiful sex life that had been and break away. When I moved to the West Side I started trying to do everything at once—work, write music, teach bass, lose pounds. A doctor in the neighborhood who was a weight specialist gave me shots and amphetamine pills to control my appetite. I took them for months and lost ninety pounds but I was all speeded up, my nerves were shot to pieces and sometimes I thought I'd go crazy from not sleeping. I'd sit at the window and stare down at the street and think maybe everybody else was crazy too, the whole streetful. I saw a guy down there who danced all the time—it would take him most of an hour to get off the block tap-dancing backwards and forwards and around in circles trying to get where he was going. He was a light chocolate-brown color and he always wore an old worn-out gabardine suit the same shade as he was. Sometimes he'd look up and see me. I'd wave and he'd wave back and dance on down the street like a rag doll with his pants falling down and his T-shirt hanging out and socks drooping over his shoes. Oh, I was very lonely when I first lived over there. I sure missed Donnalee."

"Did you still love them, Charles?"

"More than ever. Actually, I guess I left because I was jealous, I couldn't stand the phone ringing and hearing them make dates and watching them get dressed to go meet their johns. I wanted them for myself, I couldn't stand sharecropping."

"Did you ever think about dropping one and continuing with the other, as a solution?"

"One was no good without the other—it'd got so they were closer to each other than they were to me. I had to break away. I was playing concerts with a composers' group and making club and school gigs and people started sending me students. One day I was down in Philadelphia at some college, and a girl was waiting after the concert. She said she was a classical harpist and wanted to study jazz with me and she'd come to New York for it, so I gave her my address and phone number. Her name was Louise.

In the middle of her first lesson at my pad all of a sudden she said, 'Show it hard and I'll suck it!' I was *shocked* into complete readiness! I never had anything like that—it turned into an almost endless fellatio come. It was so good with this girl that I wanted to share it with Donna and I told her about it—she loved the idea of grooving with us and planned the whole scene. I was supposed to leave the door unlocked next time and Donna would tip-toe in and catch us naked and get furious and say, 'Aha! I caught you freefucking, Mingus, so now I'm going to fuck her too!' We thought Louise would dig it—she'd do anything every kind of way with me alone. But when Donna started taking off her clothes this girl began to scream out so loud—'Get that freak out of here! Freak! Freak!' Funny, she didn't blame me at all, she only called Donna a freak. I felt ashamed and I was convinced something was dreadfully wrong with me to want to add still another girl to my—"

"Your what, Charles?"

"I was going to say harem. And there was Louise running out of the room looking so good bare-ass screaming 'Freak!' and Donna coldly going right on undressing like nothing was happening. Then Lee-Marie walked in and I knew Donna had set that up too, only the first thing she said was, 'Donna, the airline will call us here about the reservations to Acapulco,' and I knew all she was thinking about was business—commercial pussy. That was the first I heard about Acapulco and I grabbed her and made her tell the whole story. Somebody'd set up a contact for Donna, a john, and she was supposed to fly down and stay at an expensive hotel and act aloof and ignore all advances from other male poodles until the guy showed

up she had a picture of. Then she was to pretend to fall
for him—he wanted to look like a big lover type to his
friends. And for this she got three thousand dollars paid
in New York and all expenses. So she gets creative—she
decides to take Lee-Marie with her so in case of party-
style she can get more bread by bringing in a colored girl!
Well, I thought, fuck it—I'm not Billy Bones to know all
the right moves. 'I'm not Billy,' I told her, 'I'm not a pimp!
I don't want you to go, I don't want you to hustle. Give all
this up. I'm a musician, this is my pad and don't come in
here with your fucking commercial plans! And leave
Lee-Marie out of them and no one's going to answer the
phone here!' Donna started yelling, 'You *are* a pimp! Look
at all my money you took!' And I said 'I told you every
dime you handed me is still under your fucking mattress!'
And here were three people who had really loved each
other at one time fighting uncontrollably, me standing
buck-naked and Donna in bra and garter belt and Lee-
Marie in the middle and we were fighting and not knowing
why and all the things that had been heaven stood for
pure hell! I looked at Donna's trim figure—sleek and not
cheap— and was thinking how it had always been the
first time over again to make love with her. She'd make
any scene but you could never take her for granted and
just fuck her in the mouth or ass like Louise or a bitch
you're paying for. Donna had class, she was like a wonderful, free virgin who would discover each act with you
but would never repeat it at your demand. Every time
she made love it was a whole new chain of events. And it
wasn't just Donna standing here screaming, it was Lee-
Marie too, the childhood love, who was part of this strange
trio. When the phone rang Donna grabbed it and I heard

her saying something like, 'Yes, Flight six four seven TWA, Idlewild to Miami, Miami to Mexico City, Mexico City to Acapulco—' and I knew I had to cut out for good or I'd be a dead man though it could also kill me to give up Donnalee. I knew it had to end or I couldn't write no more music, play no more bass or even tinkle at the piano. I knew that with just one of these brawds there'd be no place for music in my life and no woman can ever respect a man who lets her know there's nothing more to his life than what he has with her. The day you say to a woman 'I can't live without you' is the day she says 'Prove it by loving only me, don't love your work or anything else.' So when they left my house I put on some clothes, shut the windows and locked the door and went out to the airport and got on a plane for San Francisco."

"Back to Billy Bones, Charles?"

"I didn't even contact him, I was down on the whole hustling life and wanted no part of it. I went to my artist friend and stayed in his studio just like I did before. He'd come every day and paint and I'd work at the piano. This was a good period again, the way it always is with Farwell. Then Billie Holiday came to town and Fats Navarro —it was the next to last time I talked to him. They were playing a concert for Norman Granz and I went over to the theater to see them."

INKUS FINKUS! I heared you was here, I knewed you'd come!"

"I been here awhile, Fats."

"I know, I heared. Come on backstage and meet the folks. You losed a lot of weight too, huh, Mingus? Look at me—I made a record with Jacquet under the name of *Slim* Romero, how 'bout that! Billie, here's Ming!"

"Mingus, honey! You on the show?"

"Just come to listen, Billie."

"Give me some sugar, baby—mmmmm! Want to gig? Norman needs another bass man on the show, you know?"

"That would do me good, Billie."

"How're you doing with your girls?"

"That's all over. It was too much for a man of high degree."

"Solid, baby."

"Remember that song I wrote for you, Billie— 'Eclipse'? You never did sing it."

"Go home and get your bass and bring the song with you. You're working, 'cause I'm the star of the show and I say so."

H, THERE'S NO WAY to describe how my boy feels when he's all tied up inside digging the mood conjured up by a Lady in Philharmonic Hall singing to an audience that's with her every note and innuendo and someone calls a tune that's great and Lady Soul who has already blessed the entire evening with her presence says, "You got it, Mingus, what's your 'Sophisticated Lady' like tonight?" Just pure music, no funny clothes or trick effects, 'cause that Lady's elegant in dress and manner and mind. She *is* the song and the people are pleased and show it with their Bravos! and Encores! After the last curtain call, a few voices call out on the dimly lighted stage—"Be with you in a moment, hon!" . . . "Who's coming for something to eat?"—and Mingus is feeling at home again, packing his bass and waiting for Fats. Two girls come by that he used to know, their names are Bobbie and Jo. They sit on his knees, hugging and saying, "Come with us to Jimbo's!" He thinks he'll save one of them for Fats but Fats has a different girl on his mind, you take her inside your veins in your arm at night when you're alone and Fats can't wait to get home. So Mingus goes with the two girls who are so completely different from the kind of women he's always liked. Bobbie looks straight out of a Turkish harem, dark and curvy, and Jo is tall and strongly built, brunette and huge-breasted. That night, just hanging out together, the memory of Donnalee is banished, at least for a little while.

EXT DAY my boy walked past a man on Fillmore Street whose suit, three sizes too large, hung on him in folds.

"Minkus! Hey, Minkus! Dat-chew, baby?"

"Girl! Fat Girl!"

"Goddamn, Mingus, why you still got to call me Girl? Fats was bad enough. What's wrong with calling me by my name which is Theodore Navarro?"

"I'm sorry, Theodore."

"Well, you can call me Fats now 'cause I'm gettin' skinny and I know you love me, Mingus, you ain't like some them other motherfuckers that don't like me but don't even know it."

"I love you, Mr. Navarro."

"So be sure, 'cause I'm leaving soon."

"Got your bags packed right, Fats?"

"What's that bag schitt you talkin' outta, Ming?"

"Well, if I'm going somewhere I pack up the things I want to take with me."

"I'm going to nothing so I'm taking nothing—but I still ain't afraid to die like you, Mingus."

"That's where we clashed before, Fats, when you took those fifty dexedrines plus a handful of bennies all at once and said 'Fuck God!' You scared me at first till I got it figured out. When you said 'Fuck God' you really said fuck yourself. But since it is the omni-invisible, in order for you to fuck the invisible you have to stick it in yourself 'cause to be fucking nothing but the wind itself is fucking alone by yourself. And since you believe there ain't no God, you're fucking yourself, hurting, killing yourself long before your time. I can't even get you to go see a doctor to see why you're bleeding inside."

"Mingus, I'm bleeding 'cause I want to bleed. I got T.B. intentionally and I'm hoping there ain't no heaven or hell like you say there is. Think how drug I'd be to get there and find the white man owns that too and it's rent-controlled in heaven and hell's the slums. I'd tell them, 'Kill me, white faggot cocksucking angels, like you did down on earth, 'cause you sure ain't gonna get no work or rent from my soul!' Dig it for yourself: unless you let his earthly white angels schitt all over you, you can't even have your soul cleansed white. Like picture me giving my enemy my coat—not in New York City! Not me! Turn *whose* cheek to be smite on the other side! Schitt! Dig how the white man's black Bible is always gonna make some money and make somebody do something! Jeremiah, sixteenth chapter, twenty-first verse—'Behold, I will this once cause them to know, I will cause them to know mine hand and my might and they shall know that my name *is* the Lord.' See, I remember that chapter and verse 'cause I had a girl named Mary and I got her cherry when she was sixteen years old on my twenty-first birthday. That verse shows you right there God is white, 'cause the white man's the only thing I know can cause, make or force people to do his bid—mostly us. I don't dig nobody making me do nothing. I'm about to let God kill me just so I can meet him. And if he's white I don't dig him in the first place or in my place either. Then soon as the white angels Crow me out of heaven I'm gonna take my shiv and peel the devil in his sleep, put on his black skin suit, horns and tail, and stab the white man's god with old Dev's pitchfork right in his fat rich old ass, find his old lady, suck her cunt and fuck her good, then make her kiss me all over my black ass while I beat her with my arrow-pointed tail. See, Mingus? Aw, you look scared for me. Don't be scared if all you believe in don't exist for me. I'll burn for my sins gladly when I know them white cock-suckers so full of hate gonna burn for theirs. Mingus, I still ain't as scared to die as I am to go home to see my mother and family in Florida. You should see all the churches we got out in Key West. The white man's got 'em too, I heard 'em praying once when I was little in some kind of weird tongue. I later found out it was Latin. Imagine! Nigger-hating Southern white man that can't hardly read or write English sitting up in a church looking holy with his big red turkey neck, speaking in Latin! I snuck in back trying to get some of that white man's God-magic-spirit. The priest caught me and you know what he said? God didn't want no little black niggers stinkin' up heaven! That's why when Mary gave me her cherry I was fuckin' and cussin' right in that priest's church under the Virgin's statue and all over his altar, I got that good red ass white pussy hole condoned by the permission of the Southern Catholic Church of Key West, Florida. I also got myself a picture of the Virgin on a Sunday school card and I peed all over it and put it in the suggestion box and Mary and I split out for New York City. . . . Well, Minkus, you gettin' famous back in the Apple?"

"No, no star eyes, Fats, not even for playing there right now. Listen, I asked Max Roach what you meant when we were with Hamp and you said I was helping you carry the stick. Max said, 'Why, Fats was talking about you carrying the cross with him like Simon the black Cyrenian who helped Jesus.' Was he putting me on?"

"Yeah, Ming. Carrying the stick, further than it would go otherwise, that's when you can't get none or you're kicking yourself with no help, carrying yourself dead on your feet without putting that dumb schitt in your arm to make your burden lighter. But it only gets heavier each time you lose your will power and stick yourself again. You're drug with yourself, hate yourself coming and going —you wish you didn't have to get high but you carried the stick so long and so far you know your next sober step alone will be into your grave. After you're high you forget for awhile but the time of forgetting gets shorter and shorter and you up to one and a half grains every four hours. Mingus, I'm over twelve grains a day, day and night, twenty-four hours, 'cause I don't sleep no more. That's two hundred and fifty to two hundred and seventy dollars a day."

"Impossible, Fats—you're putting me on, too."

"No, Mingus, I gotta be serious with somebody. You lucky or something, most cats ain't like you—try schitt three, four times and forget it. I wish I could get turned on with some of that God-junk you got so I don't have to buy no more highs. . . . Hey, Ming, if you gettin' rich back east you sure is cool 'cause you sure is raggedy! You dress like a farmer, a poor farmer ain't got no seeds to plant. Milkman's overhalls, old sweaters—what kind of shoes? Oh, I see *dey* do cos' a nice taste of bread."

"Well, I been getting in a lot of rumbles lately and I guess I'm looking like it. Not long ago I went in a club in New York and started drinking, and suddenly everything just turned white. I started to read ofays' minds and challenged the whole joint. Twenty cats at least, I don't know how I did it. I didn't get a scratch on me, I was so drunk. Tore the raggedy joint up and I still went back in after they barred me out. Maybe I want to die, like you, Fats, but I only feel that way when I'm juiced. In a way these clothes are my protest to Whitey, I don't want him to forget that he don't have to dress ragged. Neither do I, right now, but my underdog brothers can't afford to dress like the white man who comes to hear me play. When they see me ragged, I remind them subconsciously of a poor black farmer ain't got no seeds to plant, like you said. Playing in their expensive drinking joints, I dress like this to remind them who I am. They can't tell me how to dress. If they dress more casual, *I'll* put on evening clothes."

"Mingus, they own us and howeverwhichway you dress ain't gonna make de master free de slaves."

"You leaving tomorrow, Fats? When I'm gonna see you again?"

"I be out here in a coupla months for a record date."

"See you then, Fats?"

"See you then, Minkus."

SO NOW YOU'VE GOT A JOB AGAIN, boy, in a trio, boy, with a famous name. The leader has red hair, boy, and the guitar player is a white man too, from North Carolina. You're playing in San Francisco and making records and the critics are writing good things. Boy! Boy! Boy!

Then you go on the road. How does it feel to drive through the South as a member of an otherwise all-white trio and in addition to that you've got a white girl traveling with you? How do you do it? I'll tell you. First you straighten your hair. That's before you start. You're traveling in two cars and your girl rides with you on the road. But before you get to another town, out on the empty highway your girl changes cars and pretends to be the wife of one of the white men so you can check into hotels. You trade rooms that night and again in the morning so she can walk out with her "husband."

How do you go into restaurants? Your girl and her "husband" go in first, then the leader of the band takes you in, big white-man style. You've got straight hair and your skin isn't too dark and you're in the company of a famous guy. But the bouncer looks right at you, looks at you hard, slamming his fist into his palm again and again. He doesn't say anything but you know what he's thinking and he wants you to know.

How does it feel on your last overnight stop in the South when you find in the morning the two white guys have checked out and you're left there in that hotel, boy, alone with a white woman? It feels very dangerous, that's how it feels. You pack and go downstairs separately not knowing what's going to happen. But thank God nobody says anything, they just *look* at you funny. You get out as fast as you can, get in your car and drive out of that town, and down the road apiece in front of a restaurant you see your leader's car and inside are the two dumb white boys having breakfast.

The trip is almost over so you don't quit. You drive straight through to New York in two cars and go in with this trio to a famous jazz club on the Upper East Side. You want to work and the critics are making it worthwhile— if the bread's low, they at least boost your ego.

How does it feel when the Redhead's trio is asked to do an important, special television show in *color?* It feels great. At night you're playing this first-class club and daytimes you're rehearsing in the studio. One day during a break you're tuning the bass and you see this producer or somebody talking to the Redhead across the room and they're both looking at you. You feel something is wrong but you don't know what. In a few minutes some guy calls out: "That's all for today, tomorrow at ten," and everyone leaves. While you're packing up, the Redhead comes over and says something like this: "Charlie, I'm sorry to tell you but I have to get another bassist for this show.

We'll continue at the club but I can't use you here."
What do you say? You ask the name of the new bassist, of
course. He tells you. The bassist is white. Now what do
you do, curse him out? Probably. You don't remember
what you said. He goes away fast. That night he doesn't
come to the club, he sends word he's sick. After that
somehow you never get a chance to talk to him, he comes
late and cuts out early. You have to find out. You start
going by where he's staying, at a residential hotel on
Broadway. But the desk always says he's not in, they won't
even ring. You never get a chance to discuss it with him.
Schitt, he can't talk anyway—can't talk about anything
real, only about what chick you're going with and like that.
You can't talk to the guitarist about it either, he never says
anything. Two dumb white boys that can't talk to you.
So you quit the trio. How can you play with guys you
can't talk to? You wonder and wonder why he didn't tell
you face to face or why he didn't walk off the TV job—
some leaders would have. He wanted the money too bad.
If he had hired Red Mitchell or somebody like that to re-
place you, you might have even believed it was something
to do with your playing. But what's good in a club is
good anywhere else, wouldn't you think? It didn't take
much to figure it out. The way television was in those
days, they had sponsors who worried about "the Southern
market" and "mixing" was taboo.

Yeah, there are certain things in this life that nobody
likes to talk about. Nobody white, that is.

So what do you do after that? Maybe you get a job
with the Duke himself. This is The Hero, and this is the
band you don't quit, but this time you're asked to leave

because of an incident with a trombone player and ar-
ranger named Juan Tizol. Tizol wants you to play a solo
he's written where bowing is required. You raise the solo
an octave, where the bass isn't too muddy. He doesn't like
that and he comes to the room under the stage where
you're practicing at intermission and comments that
you're like the rest of the niggers in the band, you can't
read. You ask Juan how he's different from the other
niggers and he states that one of the ways he's different is
that HE IS WHITE. So you run his ass upstairs. You leave
the rehearsal room, proceed toward the stage with your
bass and take your place and at the moment Duke brings
down the baton for "A-Train" and the curtain of the Apollo
Theatre goes up, a yelling, whooping Tizol rushes out and
lunges at you with a bolo knife. The rest you remember
mostly from Duke's own words in his dressing room as he
changes after the show.

"Now, Charles," he says, looking amused, putting
Cartier links into the cuffs of his beautiful handmade shirt,
"you could have forewarned me—you left me out of the
act entirely! At least you could have let me cue in a few
chords as you ran through that Nijinsky routine. I con-
gratulate you on your performance, but why didn't you
and Juan inform me about the adagio you planned so that
we could score it? I must say I never saw a large man so
agile—I never saw *anybody* make such tremendous leaps!
The gambado over the piano carrying your bass was
colossal. When you exited after that I thought, 'That
man's really afraid of Juan's knife and at the speed he's
going he's probably home in bed by now.' But no, back
you came through the same door with your bass still in-

tact. For a moment I was hopeful you'd decided to sit down and play but instead you slashed Juan's chair in two with a fire axe! Really, Charles, that's destructive. Everybody knows Juan has a knife but nobody ever took it seriously—he likes to pull it out and show it to people, you understand. So I'm afraid, Charles—I've never fired anybody—you'll have to quit my band. I don't need any new problems. Juan's an old problem, I can cope with that, but you seem to have a whole bag of new tricks. I must ask you to be kind enough to give me your notice, Mingus."

The charming way he says it, it's like he's paying you a compliment. Feeling honored, you shake hands and resign.

What do you do after that? You start with the gigs again. Maybe you go to Boston and play a tiddy at Storyville. And in Boston you meet a very sensitive cat named Nat Hentoff who interviews you on his radio show and turned out to be one of the few white guys you could really talk to in your life. Afterwards you get in the habit of writing to him from time to time when you're feeling the pain in the middle of the night and the larger questions that seem to have no answers loom up before your eyes but Hentoff always digs the meaning of the question and replies, all in caps on yellow paper like a story off the wires.

CHARLIE, THIS IS WHAT I THINK: LOVE, THE DIFFI-CULTIES OF REAL COMMUNICATION, THE REASON FOR WANTING TO HAVE A REASON FOR STAYING ALIVE, THESE HAVE CONCERNED ME TOO EVER SINCE I CAN REMEMBER.

I LAY NO CLAIM TO HAVING ACHIEVED ANY ROCK-LIKE EQUILIBRIUM NOR TO HAVE ANSWERED THE QUESTIONS FOR ANYONE BUT MYSELF. BUT SO FAR THIS IS WHAT I VE FOUND. THE REASON FOR HATING OTHERS IS HATE OF ONESELF, FEELING THE SELF IS INADEQUATE IN SOME VAGUE OR SPECIFIC WAY, AND PROJECTING THAT TO OTHER OBJECTS. HATE IS A DESTRUCTIVE EMOTION IN-CAPABLE OF DOING ANY GOOD OR CREATING ANYTHING AND DESTROYS THE MAN WHO HATES MORE PAINFULLY AND THOROUGHLY THAN THE MAN HE HATES. THE MAN WHO HATES DOESN T REALIZE EVERYONE ELSE IS AS COMPLEX AS HE KNOWS HIMSELF TO BE. NOT THAT THERE AREN T MANY PEOPLE WHO DO EVIL THINGS AND IN THAT RESPECT ARE EVIL. . . . BUT WHAT MADE THEM THAT WAY? NO ONE IS BORN TO DESTROY. THIS IS SOUNDING MORALISTIC, A TONE I TRY TO AVOID, BUT BE-CAUSE WE KNOW EACH OTHER SO WELL IF MAINLY THROUGH LETTERS I LL GO ON. AT THE POINT A GUY BE-GINS TO REALIZE THE AMAZING EXTENT OF HIS OWN POTENTIALITY HE BEGINS TO KNOW HE S BEEN WASTING PAIN AND ENERGY IN BLAMING HIMSELF AND HATING OTHERS FOR THINGS THAT HAVE BEEN, THAT WERE DONE, THAT WERE NOT DONE, TO HIMSELF, TO A RACE, TO A UNI-VERSE. AT THAT POINT HE SEES THAT LIFE, AS CHAPLIN SAYS, IS A DESIRE NOT A MEANING, WHICH IS WHY A ROSE OR A BIRD HAS TO BE. AFTER ACCEPTING THE SHEER PLEAS-URE OF WALKING AND BREATHING AND SEEING A SKY, THEN THE QUESTION OF MEANING ARISES.

FOR ME A MAN S MEANING, THE REASON HE HAS TO KEEP ON LIVING, IS THAT WERE HE TO LIVE THOUSANDS OF YEARS HE WOULD NEVER FULFILL ALL HIS POSSIBILITIES,

NEVER COMMUNICATE OR CREATE ALL HE IS CAPABLE OF.
SO HE MUST USE WHAT TIME HE HAS CREATING NOW FOR
THE FUTURE AND UTILIZE THE PAST ONLY TO HELP THE
FUTURE, NOT AS A RAZOR STROP FOR GUILTS AND FEARS
THAT INHIBIT HIS VERY BEING. OR LIKE IT SAID AT THE
END OF A LABOR UNION SONG I LIKED A LOT WHEN I WAS A
KID: WHAT I MEAN IS, TAKE IT EASY, BUT TAKE IT.

I DON T KNOW IF THIS HAS MADE SENSE OR IS OF ANY USE
BUT IT S WHAT I THINK.   NAT.

34

"HELLO, NAT, I'M IN BELLEVUE, I can't talk long. There's a Nazi-thinking Jew called Dr. Bonk or something down here saying all Negroes are paranoid and he knows just the treatment for them, which is frontal lobotomy. He's a prejudiced white cocksucker so high on white supremacy that he's blowing the whole U.S.A. scene on integration singlehanded. Nat, I'm scared and they won't let me leave. You got to get me out of here—"

"Wait, wait, Charles! How'd you get yourself in there in the first place?"

"If you have a toothache you go to a dentist and I thought if you have head problems you come down here."

"Didn't you call your analyst?"

"I couldn't remember his number."

"I'll do all I can, Charlie, you know that. I'll call him, and who's your attorney?"

"Marvin Karpatkin."

"Okay. Anyone else?"

"Nat, do you ever see Donna or Lee-Marie? Tell them I'm down here. Please."

"I haven't run into them in a long time, Charles. Someone said Lee-Marie got married and Donna was living with some guy in France."

"Nat, see if you can find out if either one of them's in town."

"Of course, Charles—hang on there, don't worry, try to rest."

S THAT REALLY why you didn't call me the night you went to Bellevue, Charles? You couldn't remember my number?"

"I don't know, Dr. Wallach."

"As it happens, I was away for those few days— perhaps it was just as well? . . . Try to talk, Charles, come on, man, open up and talk to me."

"Nothing don't want to come out."

"Try."

"I was angry. You were gaming with me. When I broke two appointments you wrote and said I couldn't come back, don't you remember that? You cancelled me out. Doctor, you're everything I could be myself if I could just find my hang-out, my notch on the stick, my crowd of people. I didn't want to impose on you after you said that and besides I owed you money. Of course, I didn't know what Bellevue would mean—I thought they just put you to bed and let you rest. I was sped up, tired out, I couldn't think who I was, I wanted to lay down and sleep. I was like a child lost with people milling all around me and no one to love me. My brain was like a crazy TV set flicking picture stories in color and black-and-white. I could see faces and bodies, speaking out to me—Barbara, my chil-

dren, Donna and Lee-Marie, agents, club-owners, you.
. . . I walked by Birdland and thought I'd go in and talk
to some of the cats but I cancelled out on that idea, they
wouldn't understand. I decided if I called anybody they'd
think I was only trying to get sympathy and attention. I
kept on walking across town, trying to think what in hell
I'd done with my life. At least I'd made about fifteen albums of my own and hundreds of records and played in
more clubs and concerts and was recognized high on more
polls than I could remember, and did some good writing
and work with people I liked. Not long before I worked
with a poet named Patchen. He was wearing his scarlet
jacket and sitting on a stool on a little stage in a theater
you walk upstairs to down on Fourteenth Street. We improvised behind him while he read his poems, which I
studied ahead of time. 'It's dark out, Jack—' this was one
of his poems—'It's dark out, Jack, the stations out there
don't identify themselves, we're in it raw-blind like burned
rats, it's running out all around us, the footprints of the
beast, one nobody has any notion of. The white and vacant eyes of something above there, something that
doesn't know we exist. I smell heartbreak up there, Jack,
a heartbreak at the center of things, and in which we don't
figure at all.' Patchen's a real artist, you'd dig him, doctor.
'I believe in the truth,' he said, 'I believe that every good
thought I have, all men shall have. I believe that the perfect shape of everything has been prepared.' Anyway, I
kept walking east on Fifty-first Street and turned down
on First Avenue, I guess I knew where I was going. I
remember it was late and cold and I don't think I was
even wearing a jacket. I kept on till I saw the gates of

Bellevue Hospital. There was a guy in a sort of booth or sentry-box and I went to him and asked him how to get in. He wouldn't open the gates, we talked through the bars. I said, 'Look, man, I haven't slept in three weeks,' and he said, 'This is no rest home, this place is for the mentally disturbed.' 'Look, man,' I said, 'I *am* mentally disturbed. I'm a musician, I need help, and I once saw a film that said if you need help the first and most difficult task is having the guts to ask for it, so help me, man!' The gatekeeper said, 'I done told you this is not where you want to go if you just sleepy. I can see from here you look a little tired, so go home, man, and go to bed. Ain't crazy or nothing, are you?' I said, 'Maybe I am, maybe I'm not.' And he said, 'Well, take my word for it, you don't want to come in *here*. If I was to let you in first thing you'd say when I close that door behind you is *Lemme out, I ain't crazy!* . . . How'd you say you feel?' 'Like I'm walking on air, man. But when I lay down I can't sleep.' 'Ever think of killing yourself?' 'Not seriously but if I don't get some sleep I might.' 'Ever think you could hurt somebody else?' 'Only if they hurt me first.' It was about midnight when I arrived—I stood and begged that guard to let me in till the sky was getting light. He was a big black man and he still spoke polite when he opened the gate and told me to come on. As soon as I got to the second door I could sense the difference—like 'Surprise, stupid! We been waiting on you, a real special case!' My friend the guard said, 'Bill, here's that crazy one,' and two big white guys in white coats, six-footers, over two hundred pounds apiece, had me in a strait jacket before I knew it and I'm telling the guard, 'Maybe you were right, I don't feel so bad after all.' 'What you mean, you don't feel so bad!' he yelled at me. 'You calling *me* crazy? Ain't I heard you for six-and-one-half hours beggin' to be let in here?' And one of the whitecoats said: 'Come on, Bill, let's get this nut up to the cell block.' Right that second I knew Bellevue wasn't the right place to go and cry help, 'cause their idea was to *scare* people back to normal."

"Were you angry, Charles?"

"No. Anger is an emotion that has some hope in it. I felt hopeless. The gateman was so polite and proper as long as I was outside but now I was in the looney bin and I saw I'd been fooled so I went quiet and didn't offer any counter-moves. They took me to a little room next to a ward. The lights were all on and through the glass I could see hundreds of people in there asleep. Bill took the strait jacket off me and said, 'Get undressed and put these on,'— meaning pajamas with a top that snaps in the back and a bathrobe and some cotton slippers. There was a desk where they kept medication and he gave me a pill and said, 'Get some rest. It's an hour or two to breakfast.' 'Breakfast! I'm not hungry! I haven't slept in three weeks! Can't you let me get some sleep?' He said, 'Whattya think this is, a hotel? When that bell goes, it's everybody on their feet, up and moving!' He took me to a bunk bed in the ward. People were groaning and snoring and crying all around. I asked him, 'Can't I have a quiet room?' He said, 'The private rooms are padded cells. Want one?' I really wouldn't have cared if I could have slept. It seemed like two minutes later a huge loud bell blasted off in my ear and there was a crescendo of sound, people coming to life, everybody getting up. I hadn't even closed my eyes. I followed the crowd to the washrooms. The attendants were cold and standoffish and kept their distance like they thought craziness was a contagious disease. I couldn't eat any breakfast. I wanted to phone someone, anyone, to get me out of there but they wouldn't let me. After a few hours they took me in to see a short dumpy man, built like Winston Churchill, with a round, shiny bald head and a name that sounded like Dr. Bonk. He was wearing a hearing aid, and I was so tired I could hardly hear *him* asking questions. He kept saying, 'We are here at Bellevue to help you,' and 'I am from another country, Switzerland.' I had a small fatty tumor on my arm and he found needle marks from the shots the reducing doctor was giving me. Right away he asked if I was a junkie. I tried to explain but he didn't believe me, I could tell by the way his eyes looked at me behind his rimless glasses. Then I heard him say to the other doctor, 'Negroes are paranoiac, unrealistic people who believe the whole world is against them.' I said, 'Tell me, doctor, do you mean all Negroes on this earth or only the Negroes in this room?' He said, 'I see I'm getting through to Mingus now,' and I said, 'That you are, Herr Doktor. Tell me, is this paranoia we all have curable?' And he said, 'Yes, this is what I am so happy to tell you. I can cure this disease with a simple operation on the frontal lobe, called a lobotomy, and then you'll be all right.' So here I am on my first day in Bellevue and nobody knows where I am and before lunch I'm told Negroes are paranoiac and threatened with a lobotomy!"

"Did you know what a lobotomy was, Charles?"

"Yeah, that's why I was so scared. I read a piece about it in *Life* Magazine a long time back and I thought 'Now I know what Bud Powell meant by his tune 'Glass Enclosure' —they didn't have to cut the front of *his* head off to teach him to shield himself from the devils.' Oh, I was definitely afraid of Dr. Bonk, he was too eager to pounce on me and carve out a piece of my mental unrest. When I left that maniac's office I knew I was going to get in touch with the outside if I had to break in somewhere to use a phone. I felt totally alone. Then I saw The Dancer, tap-tap-tapping down the corridor just like on Fifty-first Street, only now he was wearing pajamas and a bathrobe like me and it crossed my mind that since he was one of us paranoid, unrealistic black men he might have been in here before and got himself fixed up by Herr Doktor which might account for his behavior. I kept trying doors until I found an empty office with a phone and I went in and called Nat. I felt a little better after that but later in the afternoon they told me I'd have to stay in there ten days for observation, because of the needle marks. I walked around . . . and around . . . that's what people do at Bellevue, they walk around. I found an art room with watercolors and oil paintings done by former inmates and saw a painting they said Monk did—I think it was an apple and a hatchet. The perspective was like a professional—I never knew Monk could paint. I borrowed a pencil and paper— you could sit down at the tables where we ate—and tried to write something that would make some sense."

I have not vanished or given up music although to many it may seem that I have. For whatever reason, the only albums of my recordings that have been recently made available to the public are at least three years old. I have worked in a few jazz clubs lately but from the people outside New York who have liked my music I have gotten letters wondering where I disappeared to. Before and during this apparent layoff from productivity, however, I have been producing as always and perhaps more because there were few to hear my voice and my need is to express my thoughts and feelings as fully as is humanly possible all the time. I have worked and I have produced music that has not been played and I have written words that have not been read. . . .

"But I couldn't concentrate in there, doctor. There was a boy sitting across the table from me reading a book on mathematics—I could see the equations and symbols. I saw him walking around earlier that morning—very tall and gangly, sandy-haired, only about eighteen years old. I later learned he was a champion chess player and spoke seven languages. He was a genius, I guess. His parents had him committed, he told me, but he didn't say why. He didn't seem to mind, he was quiet and good-natured and always busy doing something. When he saw me looking at him he asked if I wanted to play a game of chess and he brought out his board. I showed him what I just wrote. He looked very thoughtful and said, 'I don't have time to hear everything but I'm interested in music and keep abreast of what's happening. It's odd you say you haven't been productive. It seems to me you have several—let's see—' and he counted in his head—'I'd say six or seven albums that came out last year. That isn't bad.' I was amazed, but he was right and I realized last year seemed like ten years ago to me. He checkmated me three times in a row and I could see he was getting bored so I went back to my bunk and tried to write some poetry. A good title came to my mind—'Nice of You to Have Come to My Funeral.' 'Blues is a man on an icy cold night, walking an eternity, site to site, Sutton Place or Bowery, living. No! Not living. He is that memory alive but not sharing, living the sight that we see alive and living. Content? Why ridicule? He sleeps on armed-in pillows in spilled pee, piss splashed to the gutters not or even not as his own knowingless leaks soaked to his clothed groin and seeped on in through the clothed rest of him. Smelling even in his mooched coin that is turned to paper seldom, in change for his reason, drink, life's answers to ever-knowing, dare he did with women, wine, song, dance or drug-out. Old cold facts sounds, he is of breathing living in off moments of extravagant blessed love moments, all lies, lying of untruth to each other than unfortunately came together and hated truths of it all, inside or out, depending that is assuming he is not a she. Oh damn it all blues. Screwed to the melting frozen walk of dared-to-embrace stone, concrete hard, imagined soft only to overdue erections of loneliness that turned feminine and speaks back wet, warm tears, not too far removed from its common denominator, iced urine melting at dared hot death that clings to life for love at thought of some response, be it only the clay, dirt or pavement I behold in my drunken fevered search for a true woman's groin, wanting me as I want her, to never hate me because we found refuge of satisfaction as two drunken stones warmed themselves side by side, in outside our guttered ideas of opposite sides fucking.' Do you understand that poem, Doctor Wallach?"

"Well, Charles, it certainly is a very personal expression."

35

"BY THE SECOND DAY at Bellevue I was crazy for sleep. I don't sleep at night like other people do and in the daytime the minute you lay down there somebody sends for you. Nobody would give me a pill but I went back to my bunk after breakfast anyway. Right away I hear MINGUS! PAGING MR. MINGUS! Oh, schitt, now what, more Dr. Bonk? But this time it was a young intern who turned out to be my lawyer's brother. Damn, was I glad to see him! I said, 'Doctor, I want to thank all of you for this experience which will live with me for the rest of my life. I actually feel I've been born again. Now will you let me out of here so I can go home and pull down the shades and get some rest?' He was very nice but he said, 'I don't think they'll let you go just yet, Charlie. They tell me you tried pretty hard to get in and you've only been here a couple of days. Why don't you get some good out of it?' I told him I couldn't see any good coming out of being locked up and I knew my own doctor could help me more. 'We're here at Bellevue to help you, Charlie,' he said— that seemed to be the slogan around there—'but you sit down and write out the reasons you think your own doctor would be better.' So I went back to my bunk and wrote it."

WHY THIS IS NOT AS GOOD AS BEING
TREATED PRIVATELY BY MY OWN
PSYCHOLOGIST

or

HELLVIEW OF BELLEVUE

1. The time schedule alone is enough to destroy a night worker like me. They shout in my ear to get up before I even get to sleep.

2. Some kind of bugs are leaving marks all over me. They itch.

3. The toilets are a drag. Men vomit and stand or stoop over the seats during bowel movements and miss their aim when they urinate. I have long been removed from filth, dirt, homosexuals and criminals. I am a composer.

4. Dr. Bonk keeps saying I am a failure. I did not come here to discuss my career or I would have brought a press agent.

5. I know now the reason I came was a childish protest against my doctor because when I missed two weeks in a row he wrote and said he could hold no more time open for me.

6. Dr. Bonk talks to me two minutes at a time and hurries me off. What does he expect me to say in two minutes? When I ask for more time he complains he is over-worked and the wards are overcrowded. My doctor is not overworked and his office is not overcrowded and he does not do all the talking.

7. I have learned my lesson. Let me have my freedom. Thank you and good-bye.

338

"Well, that was nice of you, Charles, to say those things about me."

"That's all right, Dr. Wallach, it was true. When I went to the office to turn it in the Chess Champ was sitting on a bench waiting for an interview. That boy always seemed about as *together* as anybody could be. He had a portable radio with him and he said there was some good Bartok on and I could borrow it for a while."

Dear Nat, bulletin from Bellevue. I've seen this point in my life coming and I need to know someone human understands, not mechanical men paid to listen and trained to react—a *machine* fed the same information could come up with just as good an analysis of my problems. I've just been listening to Bartok quartets and wow! It's not the composer so much that prompted this writing as the musicians—the players, as Rhein-schagen used to say. Their names were not announced, just "The Juilliard String Quartet." That's the way it should be. They're good, good players and their names are unimportant except they must live somewhere in houses with street numbers and telephone numbers that one needs to reach them, to ask them to play another man's music sometime—maybe mine, if I had anything worthy. They are good, very good, close to perfection, very important men. They have the ability to transform in a second a listener's soul and make it throb with love and beauty—just by following the scratches of a pen on a scroll. Hearing artists like this reminds me of my original goal but a thing called "jazz" took me far off the path and I don't know if I'll

ever get back. I am a good composer with great possibilities and I made an easy success through jazz but
it wasn't really success—jazz has too many strangling
qualities for a composer. I wonder if there are *any* jazz
players as fine as these cats. Something's so wrong it's
pitiful. We have children on stage, acclaimed, who
can barely play. I myself and all the other jazz bassists
should be able to play cello or even viola parts in the
most difficult chamber music but the incentive to play
at that peak in this country is not there. (This is not to
say that these men doing the near-impossible with the
bow would all be able to keep a swinging four-four
beat like jazz men.) But if music lovers knew the
wealth of talent being wasted in the name of jazz
they'd storm the managers' and bookers' offices and
tell them they refuse to settle for the crap they're getting! How many jazz musicians would stay in the clubs
if they could even make a *living* playing in parks and
simple places without the big build-up that's now an
absolute necessity for survival? Tote that Down Beat,
win that poll, hope I get a mention before I'm too old!
Oh, to be the nameless member of a quartet like I
heard today! If I want it right, Nat, guess I'll have to
leave jazz—that word leaves room for too much fooling.

Chazz.

36

"ON THE THIRD DAY at Bellevue I was sitting in the gymnasium writing a song called 'All the Things You Could Be by Now If Sigmund Freud's Wife Was Your Mother,' which I later recorded, when who should walk in but Donnalee—yeah, sweet-and-hot marshmallow-and-chocolate walked right in. It was the strangest feeling to see them after so long, I'd almost forgotten how beautiful they were. They looked unshook by the whole scene of all the loonies jumping around playing basketball and people gibbering in the halls. For me Bellevue stopped existing in the presence of their beauty. It seemed impossible to believe what these women had once been in my life. I felt so complimented that they had come to see me and so proud that I showed them off like a father or a brother."

"I'm interested, Charles, that you now speak so well of Donnalee. Remember after you left them you called them stupid brawds, hopeless creatures, and said they were deliberately destroying you?"

"I had to blame them. The truth is, doctor, I'm insecure and I'm black and I'm scared to death of poverty and especially poverty alone. I'm helpless without a

341

woman, afraid of tomorrow. But I was the stupid one,
because what Lee-Marie and Donna did was for real and
I could never do it. I could never any way end up on my
back spread-eagle and know how it feels doing it for him
who has the price. It was easy to be proud and feel contempt and say to those beautiful women 'I don't want your
dirty money!' I never knew how it felt and never had to
do it that way for the rent man or anybody else. So that
was one good thing that happened in Bellevue, having a
feeling of love and respect for them again and being glad
they found good lives for themselves, 'cause they were
both married and Donna had a baby. I don't know where
they are now. . . . . The fourth day I had to do
something so I hunted up Chess Champ and found him
sitting on the hall steps looking at a folding pocket chess-
board he had on his lap and listening to his radio with an
ear-plug. I said, 'Hey there, Chess!' and he just raised his
palm to me without looking up. After awhile he moved a
wooden peg and stuck it in another hole in the board and
said 'Hello, Charlie.' I told him I had an idea. 'Why don't
you and me and The Dancer get all these nuts together
and start up a school? Look around at these poor bastards,
look at all this confusion. Between the three of us we got a
university—math, chess, languages, music, dancing.' He
said, 'Sure, Charlie, that's a good idea.' So I went looking
for The Dancer and there he was, bobbing around the
ward, PAP TE DAP TE, RUBE DE TAP DE BAP TE. 'Dancer,'
I asked him, 'would you teach a group of fellows the
time-step in a class Chess and I are forming?' Poor old
Dancer was so tickled. His head lolled around and he
said, 'Ug hug! Yea! Yea! Yea!' I went to one of the nurses

and told her we needed a room and a blackboard and what we were going to do. She said, 'Oh, I think that's just fine! I'll put in the order for tomorrow.' But it wasn't an hour later that Dr. Bonk sent for me. He was waiting in his office with some other doctors and they asked me what these plans were all about and why. I said to keep people from going to waste in this place. Dr. Bonk raised his eyebrows and looked at the others and spoke as if I wasn't even there. 'Mr. Mingus is going to organize Bellevue for us. May I comment that compulsive organization is one of the prime traits of paranoia.' I left, and we didn't get our classroom or blackboard and Dancer went on weaving and tapping up and down the halls and Chess Champ talked to himself in seven languages and I went back to composing by solfeggio and writing down my thoughts."

My music is evidence of my soul's will to live beyond my sperm's grave, my metathesis or eternal soul's new encasement. Loved and lovers, oneness, love. Conception, one and one is two is four, eight, sixteen, thirty-two equals you. Youman, human, newman, new man. Me. My I's personal private sacred knowing the moment of coming together with my creator or all creations' I, as one, knowing God, living as life itself for love of loving to do so and living with this, its own life secret, in and again of life loving itself, loving of life itself for good and evil because it is beautiful to have this life in itself alive, to grow, see it be it watch it love it, and know it is I and you that make it so as we each love it in our way. And that is why it is that thought came to be in us human beings that can know if we care to

that we are that secret knowing of the sacred conception as two opposites in force of love's expression grew
in a togetherness out of the nothingnesses of empty
space and times and this our universe of knowing and
talking about it all is where the womb of the creative
knowledge lay to all the knowledges of life or death.
Alone lonely lonesome life living alive and caring to
commune or speak with itself of its sacred knowing of
its own creation cannot speak to itself except through
its mind in us of its personal sacred secrets of knowing
and not knowing life was born out of nothingness, time
in space, or an I and an I and an I that we do compre-
hend, but it is impossible that it came to be other than I
plus *the* I equals a new I of mating of something and
nothingness of two or love *and* loving to do so and born
alive to this life as one knowing its beginning as no more
threat as its knowing, and its knowing has no more ending than its beginning from nothing to nothing but
knowing all the while the eternities' incarnation is proof
of my lives' graves and incarnations.

37

THEN IT SEEMED that days went by, my boy no longer counted, but one afternoon he found himself facing a lady across a desk in an office he had never been called to before. She was an attractive woman, a staff psychiatrist or possibly even head of the department, obviously someone important, and her name was Dr. Jewel. She looked at him with sympathy as he sat there in his bunchy bathrobe.

"Mr. Mingus, I understand the complexities life can hold for a person in the professional world but somehow we must go on living and solve our problems in this life by ourselves, isn't that so? I talked with your psychologist outside, Dr. Wallach, and we decided you could be released in the custody of a relative. If there is anyone related to you here in the city, you may call them now if you care to."

"I'll call my uncle in Brooklyn. His name is Fess Williams."

"He is truly a relative?"

"He's married to my mother's sister. I hope you don't need a birth certificate or marriage license or a writ of habeas corpus, Dr. Jewel?"

She smiled very gently. "We are only trying to help you here at Bellevue."

NFORMATION, give me the number of Fess Williams, three sixty-five Waltham Street, Jamaica, Long Island. Hey, Phil?—Mingus. Where's Fess? Oh, schitt, well, you'll do. Come on over to Bellevue and sign me out, will you? Not tomorrow—*now!* —okay, doctor? Okay, Cousin Phil, see you later. . . . Excuse me, Doctor Jewel, I can't wait to get into my own clothes."

EY, PHIL, isn't it beautiful being crazy? That view from Bellevue is *no* view compared to the view from this here window which is wild! Only thing missing down there on the street is The Dancer, who probably don't have nobody to spring him, poor motherfucker. Pass that jug of wine."

"Yeah, Cousin Charles. Let's call some chicks over and have a ball."

"Later, Phil, I gotta get used to freedom. Speaking of chicks, know something? I could be living the life of kings but I just couldn't make the scene."

"What scene's that, Chazz?"

"Never mind. I'll bet you there's a heaven and hell, cousin."

"Let's bet on something you can lay the results down."

"Well, then, let's drink to death—that's where they're both at. So later with that guessing game and that believing bag, right now I just want to rest over from resting. I'm tired of thinking over what's none of my business. You know Timmy Rogers, Phil?"

"Pass the wine. Sure, I know Timmy. 'Everybody's talkin' 'bout heaven but nobody wants to die,' that's Timmy's song."

"You know, I believe Bellevue did me some good. How could anybody outside bug me when I remember those closed-in helpless people? Everywhere I go I'll take those bars with me in my mind."

"Why you going to do that, man?"

"Those bars stand for power over others, the power to make you hold still and take it. Is that why I feel so much better out here where the real insanity is? See that guy down there, waiting to cross the street? Look at his face, he could be planning a murder, probably is. I wonder what will happen to The Dancer and Chess—if they're crazy they're not crazy like *that*. There was one old man who had conversations all day on a make-believe telephone with President Eisenhower. Guys in the ward would get tired of listening to him rapping on the red line and yell, 'Cut it out! You got no phone there!' He'd look at them with such pity and say, 'You mean you ain't never seen one of these little phones? You can talk to anybody you want to anywhere in the world. The President got one. He can hear me and I can hear him!' "

"Maybe he *could* hear the President, Chazz."

"That's possible, Phil, it's possible. Let's go down to the corner restaurant and get us some of that French cuisine—it'll really shake you up!"

THE FAST BUCK IS PACKED AS USUAL and several cars with chauffeurs are waiting outside, parked against the mountains of snow piled up in the dark streets, with motors running to keep the drivers warm. My boy is back playing in a small club deep in the warehouse district on the Lower West Side of Manhattan. Bellevue seems far in the past, Dr. Wallach is again in charge of his head and women are his escape from reality.

The club is definitely the place this season for society and college girls from New York and out-of-town who want to have a fling at life via the bandstand or the single male customers who press around the bar and it's nothing wild to walk in on a crowded night and find Mingus at a table with half a dozen girls huddled around him or sitting on his knees or him perching on theirs. The owner, Mr. Caligari, calls him son and his two sons call my boy brother and they've given him a contract saying he can always return with his group anytime he chooses no matter who's playing there. These days Charles feels wholly free and not only as good as any white people but better than most and he's found a musical home, a place to play for people who really seem to want to hear.

But there's lumps in everything in this life. My boy can't help having a hunch that the Police Department really enjoys harassing any club where a healthy integrated feeling is a little too out in the open—like the night he sees through a crack from a cubicle in the men's room a uniformed policeman remove and pocket a bar of soap from the washbasin. As soon as the cop walks out my boy finds himself a sliver, quickly lathers his face and runs out to face Mr. Blue writing up a no-soap-in-the-men's-room citation. Perhaps he suspects it the night another cop walks up outside the big street window, pulls out his penis and pisses right in front of the customers, or when still another one is seen unobtrusively dropping a cigarette butt on the floor, "discovering" it and then writing out a ticket for violation. Perhaps it's the presents of money in brown paper bags going out of the place as "sandwiches" to cops on the beat, and what he sees written all over fuzz faces when he's making what some folks call free with the white ladies. Maybe it doesn't go down well either when he talks about all these things and doesn't care who hears.

Tonight the tall, blue-eyed student nurse with short blonde hair and the kind of bony face he's always liked is sitting at Table Four with her two girlfriends. They've come all the way in from White Plains to hear Mingus and they're in high spirits. When he joins them between sets there's much laughter over very little. She's in her twenties, her father is a milkman, she's going to nursing school in Westchester, she loves jazz, her name is Judy. My boy asks if he can drive her home. All the way to *Westchester?*— groovy, but he'll have to take Roxanne and Mary Lou home too, okay? And she flirts and asks him a lot of fresh questions. He loves her jovial attitude. But she becomes quiet and listens with interest when the English critic comes over and asks for an interview. "Do excuse me, Mr. Mingus, I can see you're awfully busy, but may I ask a question or two for my paper? For instance, what do you feel about jazz?" "Man, just listen, it's all there." "No, actually, they'd like to know what you think in England, just a few words?" "Well . . . I can tell you how I feel tonight anyway. Up to now, I don't think *nobody* has given *nothing* important since Bird died except his contemporaries who were overlooked at the time—Monk, Max, Rollins, Bud, others, maybe even me. Bird was playing then what they're calling avant-garde today—putting major sevenths with minor sevenths, playing a fourth away from the key, things like that, and people would say he squeaked. Well, now they hear what those squeaks meant. All this free-form business isn't new—dropping bar lines and all. I was doing it and Duke before me and Jelly Roll before that. I wrote 'What Love' back in '42 and played it with Buddy Collette and Britt Woodman and just recently some horn men looked at it and said it couldn't be played—too freaky, too hard."

"How would you characterize the kind of music you play now?"

"There once was a word used—swing. Swing went in one direction, it was linear, and everything had to be played with an obvious pulse and that's very restrictive. But I use the term 'rotary perception.' If you get a mental picture of the beat existing within a circle you're more free to improvise. People used to think the notes had to fall on the center of the beats in the bar at intervals like a metronome, with three or four men in the rhythm section accenting the same pulse. That's like parade music or dance music. But imagine a circle surrounding each beat— each guy can play his notes anywhere in that circle and it gives him a feeling he has more space. The notes fall anywhere inside the circle but the original feeling for the beat isn't changed. If one in the group loses confidence, somebody hits the beat again. The pulse is inside you. When you're playing with musicians who think this way you can do anything. Anybody can stop and let the others go on. It's called strolling. In the old days when we got arrogant players on the stand we'd do that—just stop playing and a bad musician would be thrown."

"What about the Mingus extended forms?"

"I've been using extended forms and prolonged chords for years and I wasn't the first with that either. I got ideas from Spanish and Arab music. And much more can be done with pedal points—you know, notes sustained underneath changing harmonies but above these notes the keys can be varied so you get all kinds of effects." My boy put his foot against Judy's under the table. "Is that all?" he asked the Englishman.

"What about British jazz? Have we got the feeling?"

"If you're talking about technique, musicianship, I guess the British can be as good as anybody else. But what do they need to play jazz for? It's the American Negro's tradition, it's his music. White people don't have a right to play it, it's colored folk music. When I was learning bass with Rheinschagen he was teaching me to play classical music. He said I was close but I'd never really get it. So I took some Paul Robeson and Marian Anderson records to my next lesson and asked him if he thought *those* artists had got it. He said they were *Negroes trying* to sing music that was foreign to them. Solid, so white society has its own traditions, let 'em leave ours to us. You had your Shakespeare and Marx and Freud and Einstein and Jesus Christ and Guy Lombardo but we came up with *jazz*, don't forget it, and all the pop music in the world today is from that primary cause. British cats listen to our records and copy them, why don't they develop something of their own? White cats take our music and make more money out of it than we ever did or do now! My friend Max Roach has been voted best drummer in many polls but he's offered less than half of what Buddy Rich gets to play the same places—what kind of schitt is that? The commercial people are so busy selling what's hot commercially they're choking to death the goose that's laid all them golden eggs. They killed Lester and Bird and Fats Navarro and they'll kill more, probably me. I'll never make money and I'll always suffer 'cause I shoot off my mouth about agents and crooks and that's all I feel like saying tonight!"

My boy gets up thinking now what did I get into that for? He doesn't like to talk on serious subjects when he's working, it interrupts the natural mood that should sustain itself between sets, so he goes back to the bandstand angry, calls the first number—"Hellview of Bellevue!"—and stomps off a furiously fast tempo. The musicians respond with a great burst of power, the horns run unbelievable frantic phrases leaping up and down octaves, tied to whole-note end phrases. It's an insane set.

At closing time the student nurse and her friends are still waiting. He drives the other girls home first because this Judy laughs a lot and makes him laugh and besides, she's exciting. But she cries a little and touches his heart when she tells him she's just broken up with her boyfriend, whose name was Charles too. They agree that much as they need the opposite gender neither of them will *ever* be in love again and that the ideal life is a peaceful, friendly relationship with plenty of sex. By dawn, still riding around near the student nurses' quarters, they're saying they're obviously the kind of people who should be married to each other.

"What would you do," Judy asks my boy, "if you had your life to live all over again?"

"That's easy," Mingus says. "I'd become a pimp, bigger and better than my cousin Billy Bones out in San Francisco. I wouldn't get involved with music or women at all, other than what they could do for me. My main motive for living would be getting money to buy my way out of a decaying society that's destroying itself while it tries to figure out what to do with the new kind of 'black' it produced. But I'd have nothing to do with black or white, I'd be a member of the raceless people of this earth. When one part of this uncivilized society got around to blowing up the others I'd be in some other country eating caviar and reading the news for the sole purpose of finding out where to move next to keep one jump ahead of the assholes who want to fight. But I'd keep me a loaded forty-five in event of any personal affront and my whores would be non-racist and agree fully with me and they'd carry forty-five automatics too. I state forty-fives because that means business, I wouldn't be carrying a gun to bluff—if I had to use it I'd want it to make a full-size hole that couldn't be patched.

I'd live to enjoy life, not to lecture or preach. I wouldn't believe in any bullschitt like 'love' and I wouldn't get involved with any woman who talked it—any woman in my company would have to admit that what she loved was money. I'd play music as a hobby and only for close friends in the raceless set. I'd study bass for kicks, I wouldn't get involved in commercial competition. I might even become a junkie if my bank roll could stand it and I felt like that scene. That's what I'd do if I had my life to live all over again."

The girl Judy laughs. She's entertained and amused and she doesn't believe a word of it, otherwise she never would have married him and borne his two youngest children, would she?

39

"AND HOW ARE YOU SLEEPING these days, Charles?"

"Sometimes I think there's a curse on me that way, Dr. Wallach. I can't get a night's sleep like other people do, I only sleep a little at a time and wake up tired. Sometimes I give up and don't even try. Last night I started thinking about my last meeting with Fats. I was working at the Surf Club in Hollywood and he was out there for a record date and fell by to say hello. After the gig we had something to eat at the Chicken Shack then I drove him back to the Dunbar on Central Avenue and we sat in the car talking for a while. He was the one who deep down understood me most clearly, I now believe, and I dug him too. We didn't see too much of each other during his lifetime but every time we talked it counted and it may be he was the closest friend I ever had."

INKUS, you start telling about your book you gonna write then you modulate and go into something completely else like hearing the thoughts of your friends who ain't in the same city and hypnotizing old

Hamp and all that spooky stuff. But you got me so interested in your bitches and whores where you coulda made
a million, I want you to go on and tell me that."

"I didn't get to that yet, Fats, or maybe I got past it.
To understand that you gotta understand the first part.
So listen to me."

"You ain't gonna let me go upstairs and get high. Hot
dog, baby, okay, go ahead!"

"It's about a kid like you were who believed. He was
born believing but as he grew, everything around him,
beginning with his parents and sisters and teachers, everybody seemed to say that what he believed wasn't so. Sure,
they said they believed and they prayed and cried to God
and Jesus Christ Almighty but that was a few moments
out of a couple of hours in church each week. So somehow
he became two personalities, one as sincere as the other,
and then three, because he could stand off and watch the
other two. The reason was that he suspected maybe the
people who didn't believe might be right, that there was
nothing to believe in. But if he accepted this and put down
the beautiful honest good things he'd lose out on all he
could have gained if he'd never lost his belief in believing."

"What was that you said, Mingus?"

"He had to hold onto both believing in disbelief and
believing in belief. The real search began with the kid
being aware of his two complete selves, as different as
man is to woman, that belong together but don't look alike,
perfect opposites that can form a new perfection with
each other. Look, Fats, suppose you show a man a large
board with some different-sized holes cut out and you
take him to a lumber yard and say, 'Match this board for

me.' He can't find a board with those same kind of holes. But then a child comes to you with five pieces of plank in his hands and says, 'Place some hinges on these planks and your board and add doorknobs or latches. Put this wall of doors where you want to. Close some doors when you wish for silence, open some when you wish for truth. Because I know better than to think I can find another to match the truth of your board by chance or luck, unless you cut two boards of the same truth at the same time.' "

"What, Mingus? You a prophet or something? What kind of board is that? Is it a white board or a black board?"

"I'm not trying to sell you nothing, Fats. You asked me to tell you."

"Finish, baby, make it your best solo for old Fat Girl's soul. But see if I got you right so far—two selves that belong together but they don't look alike, like a man's got a joint and a bitch's got a pussy."

"I'm trying to talk about opposites, Fats, two complete opposites. Exact perfection or exact imperfection are both perfection when they stand to be judged alone, separate from each other. Destruction begins with the very idea of contest."

"Go ahead, Mingus, swing, baby! I won't ask why destruction begins with the very idea of contest."

"Contest and competition between the animal-devil I and the God-good I makes it like one exists at the expense of the other."

"Look, Mingus, I don't wish to bug you but why is it every time someone like me asks someone like you to explain God, G-O-D, people like you start with that off-the-wall schitt, talking in parables and telling riddles. Why can't they say it simple like I do? I'm Fats Navarro. I stand five feet and nine and three-quarters inches tall. Look almost Mexican with kinky, nappy hair. Used to weigh three hundred and fifty pounds. Now weigh one hundred and ten. Considered to be a member of the Negro race according to the white man who don't like me and I like him even less than that. But the way you're starting so slow I'll be dead before you tell me if God goes to the bathroom or not."

"Fats, you keep talking it in your direction, that's what takes so much time. Each time I get started you come up with a question. If I don't answer that, the one I'm on don't make sense."

"Okay, answer that one then. Why all that off-the-wall schitt?"

"All *right*, Fats. If you're going to California from New York and you know California exists, you don't guess all over the place. You look up what direction it's in and then you find where it is on the map."

"They got road maps to Heaven?"

"I got one, but you gotta make your own. Unless you get out a pencil and pick what you think is the best route you're not about to get there from looking at New York City and jumping your eyes to California, no matter what kind of imagination you got. And as for the place you're talking about, the few maps available are so old and strangely translated that you can't expect intelligent human beings to try to use the kind they been selling."

"You mean bibles, parchments, rocks and things like that?"

"Yes, and we got no new directions or visions from the

modern holy men who are growing in doubt of themselves. Are the powers of man to commune with the Divine Laws any less today than in Christ's time and before? He said, 'Seek and ye shall find. . . . Ye too have the powers to become the Sons of God.' Don't these words show God isn't to be deserted for the *church* to handle our lives and sins the same as the Chinese handle our laundry? But the church waves a magic wand and says, 'Man can kill or do anything and atone himself through *me*, without ever passing up his TV set to commune with the Divine Spirit.' "

"There you go again, Mingus. I was asking about God, G-O-D. How much does he weigh? Where is he? How far off?"

"Fats, what's five and five?"

"Ten, baby."

"It could be twenty."

"It could not, Mingus."

"It could, Fats, you're stupid to restrict yourself. You didn't ask five *what*. I was thinking of five married couples, males and females, traveling in Pullman compartments. When they board it's as couples, when they're counted it's as individuals. So I meant five twos and five twos, which is twenty. The answer can be whatever the searcher prefers it to be—five twos, five threes, five fives, anything. God is the product of the parts added, subtracted, multiplied, divided. Ten alone don't equal God, neither does twenty. So how can any sensible being start with the answer and call it a total? You told me your collected knowledge gotten from living in this world, Fats, equals nothing— *nought*. There's no harm for anyone else in your mathematics. But don't forget that once, standing on your feet,

359

out of your huge three-hundred-pound frame through your own lungs came a beautiful burst of sound like the voices of the elements clashing together as your trumpet changed the velocity of the winds! And now you're asking to die because you've judged yourself not even schitt in this world. I'm sorry, Fats. But I've been true enough to myself to know a lie—even if I am telling it—and that's the only truth necessary. Your horn has never lied about you. You love *more* than I do and for this you desire to die. Only you can change this."

"You mean you still say I believe even if I don't believe?"

"Yes, and I say you believe more than the believers who can't bear to think there might *not* be a God. They go to church out of fear, and the church says, 'Come here for forgiveness—but don't change! Stay drunk, poor and ragged—we need you stupid, to fight our wars and kill for the God we tell you exists!' "

"Mingus, are you a Communist or something?"

"What I'm saying is as old as Man's first time out. During the Stone Age while the others were out with clubs beating each other up some cats were thinking this way. Bird and I talked about this."

"Bird believes in God, Mingus?"

"You know he does. Someday one of us put-down, outcast makers of jazz music should show those church-going clock-punchers that people like Monk and Bird are dying for what they believe. That duty's supposed to be left to holy men but they're so busy building temples they haven't got time for you and me. Dig? You say you're dying and know it, Fats, and you aren't afraid. Then why don't you die now? If you know there's no God then you have the power of God. There's no need to kill yourself—*think* yourself to death. Go ahead, Fats, you know you're right, there ain't no God. You know more than Christ, Buddha, Socrates, Plato, Mohammed, Bird, Judas, Mingus, Casals, Stravinsky, Benjamin Franklin, Swami Vivikananda and Norman Mailer! You know there ain't no God, you know more than anyone except some of them dumb agents, critics and congressmen. But it's lucky for you *I* believe, 'cause you come here with a suicide complex like that's original and you weigh one hundred and ten pounds and I could oblige your wish in seconds. But I know that's wrong, I know I was born an extension of life itself—the whole outdoor scene, sky, moon, sun, universe, space, the whole scene is me. I remember once I was talking to Bird like this. Suddenly he said, 'Mingus! Don't take that breath!' I didn't. He had his mind tuned to my thoughts and when I felt it time to breathe again he said to me, 'Don't take that breath either.' I didn't. A few minutes later I spoke to him. 'Why should I die for you, Bird? You wouldn't believe it after it happened, you'd think it was just an accident.' 'No, I wouldn't, Mingus,' Bird said. So I began to die for him. Tears came to his eyes. He said, 'Don't waste yourself—it wouldn't do any good anyway.' Later Lennie Tristano got into this discussion with me and Bird. It was out near Boston, Massachusetts—Christy's, Eddie Kern's club. Tristano was confirming to be an atheist and I remember Eddie interrupted and gave Lennie his cross. Eddie gave it because he thought me and Bird was trying to destroy Lennie when we were actually trying to *save* him from his disbelief. When Bird saw that Eddie had given his cross to Lennie he started to cry to Eddie, 'You're white! You're white! You come to save your blind white brother from the cold ruthless clutches of black magic! You ripped your cross from your neck and handed it to the blind man because you see his eyes and not his soul. You're supposed to give *me* the cross—I was speaking love! Lennie was speaking hate! Give me the cross, give me something so I can give it to Mingus who would die for me! Mingus! Mingus!' Bird ran his fist through the glass door and passed out. I picked up the beautiful fallen giant to my shoulders and carried him to his car. I remember him so well that night. 'Mingus, feel this coat. What is it, Mingus, what is it?' 'I don't know, Bird.' 'It's cashmere, the finest wool on earth. Now once again, Mingus, feel my coat. What is it?' 'Cashmere, Bird.' 'Mingus, this coat ain't schitt! Dead goats' hair from the mountains of Tibet. Goat coat, Mingus! Goat coat!' I don't know how it is all these beautiful things seem to find me luckily standing by. But I was there with Bird as Lennie tried to tell him there was no God. And Bird said, 'Are you sure, Lennie? The job is open? I'll take it. On your knees, Tristano. Thank me for all I have given you. On your knees, blind fool without any eyes within his soul. Worship the bird that flies without wing!' If Eddie Kern hadn't interrupted, Lennie might have been where it was, that night."

"Mingus, who's God?"

"Bird without wings, motherfucker! Bird!"

"Mingus, you think I could fly, now that I've lost so much weight?"

"How else you gonna get out of your head, Fats?"

"Mingus, you a bitch, a bitch cat."

"You almost got me covered—I could be a *witch*. I got three titties, you know."

"You do?"

"In the Middle Ages they'd've burned me at birth as a warlock."

"Where is the third titty located, Mingus?"

"It's always below the right or left breast."

"Oh, I dig that. I thought it might be in the middle where it could mess up the scenery. Them really was the dark ages, Mingus. How many did they burn?"

"What?"

"Witches!"

"Thousands, I guess."

"How many thousand?"

"Couple, I guess."

"Lemme see. Three times. . . . Think of all them titties we coulda sucked!"

"No, Fats, they were babies."

"Oh. Okay, Mingus, so five and five ain't ten. It's thirty, 'cause I'm thinking about five threes and five threes. Dig? Now tell me some more stories to make me scared to die."

"You don't listen, Fats. You're dying in your mind, killing yourself 'cause you want to. You don't go to bed five and six nights in a row. It's like talking to a man who has a razor at his jugular vein—I'm reaching out to stop him as the first gush of blood tells him he's on his way and he still doesn't realize it's his own hand with the razor."

"I do, Mingus. But I want to watch my enemies as I die and see their faces when they know they lost a steady client. I go out, kick my habit, come home clean. And right away there's some dirty motherfucker pulling on my arm to come and get high free this time 'cause he knows next I'll be knocking down his door to get in. Mingus, don't ever be no junkie. This world is a dirty place. They take and hold little boys and girls down to get the young kids started."

"Somebody hold me or mine down, Fats, I don't stop till I get him, his sisters, brothers, mama and papa and doctors and nurses that brought him here. The day anything is done to mine against their will, that's the day Dillinger becomes a faggot—everybody goes!"

"Oh, that's the kind of Christian gentleman you are. You don't turn the other cheek?"

"Cheeks have been turned by great men, closer to God than me. No, I sincerely believe that's the day. If He or His Father don't reach down and stop my hand that will be the day."

"Aw, Mingus. Just when you start winning me over, before I know it I done did you up and you lose your faith!"

"Fats, as soon as I say something you turn it! If a man don't even believe the places exist, you can't give him any kind of directions to get to California *or* the Holy Land!"

"I just feel left out of that whole scene you talking about, Ming. Like some kids got ice cream. I didn't, I just watched them. Even today I don't eat it. It don't exist for me. There is no ice cream. But when I cursed God I didn't mean to hurt you. 'Cause I love you, I love deep in my heart. That's why I'm leaving, 'cause the white man and people in *general* don't love. Fuck 'em. Mingus, I don't *really* want to die but I am and I ain't afraid. I got one thing I did right. I really loved, you know I loved."

"Fats, can I try one more time? Listen, did you make yourself?"

"No. My daddy fucked my old lady and knocked her up like your daddy did your mama and their daddys did their mamas."

"You mean it always just *was*? Like that tree there was always just like that?"

"No. It was a seed like I was one time. All the things on earth was a seed at one time. Has to be. If I was some come, then everything once was some come."

"How about the earth, Fats? Was it some come, too?"

"It stands to reason."

"Then where is the mother of this earth and these planets?"

"Yeah. . . . Well, we got this far, Mingus. . . . The earth, the stars, the moon is still babies 'cause they're in their mama's womb, which is the universe."

"But what's *outside* the universe, Fats?"

"Her stomach and legs, et cetera. God's old lady?— she sure is a big chick."

"So what's outside his old lady, in space?"

"The rest of his harem? If there's no end, he must have quite a few old ladies."

"He who, Fats?"

"God! Isn't that the cat we're trying to find before I die?"

"Yeah, but I didn't bring Him up at this point. Why did you?"

"Mingus . . . if I get out there, you can bet I'll try and let you know what's happening 'cause you sure are a believing cat. You done believed me mentally all out into space with you till I almost forgot. Just how premature do you suppose the bodies of this universe are in relation to those other universes out there?"

"I'd say just as premature as earthman is in relation to the Man who dies again and again to save all men from their fear of the unknown."

"You mean He dies to save *me*, Mingus?"

"You too."

". . . I guess I am a little afraid that it might *hurt* or something to die, maybe like getting busted by an auto. But somehow thinking of space and all that, funny as it sounds, it feels like I got more room than I had before, like how big you suppose Central Park is to a squirrel? It's big enough for him. It's really more than he needs for himself. Like I'm beginning to feel even this earth is more than man needs for himself if he loved his brother."

"Fats, that's where it is. Love."

"Then you don't have to worry about me no more. Worry about yourself. I done my share of loving till they killed me. . . . Well, take care of yourself, Mingus. I love you."

"I love you, Fats. Later."

"Maybe, maybe. Right now it seems more like good-bye."

"I was talking about that. So . . . Later, hear me?"

"I dig. Mingus, when you think you due?"

"I don't know, Fats. Not until I write it down, I guess. Those are my orders from The Man."

"Later, Mingus."

"Later, Girl. . . ."